state functions and
linear control systems

McGraw-Hill Series in Electronic Systems

John G. Truxal and Ronald A. Rohrer   Consulting Editors

state functions and linear control systems

Donald G. Schultz

Professor of Electrical Engineering
University of Arizona

James L. Melsa

Associate Professor of Information and Control Sciences
Southern Methodist University

McGraw-Hill Book Company

New York, St. Louis, San Francisco, Toronto, London, Sydney

TO

Mr. Stove

Mr. Moke

Mr. Mutt

State functions and linear control systems

Library of Congress Catalog Card Number 67-23481

55655

1234567890 MP 7432106987

contents

preface

This book is concerned with the application of modern control theory to the fundamental problem of the control of linear systems. The obvious difference between this book and the others that treat the linear system is its use of state variables and matrix methods, a difference which is superficial rather than basic.

The fundamentally different outlook of this book is based on the use of the state function as the cohesive concept in control engineering. Use is made of the state functions of classical mechanics, the lagrangian and the hamiltonian, in the early stages of problem formulation. These result in systems automatically described in state-variable form. The use of matrix methods then follows as a simple means of manipulating these equations. The state functions of modern control theory, the V function of Liapunov and the H function of Pontryagin, are used in analysis and system synthesis.

The second fundamental difference is the simultaneous use of state variables in both the time and the frequency domain. Methods of system representation, analysis, and synthesis are discussed from the point of view of both the Laplace transform and the more recent time-domain methods. For example, system synthesis through the use of state-variable feedback is discussed from the point of view of integral performance indices as well as closed-loop transfer functions. Furthermore, the relationship between the two approaches is investigated in detail, and methods of relating one design to the other are explicitly pointed out.

By concentrating almost exclusively on the linear system rather than the general case, the authors attempt to make clear ideas that might otherwise be lost in computational difficulty. However, the point is made throughout the book that the inherent advantage of the state-function approach is that it may be extended to nonlinear and time-varying systems, though little is done here with this broader class of problems.

This book is directed toward the engineer with a bachelor of science degree, who as a control engineer faces the same problem whether he is in industry or just entering graduate school: the control theory he learned as an undergraduate is based exclusively on the use of the Laplace transform. Yet the literature he is expected to read and understand is written in matrix notation and often appears in the time domain. The aim of this book is to make modern control theory intelligible by treating the linear problem with which the engineer is already familiar. Thus the book is suitable for a beginning one-semester graduate course in automatic control or for the practitioner already acquainted with conventional control-system techniques.

Considerable effort has been expended to make the book as "self-teaching" as possible. The text material is liberally illustrated with examples. Whenever applicable, exercises are provided which pertain to each section, and they all include answers. More general problems are given at the end of the chapters, and a solution manual is available to ensure that these problems are well understood.

The material included within this book has developed from graduate courses taught at the University of Arizona, Tucson. The material was also presented to Rover Project engineers at Los Alamos Scientific Laboratory. Thus the combined needs of graduate students and practicing engineers have contributed to the overall structure and method of presentation of this book.

The authors wish to express their appreciation to their colleagues and graduate students who have provided assistance in the preparation of this manuscript. In particular, the authors are indebted to Dr. Charles Hausenbauer, of the University of Arizona, who suggested many improvements in the presentation. Special appreciation is due to Katherine S. Melsa for her untiring efforts in typing the manuscript.

Donald G. Schultz

James L. Melsa

one

introduction and outline of the book

1.1 Introduction and historical background

This book provides a new and clearer look at modern control theory, first, by interrelating it with classical mechanics through the concept of the state function and, second, by presenting an integrated approach in both the time and frequency domains. From such a viewpoint, modern control theory no longer appears as a collection of isolated facts but rather as an integral part of advanced dynamics. A brief history of control theory reveals the need for the unifying concept of state functions and the dual approach in the time and frequency domains.

The period before the Second World War may be considered as ancient history. With due respect to the early workers in the field, it must be said that no organized theory guided their efforts. The technical stimulation of the Second World War brought increasing activity in the control area. In conjunction with the "new mathematics" of the Laplace transform, the frequency-response methods of Nyquist and Bode developed into an efficient and powerful theory. On the basis of a few open-loop frequency-response measurements, not only could closed-loop response be predicted, but the dynamic behavior of large and complex systems could be predictably altered by the addition of a few relatively inexpensive electrical or mechanical components.

Soon it was realized that the Laplace variable was more than just a frequency variable and that a suitable vehicle for the discussion of the closed-loop behavior was the location of the open-loop poles and zeros. Thus, in the early 1950s, was born the root-locus method of closed-loop system analysis. The development of the root locus had one obvious but disturbing effect. Control engineers tended to divide themselves as frequency-response men or root-locus men. However, as the 1960s approached, there was a growing realization that the frequency response and the root locus were simply different viewpoints of a more basic fre-quency-domain approach.

But having resolved this question, the control engineer has now to face a similar situation. The advocates of modern control theory are motivated by the desire to go beyond the consideration of purely linear systems with constant coefficients. Hence they have abandoned the Laplace transform methods and have returned to a more basic differential-equation approach. Here matrix methods are convenient, and at least on the surface it appears that these advocates are not even treating the same problem.

This is where we find ourselves now. Although limited to linear systems, frequency-response and root-locus methods work. But the din of the modern theorists is too loud to be ignored. Unfortunately, they have already bypassed the linear problem and are either unwilling or unable to clarify the linear problem in terms of the new theory.

This book, written almost exclusively in terms of modern control theory, aims to apply modern control theory to the linear problem and, at the same time, indicate means by which the modern time-domain approaches are related to the conventional use of Laplace transforms. By restricting the discussion largely to linear systems, the authors appeal to the reader's basic knowledge of linear systems as an aid in understanding the modern approach. Even in the case of linear systems, the result is a new basic servo configuration with inherent stability characteristics.

1.2   *The conventional vs. the modern approach*

Before considering the detailed application of modern control theory to the linear control problem, it is well to view the overall approach, particularly as contrasted with the conventional approach to the control problem. A typical linear text begins with a review of Laplace transform theory and proceeds to the use of this theory in system representation in block-diagram form. The use of the block diagram is a crucial factor in the classical approach.

A block diagram is nothing more than a pictorial representation of a set of transformed differential equations. In many cases the block diagram is drawn from the physical system under consideration. In this respect the block diagram serves as a means of identifying the object being controlled in terms of a physical model and ultimately a mathematical model. In other cases the governing equations are known, and the block diagram simply serves as a way of describing the results of the modeling that has already taken place.

The basic power of the conventional approach lies in the reduction of all control systems to a common form. The configuration upon which much of linear control theory is based is pictured in Fig. 1.2-1. It is not important whether the problem in question is the control of the power level of a nuclear reactor or the position of a radar antenna or the quality of a chemical process. Once all these physical situations have been reduced to a common form, the control engineer need know nothing about reactors or radar or chemistry. He attacks the problem simply as a control problem.

The configuration of Fig. 1.2-1 is not necessarily inherent. The unalterable physical plant, pictured as $G(s)$ in Fig. 1.2-1, may itself contain a number of inner loops. But since the overall interest is usually expressible in terms of input-output relationships, these input-output characteristics dominate. In fact, this is the basic idea of feedback control: look at the desired output and use that knowledge to effect the desired control. From this point of view, any minor loops that may exist are often suppressed, so that the configuration of Fig. 1.2-1 results more or less automatically.

This classical approach is in sharp contrast to the outlook of modern control theory, which requires a system description in terms of n first-

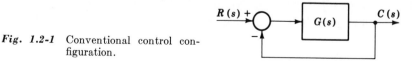

Fig. 1.2-1 Conventional control configuration.

order differential equations.   This means that n variables must somehow be considered.   Thus the unalterable plant described simply by $G(s)$ above is now discussed in terms of n variables rather than just in terms of input-output properties.   If these variables are chosen to represent physical quantities within the system to be controlled, it is not surprising that one might consider doing something with each of these n variables.   Modern control theory dictates that these n variables should *all* be fed back, after suitable weighting.   This is perhaps the most important single conclusion of modern control theory, namely, that the configuration of Fig. 1.2-1 is not basic but only a special case in which all the variables except the output have been weighted by a zero amount.

One of the basic aims of this book is to make the reader appreciate how and why all the system state variables should be fed back.   In realizing this aim, we do not abandon the familiar block diagram or transform methods but only the idea of feeding back just the output.

1.3   State functions in automatic control

In recent years the vogue in the automatic-control literature has been the second method of Liapunov and the maximum principle of Pontryagin. Both of these techniques are time-domain approaches and are based on system representation in state-variable form.   Because the state variable is common to both of these modern methods of analysis, the term state variable has acquired a mystic importance, and the concept of the state space has been postulated as the key to the new automatic control.

This book takes a more fundamental viewpoint, one inspired by the realization that both the V function of Liapunov and the H function of Pontryagin are state functions.   A state function is defined as a scalar function of the state variables, and possibly time.   Such a realization leads one to search for other state functions in problems of advanced dynamics.   The lagrangian and hamiltonian of classical mechanics also prove to be state functions.   When they are combined with the state functions of modern automatic control, the result proves to be quite powerful.   The generalized coordinates of Lagrange, some 200 years old, prove to correspond to the state variables of automatic control.   More than that, they prove to be a suitable choice of state variables because of their intimate association with energy.   Energies are usually expressed in terms of variables which are real and available for measurement.   From a control engineer's point of view, these variables are then available for control.

Through the use of Lagrange's equations and the state function of

Lagrange, the equations of motion governing the dynamic system in question are generated in a form necessary for the application of the second method and the maximum principle. This seems more than just a coincidence. The lagrangian generates the governing equations in state-variable form. The V function of Liapunov provides a test of stability, and the H function of Pontryagin serves as a synthesis tool. It is on the basis of these three state functions that the book is naturally divided into chapters on system representation, analysis, and synthesis.

1.4   Outline of contents

This introductory chapter is followed by two chapters devoted entirely to system representation and problem formulation. After a brief introduction to matrix methods, Chap. 2 discusses means by which a feedback system originally known in block-diagram form can be represented as n first-order differential equations. The idea is to proceed from the familiar directly into the modern formulation. Both analytic and block-diagram reduction methods are given.

Chapter 3 is based on the realization that systems are rarely known at the outset in sufficient detail for the block diagram to be completely specified. A return to basic principles is called for, and, as indicated above, the state function of Lagrange is used to generate the governing equations directly in state-variable form.

Chapters 4 and 5 are devoted to analysis. Here the procedure is much like that of other control texts. First, means of obtaining the complete time response are discussed. This often proves to be more information than necessary, and the designer seeks first to answer the more basic question of stability. Means of determining the total time response are discussed in Chap. 4, based upon the state-transition matrix. The second method of Liapunov is the basis for the stability analysis of Chap. 5.

Chapter 6 presents the mathematical foundations necessary for the synthesis procedures to follow. The mathematics necessary is the calculus of variations. Discussion of the calculus of variations leads directly to the maximum principle and the state function H of Pontryagin.

By relating the V function of Chap. 4 to the H of Pontryagin, it is shown that optimal control requires a design procedure based on feeding back *all* the state variables. Chapter 7 is devoted exclusively to a theoretical treatment of this problem. The theoretical results derived here are difficult to accomplish by hand calculation methods; however, these results can be interpreted in terms of the Laplace transform variable and transfer functions, and hence this chapter serves as a necessary introduction to Chaps. 8 and 9.

Practical design methods are discussed in Chaps. 8 and 9.   In Chap. 8 the performance criterion is an integral involving a quadratic form both in the state variables and in the control.   Before proceeding to specific design procedures, the performance index is given a physical interpretation in terms of a desired response.   The remainder of the chapter is devoted to frequency-domain design procedures, with the Kalman equation as the starting point.   Approximate methods are discussed on both the Bode and root-locus diagrams.

The design criteria of Chap. 9 is not the integral performance index but the desired closed-loop transfer function.   Means by which these two criteria are related serve as an introduction to the design procedure known as the *H* equivalent method.   This design procedure features the introduction of series compensation in addition to state-variable feedback to realize the desired specifications.

Actually, there is no fitting place to end the book.   Ideally the reader will consider this book as an introduction to modern control theory and to the more extensive works on the subject, published and yet to come.

two   *system representation in state-variable form*

2.1 *Introduction and outline of chapter*

This chapter introduces the concept of the state variable and the various means of representing control systems in state-variable form. Each method of state-
variable representation results in a system description
in terms of n first-order differential equations, as
opposed to the usual nth-order equation. A convenient tool for this new system representation is matrix
notation, and thus the early portion of this chapter contains a brief discussion of matrix notation and
manipulation.

The use of n first-order differential equations to
describe the dynamics of a control system is a radical

departure from the standard block-diagram, transfer-function approach. It is a basic hypothesis of this book that the state-variable description is actually more meaningful than the block-diagram representation. Because the state-variable description is as yet less familiar, a "backdoor" approach to the problem of system representation is used in this chapter. It is assumed that the governing differential equations of the various elements making up the control system are known and that the complete system is represented by a transfer function. This is nothing more than another representation of the differential equations of the system.

   With the familiar transfer-function representation as a starting point, several methods of system representation in state-variable form are discussed and compared. The relationship between the conventional and the state-variable approach is emphasized.

2.2   System state and state variables

It is important to stress at the outset that the concept of system state is, first of all, a physical concept. However, it is often convenient to describe the behavior of an actual physical system in terms of a mathematical model. Here this mathematical model is assumed to consist of ordinary differential equations which have a unique solution for all inputs and initial conditions. It is in terms of this mathematical model that the *system state*, or simply *state*, is defined.

> **Definition 2.2-1**   The *state of a system* at any time t_0 is the minimum set of numbers $x_1(t_0)$, $x_2(t_0)$, . . . , $x_n(t_0)$ which, along with the input to the system for $t \geq t_0$, is sufficient to determine the behavior of the system for all $t \geq t_0$.

In other words, the state of a system represents the minimum amount of information that we need to know about a system at t_0 such that its future behavior can be determined without reference to the input before t_0.

   The idea of state is familiar from a knowledge of the physical world and the means of solving the differential equations used to model the physical world. Consider a ball flying through the air. Intuitively we feel that if we know the ball's position and velocity, we also know its future behavior. It is on this basis that an outfielder positions himself to catch a fly ball. Exactly the same information is needed to solve a differential-equation model of the problem. Consider, for example, the second-order differential equation

$$\ddot{x} + a\dot{x} + bx = f(t)$$

The solution to this equation may be found as the sum of the forced response, due to $f(t)$, and the natural or unforced response, i.e., the solution of the homogeneous equation. However, the solution is not completely specified until initial conditions are given on x and $\dot{x}$. With reference to the definition, n is 2 in this example, and the initial values of x and $\dot{x}$ are the only two numbers necessary to define completely the solution for all time. Of course, the initial instant is completely arbitrary, so that a knowledge of x and $\dot{x}$ at any time, along with subsequent values of the input, completely describes the system.

In the example above, both x and $\dot{x}$ are functions of time; i.e., they are variables. Since they are variables capable of defining the state of the system, they are designated as state variables. In general, an nth-order system is described by a collection of n state variables. Indeed, this may be regarded as the definition of the state variable: a state variable is one of a set of n variables the knowledge of which is sufficient to describe completely the behavior of the system. In a third-order system, for example, a knowledge of x, $\dot{x}$, and $\ddot{x}$ would be sufficient. Clearly a knowledge of x, $\dot{x}$, and $ax + b\dot{x}$ would not be adequate, since the last expression provides no new information about the system.

Modern control theory is almost completely dependent upon a system representation in n first-order differential equations. It is shown in the following sections that this representation is not unique and, in fact, that there is an infinite number of choices of state variables that can correctly describe the system. Fortunately, only a few of these are in common use—either because they give a mathematical advantage or because they have some relationship to physical reality.

Before proceeding to the various methods of system representation, we must consider the notation employed in modern control theory.

2.3 *Vectors and matrices*

This section details the notation used throughout the book and defines some of the more basic matrix manipulations. The treatment here is brief, since the rest of this chapter contains examples that amply illustrate the points made in this section.

A matrix is a rectangular array of elements arranged in m rows and n columns which obeys a certain set of manipulations discussed below. The elements of the matrix may be real or complex numbers or variables of either time or frequency. The matrix **A** is thus

$$\mathbf{A} = [a_{ij}] = \begin{bmatrix} a_{11} & a_{12} & \cdots & a_{1n} \\ a_{21} & a_{22} & \cdots & a_{2n} \\ \cdot & \cdot & \cdot & \cdot \\ a_{m1} & a_{m2} & \cdots & a_{mn} \end{bmatrix} \qquad (2.3\text{-}1)$$

Equation (2.3-1) indicates the notation that is used throughout this book. The matrix **A** is designated by a boldface capital letter as a shorthand notation for the entire array. When the array itself is given, it is always set off in brackets to emphasize that it is a matrix. The elements of the matrix are indicated by a small letter with a double subscript. Thus the element of **A** that is located in the ith row and the jth column is a_{ij}.

A matrix is classified by the number of its rows and columns; a matrix of m rows and n columns is a matrix of order $m \times n$, or an $m \times n$ matrix. If $m = n$, the matrix is called a *square matrix*. A matrix with n rows and only one column is called a *column matrix* or vector.[1] The shorthand notation for the column vector is a lowercase, boldface letter, as

$$\mathbf{x} = \begin{bmatrix} x_1 \\ x_2 \\ \cdot \\ \cdot \\ \cdot \\ x_n \end{bmatrix} = \text{col } (x_1, x_2, \ldots, x_n)$$

Note that the elements of a vector have only one subscript, to indicate their location in the column. A matrix with one row and n columns is called a *row matrix* or row vector.

The *transpose* of any matrix is formed by interchanging rows and columns of the matrix and is indicated by a superscript T, so that

$$\mathbf{A}^T = \begin{bmatrix} a_{11} & a_{21} & \cdots & a_{m1} \\ a_{12} & a_{22} & \cdots & a_{m2} \\ \cdot & \cdot & \cdot & \cdot \\ a_{1n} & a_{2n} & \cdots & a_{mn} \end{bmatrix}$$

[1] The equating of a vector to a column matrix is not exactly correct, since a vector has a fixed geometric meaning while the column matrix is only a representation of a given vector in one coordinate system. However, the usage is common in the literature and is retained here. For a more complete discussion of this subject see Huelsman (1963).

A row matrix may be thought of as the transpose of a column matrix, so that $\mathbf{x}^T$ is the row matrix

$$\mathbf{x}^T = [x_1 \quad x_2 \quad \cdots \quad x_n]$$

Matrices are also classified by their *rank*. The rank of a matrix is the largest number r such that at least one $r \times r$ matrix whose determinant[1] is nonzero may be formed from the original matrix by deleting rows and/or columns. It is obvious that the rank of a matrix may never be larger than the smaller dimension of a matrix, that is, $r \leq$ minimum (m,n). Although there are more elaborate tests, the rank of a matrix can be determined by simply testing all determinants of successively smaller size until a nonzero one is found. Consider, for example, the matrix

$$\mathbf{A} = \begin{bmatrix} 1 & 1 & 2 \\ 0 & 1 & 1 \\ 1 & 2 & 3 \end{bmatrix}$$

In this case, the single third-order determinant of the matrix itself is zero. However, every second-order determinant is nonzero, and therefore the matrix has rank 2.

Another type of classification of square matrices is concerned with the elements of the matrix. If $a_{ij} = a_{ji}$ for all i and j, the matrix is called *symmetric*, and we see that $\mathbf{A}^T = \mathbf{A}$. For example the matrix

$$\mathbf{A} = \begin{bmatrix} 1 & 2 & 7 \\ 2 & 4 & 13 \\ 7 & 13 & 0 \end{bmatrix}$$

is symmetric. On the other hand, if $a_{ij} = -a_{ji}$ for all i and j, the matrix is called *skew-symmetric*, and we observe that $\mathbf{A}^T = -\mathbf{A}$. The matrix

$$\mathbf{A} = \begin{bmatrix} 0 & 1 & -3 \\ -1 & 0 & -2 \\ 3 & 2 & 0 \end{bmatrix}$$

is skew-symmetric. We note that the diagonal elements a_{ii} of any skew-symmetric matrix must be zero, since $a_{ii} = -a_{ii}$ can be satisfied only by $a_{ii} = 0$.

---

[1] A knowledge of determinants is assumed. For reference see Hohn (1958).

It should be noted that any square matrix may be written as the sum of a symmetric matrix $\mathbf{A}_s$ and a skew-symmetric matrix $\mathbf{A}_{sk}$, as can be shown as follows.   Let

$$\mathbf{A} = \mathbf{A}_s + \mathbf{A}_{sk} \qquad\qquad (2.3\text{-}2)$$

Now take the transpose of both sides,

$$\mathbf{A}^T = \mathbf{A}_s{}^T + \mathbf{A}_{sk}{}^T$$

By the above definitions this becomes

$$\mathbf{A}^T = \mathbf{A}_s - \mathbf{A}_{sk} \qquad\qquad (2.3\text{-}3)$$

If Eqs. (2.3-2) and (2.3-3) are solved simultaneously, we have

$$\mathbf{A}_s = \frac{\mathbf{A} + \mathbf{A}^T}{2}$$

$$\mathbf{A}_{sk} = \frac{\mathbf{A} - \mathbf{A}^T}{2}$$

Therefore the sum of $\mathbf{A}_s$ and $\mathbf{A}_{sk}$ is

$$\mathbf{A}_s + \mathbf{A}_{sk} = \frac{\mathbf{A} + \mathbf{A}^T}{2} + \frac{\mathbf{A} - \mathbf{A}^T}{2} = \mathbf{A}$$

as desired.   Consider, for example, the matrix

$$\mathbf{A} = \begin{bmatrix} 1 & 3 \\ 5 & 9 \end{bmatrix}$$

which may be written as

$$\mathbf{A} = \begin{bmatrix} 1 & 4 \\ 4 & 9 \end{bmatrix} + \begin{bmatrix} 0 & -1 \\ 1 & 0 \end{bmatrix}$$

If $\mathbf{A}$ is square, and if $a_{ij} = 0$, for $i \neq j$, then $\mathbf{A}$ is called a *diagonal matrix*.   In the special case when $\mathbf{A}$ is diagonal and $a_{ii} = 1$ for all i, the matrix is known as the *identity matrix*, designated as **I**,

$$\mathbf{I} = \begin{bmatrix} 1 & 0 & \cdots & 0 & 0 \\ 0 & 1 & \cdots & 0 & 0 \\ \cdot & \cdot & \cdots & \cdot & \cdot \\ 0 & 0 & \cdots & 1 & 0 \\ 0 & 0 & \cdots & 0 & 1 \end{bmatrix} \tag{2.3-4}$$

Closely associated with the definition of a matrix is a matrix algebra governing the allowable manipulations of matrices, which are summarized below.

Equality. Two matrices **A** and **B** are equal if and only if all the elements of each matrix are equal, i.e., if $a_{ij} = b_{ij}$. Two matrices can be equal only if they are of the same order.

Addition and subtraction. The sum or difference of two matrices **A** and **B** is a matrix **C** whose elements are the sum or difference of the respective elements of **A** and **B**. That is,

$$c_{ij} = a_{ij} \pm b_{ij} \tag{2.3-5}$$

Addition and subtraction are defined only for matrices of the same order. Addition and subtraction are commutative, $\mathbf{A} + \mathbf{B} = \mathbf{B} + \mathbf{A}$, and associative, $\mathbf{A} + (\mathbf{B} + \mathbf{C}) = (\mathbf{A} + \mathbf{B}) + \mathbf{C}$.

Multiplication by a scalar. The product $h\mathbf{A}$ is formed by multiplying each element of the matrix **A** by the scalar constant h. Therefore, if $\mathbf{C} = h\mathbf{A}$, then $c_{ij} = ha_{ij}$. Scalar multiplication distributes over vector addition, $h(\mathbf{A} + \mathbf{B}) = h\mathbf{A} + h\mathbf{B}$.

Integration and differentiation of matrices is also treated on this same element basis. For example, the elements of the matrix $d\mathbf{A}(t)/dt$ are $da_{ij}(t)/dt$.

Multiplication. Two matrices may be multiplied only if they are *conformal;* that is, **AB** is defined only if the number of columns of **A** equals the number of rows of **B**. If **A** is an $n \times r$ matrix and **B** is an $r \times m$ matrix, the product $\mathbf{AB} = \mathbf{C}$ is an $n \times m$ matrix with the elements of **C** defined as

$$c_{ij} = \sum_{h=1}^{r} a_{ih} b_{hj} \tag{2.3-6}$$

Thus c_{ij} is formed as the sum of the products of the corresponding elements of the ith row of **A** and the jth column of **B**. As an example, consider the following matrix product.

$$\begin{bmatrix} 1 & -2 & 3 \\ 2 & 3 & 1 \\ -1 & 3 & 2 \end{bmatrix} \begin{bmatrix} 1 & 1 \\ -2 & 3 \\ 3 & 2 \end{bmatrix} = \begin{bmatrix} 14 & 1 \\ -1 & 13 \\ -1 & 12 \end{bmatrix} \tag{2.3-7}$$

Here the c_{21} term of the resulting matrix is determined as

$$(2)(1) + (3)(-2) + (1)(3) = -1$$

As a consequence of the requirement of conformality, note the following points:

1. An $n \times n$ square matrix times an $n \times n$ square matrix yields an $n \times n$ square matrix.
2. A row vector times an $n \times n$ square matrix yields a $1 \times n$ matrix, or row vector.
3. An $n \times n$ square matrix times a column vector yields an $n \times 1$ column matrix, or column vector.
4. A $1 \times n$ row matrix times an $n \times 1$ column matrix yields a 1×1 matrix. The 1×1 matrix has all the usual properties of a scalar and hence is defined as a scalar.

As a consequence of the definition of matrix multiplication, note also the following points:

1. **AB** is not necessarily equal to **BA**. If **AB** = **BA**, this is purely coincidence. The product **BA** may not even be defined. Consider, for example,

$$\mathbf{A} = \begin{bmatrix} 1 & 2 \\ 5 & 1 \end{bmatrix} \quad \text{and} \quad \mathbf{B} = \begin{bmatrix} 2 & 0 \\ 1 & 3 \end{bmatrix}$$

Then

$$\mathbf{AB} = \begin{bmatrix} 4 & 6 \\ 11 & 3 \end{bmatrix} \neq \begin{bmatrix} 2 & 4 \\ 16 & 5 \end{bmatrix} = \mathbf{BA}$$

Because matrix multiplication is not commutative, one must be careful to preserve the order of the matrices when making any manipulation. In addition, one often speaks of pre- or postmultiplication to indicate whether the matrix is multiplied from the right or the left. For example, in the triple matrix product **ABC**, **A** premultiplies **B** while **C** postmultiplies **B**.

2. If **AB** = 0, it cannot be concluded that either **A** or **B** is identically zero. For example, if

$$\mathbf{A} = \begin{bmatrix} 1 & 0 \\ 1 & 0 \end{bmatrix} \quad \text{and} \quad \mathbf{B} = \begin{bmatrix} 0 & 0 \\ 2 & 9 \end{bmatrix}$$

then **AB** = 0 even though neither **A** nor **B** is zero. This is simply another indication of how careful one must be in translating scalar concepts into the world of matrices.

3. If **AB** = **AC**, then **B** and **C** are not necessarily equal. This is an obvious consequence of point 2 above.

4. Multiplication is associative; that is,

$$(\mathbf{AB})\mathbf{C} = \mathbf{A}(\mathbf{BC}) \tag{2.3-8}$$

5. Multiplication is distributive with respect to addition; that is,

$$\mathbf{A}(\mathbf{B} + \mathbf{C}) = \mathbf{AB} + \mathbf{AC} \tag{2.3-9}$$

Inversion. Division is not defined for matrices. The division operation is replaced by matrix inversion for square matrices. The square matrix $\mathbf{A}^{-1}$ is said to be the *inverse* of the square matrix **A** if

$$\mathbf{AA}^{-1} = \mathbf{A}^{-1}\mathbf{A} = \mathbf{I}$$

the identity matrix. Not all square matrices have an inverse, since the existence of an inverse requires that the determinant of the matrix be nonzero. If the determinant is nonzero, the matrix has an inverse and is said to be a *nonsingular matrix*. If the determinant is zero, the matrix has no inverse and is said to be *singular*.

Consider the problem of determining the inverse of **A**. If $\mathbf{A}^{-1}$ does exist, the elements of $\mathbf{A}^{-1}$ may be determined in a brute-force manner from the defining equation $\mathbf{A}^{-1}\mathbf{A} = \mathbf{I}$ by solving these n^2 simultaneous algebraic equations for the elements of $\mathbf{A}^{-1}$. Although this procedure is possible, it is desirable to avoid the direct simultaneous-equation approach. This may be done by defining the *adjoint* of a matrix. The adjoint matrix adj **A** is related to the matrix **A** through the cofactors of the elements of **A**. The cofactor cof a_{ij} of the element a_{ij} is $(-1)^{i+j}$ times the determinant of the matrix formed by deleting the ith row and the jth column from **A**. The adjoint of the matrix **A** is then defined as the transpose of a matrix whose elements are the cofactors of **A**, or

$$\text{adj } \mathbf{A} = [\text{cof } a_{ij}]^T = \begin{bmatrix} \text{cof } a_{11} & \text{cof } a_{21} & \cdots & \text{cof } a_{n1} \\ \text{cof } a_{12} & \text{cof } a_{22} & \cdots & \text{cof } a_{n2} \\ \cdots & \cdots & \cdots & \cdots \\ \text{cof } a_{1n} & \text{cof } a_{2n} & \cdots & \text{cof } a_{nn} \end{bmatrix} \tag{2.3-10}$$

Then $\mathbf{A}^{-1}$, the inverse of **A**, is

$$\mathbf{A}^{-1} = \frac{\text{adj } \mathbf{A}}{\det \mathbf{A}} \tag{2.3-11}$$

Example 2.3-1 The following example illustrates the steps involved in taking the inverse.   Let **A** be given as

$$\mathbf{A} = \begin{bmatrix} 8 & 4 & 2 \\ 2 & 8 & 4 \\ 1 & 2 & 8 \end{bmatrix}$$

The determinant associated with the matrix **A** may be formed by expanding in terms of the minors of the elements of the first row. Thus

$$\det \mathbf{A} = 8(64 - 8) - 4(16 - 4) + 2(4 - 8) = 392 \neq 0$$

and **A** has an inverse.   The cofactor matrix is

$$[\text{cof } a_{ij}] = \begin{bmatrix} 56 & -12 & -4 \\ -28 & 62 & -12 \\ 0 & -28 & 56 \end{bmatrix}$$

Here, for example, cof a_{23} was formed as

$$\text{cof } a_{23} = (-1)^5 \det \begin{bmatrix} 8 & 4 \\ 1 & 2 \end{bmatrix} = -12$$

Thus the adjoint matrix is

$$\text{adj } \mathbf{A} = [\text{cof } a_{ij}]^T = \begin{bmatrix} 56 & -28 & 0 \\ -12 & 62 & -28 \\ -4 & -12 & 56 \end{bmatrix}$$

and the inverse $\mathbf{A}^{-1}$ is given by

$$\mathbf{A}^{-1} = \frac{\text{adj } \mathbf{A}}{\det \mathbf{A}} = \begin{bmatrix} \frac{1}{7} & -\frac{1}{14} & 0 \\ -\frac{3}{98} & \frac{31}{196} & -\frac{1}{14} \\ -\frac{1}{98} & -\frac{3}{98} & \frac{1}{7} \end{bmatrix}$$

As a check, the reader may wish to show that $\mathbf{A}^{-1}\mathbf{A} = \mathbf{I}$.

Before concluding this brief introduction to matrices, the two following identities are given for future reference:

$$(\mathbf{AB})^{-1} = \mathbf{B}^{-1}\mathbf{A}^{-1} \tag{2.3-12}$$

and

$$(\mathbf{AB})^T = \mathbf{B}^T\mathbf{A}^T \tag{2.3-13}$$

Equation (2.3-12) applies only to cases where $\mathbf{A}$ and $\mathbf{B}$ are nonsingular and therefore square and of the same order. Equation (2.3-13) applies in all cases where $\mathbf{A}$ and $\mathbf{B}$ are conformal.

The reader is referred to Bellman (1960), Hohn (1958), and Nering (1963) for a more thorough and extensive treatment of the subject of matrices. The object here is not to be definitive but to present only that material which is used in the remainder of the book.

Exercises 2.3 *2.3-1.* Perform the following matrix multiplications.

(a) $\begin{bmatrix} 1 & 0 & -1 \\ 2 & 0 & 1 \end{bmatrix} \begin{bmatrix} 1 & 2 & 3 \\ 2 & 0 & 4 \\ 0 & 0 & 1 \end{bmatrix}$ (b) $\begin{bmatrix} 2 & 0 & 3 \\ 0 & 1 & 0 \end{bmatrix} \begin{bmatrix} 10 \\ 5 \\ 4 \end{bmatrix}$

(c) $\begin{bmatrix} \frac{1}{2} & \sqrt{\frac{3}{2}} \\ -\sqrt{\frac{3}{2}} & \frac{1}{2} \end{bmatrix} \begin{bmatrix} \frac{1}{2} & -\sqrt{\frac{3}{2}} \\ \sqrt{\frac{3}{2}} & \frac{1}{2} \end{bmatrix}$

answers:

(a) $\begin{bmatrix} 1 & 2 & 2 \\ 2 & 4 & 7 \end{bmatrix}$ (b) $\begin{bmatrix} 32 \\ 5 \end{bmatrix}$ (c) $\begin{bmatrix} 1 & 0 \\ 0 & 1 \end{bmatrix}$

2.3-2. Find the inverses of the following matrices.

(a) $\begin{bmatrix} 1 & 2 & 2 \\ 2 & -2 & 1 \\ 2 & 1 & -2 \end{bmatrix}$ (b) $\begin{bmatrix} 0 & 2 & 0 \\ 1 & 3 & -1 \\ 1 & 0 & 0 \end{bmatrix}$ (c) $\begin{bmatrix} a & b \\ c & d \end{bmatrix}$

answers:

(a) $\dfrac{1}{9}\begin{bmatrix} 1 & 2 & 2 \\ 2 & -2 & 1 \\ 2 & 1 & -2 \end{bmatrix}$ (b) $\dfrac{1}{2}\begin{bmatrix} 0 & 0 & 2 \\ 1 & 0 & 0 \\ 3 & -2 & 2 \end{bmatrix}$

(c) $\dfrac{1}{ad - bc}\begin{bmatrix} d & -b \\ -c & a \end{bmatrix}$

2.3-3. Verify Eqs. (2.3-12) and (2.3-13) for

$$\mathbf{A} = \begin{bmatrix} 1 & 1 \\ 2 & 1 \end{bmatrix} \qquad \mathbf{B} = \begin{bmatrix} 1 & 2 \\ 0 & 4 \end{bmatrix}$$

2.3-4. If $\mathbf{P}$ is symmetric, show that $\mathbf{A}^T\mathbf{P} + \mathbf{PA}$ and $\mathbf{B}^T\mathbf{PB}$ are symmetric.

2.3-5. Find the rank of the following matrices.

(a) $\begin{bmatrix} 1 & -2 \\ 1 & -2 \end{bmatrix}$ (b) $\begin{bmatrix} 1 & 2 & 1 \\ 3 & 5 & 1 \\ 0 & 0 & 1 \end{bmatrix}$ (c) $\begin{bmatrix} 0 & 0 & 1 \\ 1 & 1 & 0 \\ 0 & 0 & 6 \end{bmatrix}$

answers:

(a) 1 (b) 3 (c) 2

2.4 *System representation in state-variable form*

This section contains a brief introduction to the representation of nth-order linear control systems in state-variable form as n first-order differential equations and an output expression. The most general form of the system equations considered is

$$\dot{\mathbf{x}}(t) = \mathbf{A}\mathbf{x}(t) + \mathbf{B}\mathbf{u}(t) \qquad \text{(AB)}$$
$$\mathbf{y}(t) = \mathbf{C}\mathbf{x}(t) \qquad \text{(C)}$$

Here $\mathbf{x}$ is an n-dimensional *state vector*, $\mathbf{u}$ is an r-dimensional *control vector*, $\mathbf{y}$ is an m-dimensional *output vector*, $\mathbf{A}$ is an $n \times n$ *system matrix*, $\mathbf{B}$ is an $n \times r$ *control matrix*, and $\mathbf{C}$ is an $m \times n$ *output matrix*. In expanded form these equations become

$$
\begin{bmatrix} \dot{x}_1(t) \\ \dot{x}_2(t) \\ \cdots \\ \dot{x}_n(t) \end{bmatrix} =
\begin{bmatrix} a_{11} & a_{12} & \cdots & a_{1n} \\ a_{21} & a_{22} & \cdots & a_{2n} \\ \cdots & \cdots & \cdots & \cdots \\ a_{n1} & a_{n2} & \cdots & a_{nn} \end{bmatrix}
\begin{bmatrix} x_1(t) \\ x_2(t) \\ \cdots \\ x_n(t) \end{bmatrix}
$$
$$
+ \begin{bmatrix} b_{11} & b_{12} & \cdots & b_{1r} \\ b_{21} & b_{22} & \cdots & b_{2r} \\ \cdots & \cdots & \cdots & \cdots \\ b_{n1} & b_{n2} & \cdots & b_{nr} \end{bmatrix}
\begin{bmatrix} u_1(t) \\ u_2(t) \\ \cdots \\ u_r(t) \end{bmatrix} \qquad \text{(AB)}
$$

$$
\begin{bmatrix} y_1(t) \\ y_2(t) \\ \cdots \\ y_m(t) \end{bmatrix} =
\begin{bmatrix} c_{11} & c_{12} & \cdots & c_{1n} \\ c_{21} & c_{22} & \cdots & c_{2n} \\ \cdots & \cdots & \cdots & \cdots \\ c_{m1} & c_{m2} & \cdots & c_{mn} \end{bmatrix}
\begin{bmatrix} x_1(t) \\ x_2(t) \\ \cdots \\ x_n(t) \end{bmatrix} \qquad \text{(C)}
$$

Note that this representation is quite general, as it allows for multiple inputs, r of them, and multiple outputs, m of them. Thus the general system representation of Eqs. (AB) and (C) is adequate for multiple input–multiple output systems.

Equation (AB) is a set of n first-order differential equations and is usually referred to as the *plant equation*, while Eq. (C) represents a set of m linear algebraic equations and is referred to as the *output expression*. In its most general form the output expression appears as

$$\mathbf{y}(t) = \mathbf{C}\mathbf{x}(t) + \mathbf{D}\mathbf{u}(t)$$

where the added $\mathbf{D}\mathbf{u}(t)$ term indicates a direct coupling of the input to the output. Since the direct coupling of the input to the output is rare in control systems, where power amplification is generally desired, we shall use the simpler form of Eq. (C) as an output expression.

This time-domain state-variable representation of a multiple input–multiple output system is to be contrasted with the frequency-domain transfer-function approach of classical control theory.   In the latter form, the system discussed above would become simply

$$\mathbf{y}(s) = \mathbf{G}(s)\mathbf{u}(s) \tag{2.4-1}$$

Here we have made use of the matrix notation of the preceding section to express the system in a compact form.   The matrix $\mathbf{G}(s)$ is known as the transfer-function matrix since each of its elements is a transfer function between an input and output.   For example, the $g_{ij}(s)$ element is the transfer function between the jth input and the ith output, or

$$\frac{y_i(s)}{u_j(s)} = g_{ij}(s)$$

It is usual to represent graphically the transfer function by means of a block diagram, as shown in Fig. 2.4-1a.   For comparison, a block diagram of the state-variable representation of the system is shown in Fig. 2.4-1b.   This latter diagram is nothing more than a pictorial representation of Eqs. (**AB**) and (**C**).

In order to put the reader on more familiar footing, it is perhaps of value to consider the special case when both the input and output are scalars.   The importance of this class of system is indicated by the fact that almost every basic control book treats only the single input–single

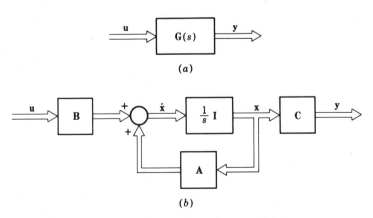

(a)

(b)

Fig. 2.4-1   Block diagrams of a multiple input–multiple output system. (a)   Transfer-function   representation;   (b)   state-variable representation.

output case.   For this case the state-variable representation becomes

$$\dot{\mathbf{x}}(t) = \mathbf{A}\mathbf{x}(t) + \mathbf{b}u(t) \tag{Ab}$$
$$y(t) = \mathbf{c}^T\mathbf{x}(t) \tag{c}$$

where the scalars u and y are the input and output, respectively, and $\mathbf{b}$ and $\mathbf{c}$ are n-dimensional vectors.   The transfer-function representation is simply

$$\frac{y(s)}{u(s)} = G(s) \tag{2.4-2}$$

where $G(s)$ is the usual scalar transfer function.   A graphical representation of this system is shown in Fig. 2.4-2 for both the state-variable and transfer-function forms.

In the classical terminology, Eqs. (**Ab**) and (**c**) represent the fixed-plant portion of the control problem, i.e., the physical object to be controlled, such as the antenna and its associated drive equipment in a radar-positioning system.   Therefore $G(s)$ is the uncompensated forward-path transfer function, while the control input $u(t)$ is the classical actuating signal, such as the armature current in a dc positioning system.

In the classical unity-ratio feedback system, $u(t)$ is formed by passing the error signal $r(t) - y(t)$ through a compensation network, as shown in Fig. 2.4-3a.   This configuration is to be contrasted with the modern con-

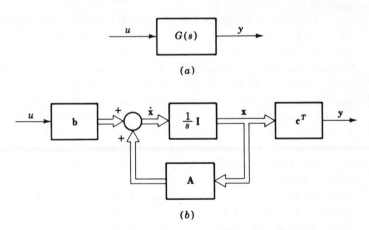

(a)

(b)

Fig. 2.4-2   Block diagrams of a single input–single output system.   (a) Transfer-function representation; (b) state-variable representation.

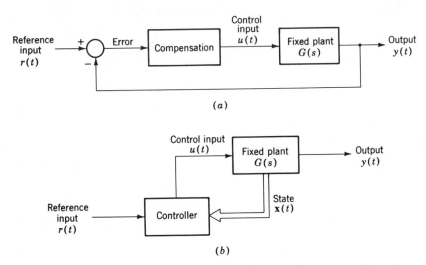

Fig. 2.4-3   Comparison of modern and classical control-system configurations.
(*a*) Classical control configuration; (*b*) modern control configuration.

figuration shown in Fig. 2.4-3*b*, where the control signal is determined by
the controller from the system state and the reference input.   The classical
configuration is simply a special case in which the controller consists of an
error detector and a compensation network.   Chapters 6 to 9 are concerned with the determination of the controller to meet certain performance
specifications.

Before continuing our comparison of the state-variable and transfer-
function methods of system representation, let us discuss some of the
notation, illustrated by the preceding discussion, that is used throughout
the text.   First, the Laplace transform of a time function, such as $y(t)$,
is indicated by simply replacing the time variable t by the frequency
variable s.   The vector $\mathbf{x}(s)$ therefore indicates a vector whose elements
are the Laplace transforms of the respective elements of $\mathbf{x}(t)$, for example,
$x_i(s) = \mathcal{L}[x_i(t)]$.   On the other hand $G(t)$ is the impulse response corresponding to the transfer function $G(s)$.   The arguments s or t are omitted
only when there is no possibility of confusion or where a dual interpretation
may be made, as on the block diagrams of Figs. 2.4-1 and 2.4-2.   There,
the variables may be interpreted as frequency-domain variables [$\mathbf{x}(s)$, for
example] and the various blocks as transfer functions, or the variables may
be interpreted as time-domain variables [$\mathbf{x}(t)$, for example] and the blocks
as linear time-domain operations with s indicating differentiation with
respect to time as usual.

The use of the broad arrow on block diagrams, as in Figs. 2.4-1 and 2.4-2, to indicate vector quantities is continued throughout the book as an assistance to the reader in identifying such quantities.

Since Eqs. (**AB**), (**C**), (**Ab**), and (**c**) play such fundamental roles, appearing over and over again in the following development, they are denoted by special symbols throughout the book for the convenience of the reader. Note also that these equation symbols have been selected to assist the reader in remembering the form of the equations.

The most obvious difference between the state-variable and transfer-function approaches is the suppression of the state vector in the transfer-function approach. This is just another way of saying that the transfer-function approach is concerned only with the input-output characteristics of a system while the state-variable approach provides, in addition, a description of the internal behavior of the system.

Two questions naturally arise with regard to these two methods of system representation. First, under what conditions are the approaches equivalent? In other words, when may a system be represented accurately by either of the two approaches? As we shall see shortly, this question could be phrased, "When is a transfer-function representation of a system adequate?"

The second question is closely related to the first, i.e., "In the cases where the two approaches are equivalent, how are they related?" In particular we are interested in knowing how to find the state-variable representation of a system, given its transfer-function representation, or how to find its transfer function, given the state-variable representation. Since the transfer-function method specifies only the input-output relations of the system, there is always a certain amount of arbitrariness in the selection of the state variables of a system specified only by a transfer function. This means that there is, in general, an infinite number of state-variable representations for a given transfer function. The next three sections discuss three of the more common methods of choosing the state variables beginning with a transfer-function representation.

On the other hand, if a state-variable representation of a system is known, the transfer function of the system is completely and uniquely specified. The fact that the state-variable representation uniquely specifies the transfer-function representation while there is an infinite number of state-variable representations for a given transfer function is simply one manifestation of the fact that the state-variable representation is a more complete description of a system. Before discussing how to determine the transfer function from the state-variable representation, let us examine more closely the question of equivalence of the two approaches.

In order to answer the question of equivalence, it is necessary to define two new concepts known as *controllability* and *observability*. These concepts can be defined and demonstrated only in terms of the state-variable representation of a system. Since the reader is probably more familiar with the transfer-function representation, it is unfortunate that this approach cannot be used. As we shall see, using a transfer function to represent a system presupposes the existence of controllability and observability in the system, and hence there is no meaningful way to discuss the concepts in terms of the transfer-function approach.

The concepts of controllability and observability were first introduced by Kalman (1960). Although these concepts may at first appear too esoteric for an engineer, nevertheless they do play important roles in almost every practical result of modern control theory. The fact that they are necessary to establish the validity of the classical transfer-function methods indicates the importance of these concepts.

The following definitions of controllability and observability are similar to the original definitions of Kalman as presented by Kreindler and Sarachik (1964).

Definition 2.4-1 A system is said to be *controllable* if any initial state $\mathbf{x}(0)$ can be transferred to any final state $\mathbf{x}(t_f)$ in a finite time, $t_f \geq 0$, by some control $\mathbf{u}$.

Controllability implies, as the word itself suggests, the ability of the control input to affect each state variable. Observability, on the other hand, is concerned with the ability of each state variable to influence the output of the system.

Definition 2.4-2 A system is said to be *observable* if every state $\mathbf{x}(0)$ can be exactly determined from measurements of the output $\mathbf{y}$ over a finite interval of time, $0 \leq t \leq t_f$.

Kalman has also defined observability in an alternate fashion by means of a concept known as a *dual system*. The dual of the system described by Eqs. (**AB**) and (**C**) is the system

$$\dot{\mathbf{x}} = \mathbf{A}^T\mathbf{x} + \mathbf{C}^T\mathbf{u}$$
$$\mathbf{y} = \mathbf{B}^T\mathbf{x}$$

with time running backward. In terms of this dual system, Kalman defines observability by saying that the original system [Eqs. (**AB**) and (**C**)] is observable if the dual system is controllable. Hence Kalman speaks of controllability and observability as dual concepts. We shall make further use of this duality property in Chap. 7 in our discussion of Kalman filters.

Quite often the controllability or observability of a system may be determined by inspection from the state-variable representation of the system or its expanded block-diagram representation. If there are states which are completely decoupled from the input, the system is obviously not controllable. If, on the other hand, some states are decoupled from the output, the system is unobservable.

The idea that some of the states may be uncontrollable or unobservable leads one to consider the possibility of dividing the system into a set of subsystems possessing different controllability and observability properties. Gilbert (1963), in fact, has shown that by proper selection of the state vector, a system may always be partitioned into four possible subsystems:

1. A subsystem S_{co} which is controllable and observable
2. A subsystem S_{cu} which is controllable but unobservable
3. A subsystem S_{uo} which is uncontrollable but observable
4. A subsystem S_{uu} which is uncontrollable and unobservable

This partitioning concept is graphically illustrated in Fig. 2.4-4 by showing the way in which the subsystems are related to the input and output. We see, for example, that the observable but uncontrollable subsystem S_{uo} is unaffected by the input **u** but does influence the output **y**.

From Fig. 2.4-4 it is obvious that the transfer function $\mathbf{G}(s)$, where $\mathbf{y}(s) = \mathbf{G}(s)\mathbf{u}(s)$, is dependent only on the controllable and observable portion of the system S_{co}. In other words, a *transfer function is an accurate*

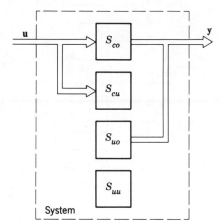

Fig. 2.4-4 Partitioning of a system.

representation of a system if and only if the system is controllable and observable. This is the desired condition of equivalence between the state-variable and transfer-function representations and is one of the primary results of the modern approach to control-system representation.

Example 2.4-1 In order to illustrate this partitioning procedure, let us consider the following state-variable representation of a system.

$$\dot{\mathbf{x}} = \begin{bmatrix} -1 & 0 & 0 \\ 0 & -2 & 0 \\ 0 & 0 & -3 \end{bmatrix} \mathbf{x} + \begin{bmatrix} 1 \\ 1 \\ 0 \end{bmatrix} u$$

$$y = \begin{bmatrix} 1 & 0 & 2 \end{bmatrix} \mathbf{x}$$

A block-diagram representation for this system is shown in Fig. 2.4-5 with the various subsystems indicated. The input-output

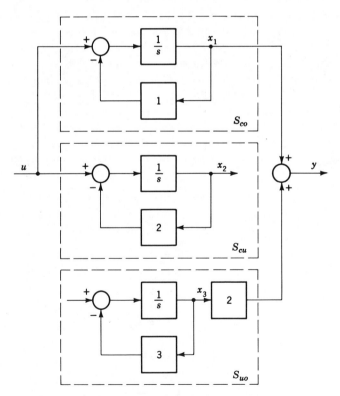

Fig. 2.4-5 Block diagram for Example 2.4-1.

transfer function for this system is obviously

$$\frac{y(s)}{u(s)} = G(s) = \frac{1}{s+1}$$

Hence we see that while the actual system is third-order, the transfer function represents only the first-order controllable and observable subsystem S_{co}.

Unfortunately in order to partition a system as discussed above, it is necessary for the system to be represented in a special and unique manner known as *normal* or *diagonal form*.   Thus, in order to use this approach to determine the controllability and observability, in general it is necessary to transform the system from its present representation into this special representation, which is often not a simple task.   This suggests the desirability of a more direct test for controllability in terms of a general system representation.

While Kalman has presented a more general partitioning procedure, it still requires a special, although not unique, *canonical* representation of the system.   Therefore, it is perhaps justifiable to conclude that partitioning is not a very useful approach to determining controllability and observability of a system, even though it is a very valuable tool in the study of these properties.   Gilbert, for example, has used this approach to investigate the controllability and observability of interconnected systems.   We shall discuss partitioning further in Sec. 2.6, on normal-form representation.   The following direct test can be used to establish the controllability and observability of a system in any state-variable representation.

Theorem 2.4-1   The nth-order multiple input–multiple output system

$$\dot{x}(t) = \mathbf{A}x(t) + \mathbf{B}u(t)$$
$$\mathbf{y}(t) = \mathbf{C}x(t)$$

is

1.   Controllable if and only if the $n \times nr$ composite matrix

$$[\mathbf{B} | \mathbf{AB} | \mathbf{A^2B} | \cdots | \mathbf{A^{n-1}B}] \tag{2.4-3}$$

is of rank n;

2. Observable if and only if the $n \times nm$ composite matrix

$$[C^T \vdots A^T C^T \vdots A^{T2} C^T \vdots \cdots \vdots A^{T(n-1)} C^T] \qquad (2.4\text{-}4)$$

is of rank n.

In the case of the single input–single output system, this test becomes:

Theorem 2.4-2   The nth-order single input–single output system

$$\dot{x}(t) = Ax(t) + bu(t)$$
$$y(t) = c^T x(t)$$

is

1. Controllable if and only if the $n \times n$ composite matrix

$$[b \vdots Ab \vdots A^2 b \vdots \cdots \vdots A^{n-1} b] \qquad (2.4\text{-}5)$$

is nonsingular; i.e., its determinant is nonzero;
2. Observable if and only if the $n \times n$ composite matrix

$$[c \vdots A^T c \vdots A^{T2} c \vdots \cdots \vdots A^{T(n-1)} c] \qquad (2.4\text{-}6)$$

is nonsingular.

These theorems are offered without proof because although the proof is not difficult, it involves concepts which have not been introduced in this treatment. The interested reader is directed to Kreindler and Sarachik (1964) for a simple proof.

Example 2.4-2   As illustration of the application of these tests, let us consider again the system of Example 2.4-1. In this case the system is single input, single output and hence Theorem 2.4-2 is applicable. For this system,

$$Ab = \begin{bmatrix} -1 \\ -2 \\ 0 \end{bmatrix} \quad \text{and} \quad A^2 b = \begin{bmatrix} 1 \\ 4 \\ 0 \end{bmatrix}$$

and the matrix (2.4-5) becomes

$$[\mathbf{b} \vdots \mathbf{Ab} \vdots \mathbf{A^2b}] = \begin{bmatrix} 1 & -1 & 1 \\ 1 & -2 & 4 \\ 0 & 0 & 0 \end{bmatrix}$$

It is obvious that the matrix is singular, since it has an all-zero row, and therefore the system is not controllable.

To check observability we form the matrix

$$[\mathbf{c} \vdots \mathbf{A^T c} \vdots \mathbf{A^{T2} c}] = \begin{bmatrix} 1 & -1 & 1 \\ 0 & 0 & 0 \\ 2 & -6 & 18 \end{bmatrix}$$

which is also singular. We therefore conclude that the system is neither controllable nor observable, as we had previously seen from the matrix partitioning.

It should be obvious to the reader that the rank of matrix (2.4-3) or (2.4-5) is equal to the number of controllable states, while the rank of matrix (2.4-4) or (2.4-6) is equal to the number of observable states.

All systems treated in this book are assumed to be both controllable and observable. This assumption is made, first of all, because almost all practical systems are controllable and observable. This does not mean that the mathematical models of these systems are always controllable and observable. On the contrary, it is quite possible for the mathematical model to lack these properties, particularly if linearization has been necessary. When this happens, however, the model is not an accurate representation of the physical system, and another model should be sought. We therefore assume that the model has been checked to ensure that the controllability and observability of the physical system have been preserved.

The assumption of controllability and observability also makes possible the meaningful use of transfer functions at various points through the book. In the next three sections, for example, we use the transfer function of a system as the starting point for a state-variable representation of the system. Such an approach is obviously senseless if the system is not controllable and observable.

In many control problems the only knowledge one has of the system is an experimentally obtained transfer function. Without an assumption of controllability and observability, such information would be useless.

In addition, this assumption has been tacitly made in every classical control book where the transfer function was the sole means of system representation.   Also there are very few results of modern control theory which deal with uncontrollable or unobservable systems.   The plain fact is that such systems are extremely difficult to treat in any reasonable fashion.   Hence the assumption of controllability and observability is neither new nor unreasonable nor unnecessary.

The reader may wonder why the transfer-function approach is used at all since the state-variable representation provides a more complete description of the system.   The simple truth is that some of the most practical results of modern control theory can be most compactly and usefully presented in terms of transfer functions.   For example, the transfer-function approach is used almost exclusively throughout Chaps. 8 and 9.   We shall therefore make use of both the state-variable and transfer-function representations throughout the book in order to present concepts in the simplest and yet most complete form and to interrelate the time-domain approach with the more familiar transform methods.

Having answered the question of equivalence of the state-variable and transfer-function representation, we turn our attention next to the question of how the two approaches are related.   Let us consider first the problem of determining the transfer function of a system given the state-variable representation

$$\dot{\mathbf{x}}(t) = \mathbf{A}\mathbf{x}(t) + \mathbf{B}u(t) \tag{AB}$$
$$\mathbf{y}(t) = \mathbf{C}\mathbf{x}(t) \tag{C}$$

Since the transfer-function representation is expressed in the frequency domain, we begin by taking the Laplace transform of both equations, assuming as usual in transfer-function determination that the initial conditions on **x** are all zero.

$$s\mathbf{x}(s) = \mathbf{A}\mathbf{x}(s) + \mathbf{B}u(s) \tag{2.4-7}$$
$$\mathbf{y}(s) = \mathbf{C}\mathbf{x}(s) \tag{2.4-8}$$

Grouping the two $\mathbf{x}(s)$ terms in Eq. (2.4-7), we have

$$(s\mathbf{I} - \mathbf{A})\mathbf{x}(s) = \mathbf{B}u(s) \tag{2.4-9}$$

where the identity matrix has been introduced to allow the indicated factoring.   If both sides of this equation are now premultiplied by $(s\mathbf{I} - \mathbf{A})^{-1}$, Eq. (2.4-9) becomes

$$\mathbf{x}(s) = (s\mathbf{I} - \mathbf{A})^{-1}\mathbf{B}u(s)$$

This result may be substituted into Eq. (2.4-8) to obtain

$$\mathbf{y}(s) = \mathbf{C}(s\mathbf{I} - \mathbf{A})^{-1}\mathbf{B}u(s)$$

Comparing this result with Eq. (2.4-1), we see that the transfer-function matrix $\mathbf{G}(s)$ is given by

$$\mathbf{G}(s) = \mathbf{C}(s\mathbf{I} - \mathbf{A})^{-1}\mathbf{B} \qquad (2.4\text{-}10)$$

In the case of the single input–single output system, this result reduces to

$$G(s) = \mathbf{c}^{T}(s\mathbf{I} - \mathbf{A})^{-1}\mathbf{b} \qquad (2.4\text{-}11)$$

The matrix $(s\mathbf{I} - \mathbf{A})^{-1}$ is commonly referred to as the *resolvent matrix* and is designated by $\mathbf{\Phi}(s)$,

$$\mathbf{\Phi}(s) = (s\mathbf{I} - \mathbf{A})^{-1} \qquad (2.4\text{-}12)$$

In terms of this notation, Eqs. (2.4-10) and (2.4-11) become

$$\mathbf{G}(s) = \mathbf{C}\mathbf{\Phi}(s)\mathbf{B} \qquad (2.4\text{-}13)$$

and

$$G(s) = \mathbf{c}^{T}\mathbf{\Phi}(s)\mathbf{b} \qquad (2.4\text{-}14)$$

Example 2.4-3   Consider the system represented by the equations

$$\dot{\mathbf{x}} = \begin{bmatrix} 0 & 1 \\ -2 & -3 \end{bmatrix}\mathbf{x} + \begin{bmatrix} 0 \\ 1 \end{bmatrix}u$$

$$y = [1 \quad 0]\mathbf{x}$$

In this case, the matrix $(s\mathbf{I} - \mathbf{A})$ becomes

$$(s\mathbf{I} - \mathbf{A}) = \begin{bmatrix} s & -1 \\ 2 & s+3 \end{bmatrix}$$

and its inverse is

$$\mathbf{\Phi}(s) = (s\mathbf{I} - \mathbf{A})^{-1} = \frac{\text{adj }(s\mathbf{I} - \mathbf{A})}{\det (s\mathbf{I} - \mathbf{A})} = \frac{\begin{bmatrix} s+3 & 1 \\ -2 & s \end{bmatrix}}{s^2 + 3s + 2}$$

The transfer function of the system is therefore

$$G(s) = \mathbf{c}^T \mathbf{\Phi}(s)\mathbf{b} = \frac{[1 \quad 0]\begin{bmatrix} s+3 & 1 \\ -2 & s \end{bmatrix}\begin{bmatrix} 0 \\ 1 \end{bmatrix}}{s^2 + 3s + 2} = \frac{1}{s^2 + 3s + 2}$$

In the above example, we observe that the determinant of the matrix $(s\mathbf{I} - \mathbf{A})$ is equal to the denominator polynomial of $G(s)$. This is always true for single input–single output systems. We shall discuss this fact further in Sec. 2.6.

Although Eqs. (2.4-13) and (2.4-14) provide a direct method for determining the transfer function of a system from a state-variable representation of the system, it is generally not the most efficient method. This is due to the fact that one must invert the matrix $(s\mathbf{I} - \mathbf{A})$. The inversion of a matrix is never an easy task, and since the elements of the matrix $(s\mathbf{I} - \mathbf{A})$ are functions of s, the job is even more difficult; in addition, it is not easy to program on a computer. Because of this problem, it is often easier to obtain the transfer function by carrying out block-diagram reductions or equivalently signal flow-graph techniques on the block diagram of the state-variable representation.

Consider, for example, the system of Example 2.4-3, which is represented in block-diagram form in Fig. 2.4-6a. By reducing the inner loop, we obtain the system of Fig. 2.4-6b, which may now be further reduced to obtain the transfer function, as shown in Fig. 2.4-6c.

In this simple example, neither the direct method nor the block-diagram approach is difficult to apply. In a more complicated problem, the block-diagram approach could be considerably easier. In fact, for certain types of state-variable representations, the transfer function may often be obtained by inspection using this approach. We shall discuss this feature further in the following sections.

The problem of determining a state-variable representation of a system whose transfer function is known is more complicated than the above problem because an arbitrary choice of state variables must be made. In essence this means that there is an infinite number of state-variable representations for a given system. In the next three sections three of the more common means for choosing the state variables are discussed.

In these sections, we restrict our attention to the single input–single output case. This is done to simplify the discussion of these methods as much as possible and with the feeling that the extension to the general case can be easily made after this special case is mastered.

The problem of state-variable representation of a given transfer

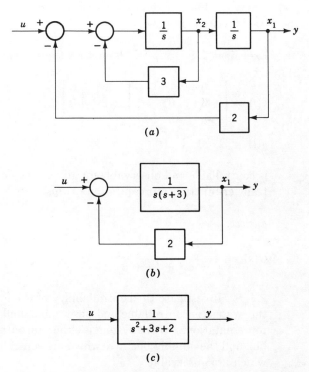

Fig. 2.4-6 (*a*) Original block diagram; (*b*) block diagram after the reduction of the inner loop; (*c*) final block diagram.

function is very closely related to the problem of analog-computer simulation of a transfer function. In fact, the reader familiar with analog-computer simulation will recognize the techniques of the next three sections as nothing more than the *direct, parallel,* and *cascade* methods of transfer-function simulation.

The results of this present section provide two valuable checks on any state-variable representation that we may obtain. First, since the system has been assumed to be controllable and observable, it is obvious that the resulting representation must satisfy these assumptions. If this is not true, we have made a mistake in our state-variable representation.

Second, we may always check to see that the transfer function associated with a state-variable representation is the same as the original transfer function. This uniqueness of the transfer-function representation is also helpful in manipulating state-variable representations. Having fixed some of the elements of the state-variable representation, for example, we may be able to determine the rest of the elements by requiring that the transfer function of the system be correct.

Exercises 2.4 *2.4-1.* Show that the system

$$\dot{x}(t) = \begin{bmatrix} 0 & 1 & 0 \\ 0 & 0 & 1 \\ -a & -b & -c \end{bmatrix} x(t) + \begin{bmatrix} 0 \\ 0 \\ 1 \end{bmatrix} u(t)$$

$$y(t) = [1 \quad 0 \quad 0]x(t)$$

is controllable and observable for all values of a, b, and c. Find the transfer-function representation of this system.

answer:

$$G(s) = \frac{1}{s^3 + cs^2 + bs + a}$$

2.4-2. Investigate the controllability of the following systems. If the system is controllable and observable, find its transfer-function representation. If the system is either uncontrollable or unobservable, find the number of states which are controllable and the number which are observable.

(a) $\dot{x} = \begin{bmatrix} 1 & 1 \\ 1 & 0 \end{bmatrix} x + \begin{bmatrix} 1 \\ 0 \end{bmatrix} u$ (b) $\dot{x} = \begin{bmatrix} 0 & 1 & 0 \\ 0 & 0 & 1 \\ 0 & -1 & -2 \end{bmatrix} x + \begin{bmatrix} 0 \\ 1 \\ 1 \end{bmatrix} u$

      $y = [1 \quad 1]x$ $y = [0 \quad 1 \quad 1]x$

(c) $\dot{x} = \begin{bmatrix} 1 & 0 & 0 \\ 0 & 0 & 1 \\ 1 & -2 & -1 \end{bmatrix} x + \begin{bmatrix} 0 \\ 0 \\ 1 \end{bmatrix} u$

      $y = [1 \quad 0 \quad 1]x$

answers:

(a) Controllable and observable,

$$\frac{y(s)}{u(s)} = \frac{s+1}{s^2 - s - 1}$$

(b) Controllable but unobservable; only one state is observable
(c) Observable but uncontrollable; only two states are controllable

2.5 Phase variables

The use of phase variables to describe a control system is simple, and hence much work has been done in this particular coordinate system. The phase variables are defined as those particular state variables which are obtained from one of the system variables and its $n-1$ derivatives. Often the variable used is the system output, and the remaining state variables are then the $n-1$ derivatives of the output. In a third-order positioning system, for example, the output might be θ, so that $x_1 = \theta$, $x_2 = \dot{\theta} = \omega$, and $x_3 = \dot{\omega}$.

As a specific example, consider the control system represented by the block diagram of Fig. 2.5-1. The transfer function for this example is

$$G(s) = \frac{y(s)}{u(s)} = \frac{K}{s^3 + a_3 s^2 + a_2 s + a_1}$$

By cross multiplying this becomes

$$(s^3 + a_3 s^2 + a_2 s + a_1)y(s) = Ku(s) \qquad (2.5\text{-}1)$$

Since, by definition, a transfer function assumes zero initial conditions, Eq. (2.5-1) is simply the Laplace transform of a third-order differential equation with zero initial conditions. It is a simple matter to reconstruct the original differential equation by identifying derivatives with powers of s, so that in the time domain Eq. (2.5-1) becomes

$$\dddot{y}(t) + a_3 \ddot{y}(t) + a_2 \dot{y}(t) + a_1 y(t) = Ku(t) \qquad (2.5\text{-}2)$$

In order to express Eq. (2.5-2) in phase variables as three first-order differential equations, let $x_1 = y(t)$, and then according to the definition of the phase variables, $x_2 = \dot{y}(t)$, and $x_3 = \ddot{y}(t)$. If these substitutions are made in Eq. (2.5-2), the result is

$$\dot{x}_3 + a_3 x_3 + a_2 x_2 + a_1 x_1 = Ku \qquad (2.5\text{-}3)$$

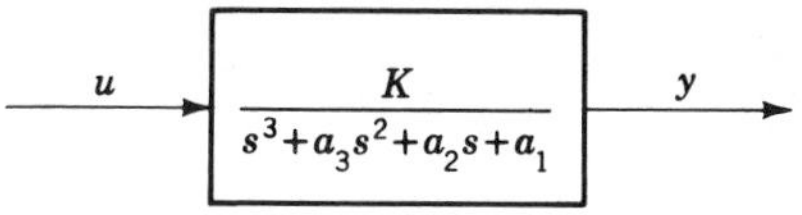

Fig. 2.5-1 System to be represented in phase variables.

and the three first-order differential equations are

$$\dot{x}_1 = x_2 \qquad \dot{x}_2 = x_3$$
$$\dot{x}_3 = -a_1 x_1 - a_2 x_2 - a_3 x_3 + Ku \qquad (2.5\text{-}4)$$

where

$$y = x_1 \qquad (2.5\text{-}5)$$

These equations are of the form (**Ab**) and (**c**), where

$$\mathbf{A} = \begin{bmatrix} 0 & 1 & 0 \\ 0 & 0 & 1 \\ -a_1 & -a_2 & -a_3 \end{bmatrix} \qquad \mathbf{b} = \begin{bmatrix} 0 \\ 0 \\ K \end{bmatrix} \quad \text{and} \quad \mathbf{c} = \begin{bmatrix} 1 \\ 0 \\ 0 \end{bmatrix}$$

and the desired system representation has been achieved.

In the nth-order case, where $G(s)$ is

$$\frac{y(s)}{u(s)} = G(s) = \frac{K}{s^n + a_n s^{n-1} + a_{n-1} s^{n-2} + \cdots + a_2 s + a_1}$$

the resulting nth-order differential equation corresponding to Eq. (2.5-2) is

$$y^{(n)}(t) + a_n y^{(n-1)}(t) + \cdots + a_2 \dot{y}(t) + a_1 y(t) = Ku(t) \qquad (2.5\text{-}6)$$

If we now let $x_1 = y$ and $x_2 = \dot{x}_1, \ldots, x_n = \dot{x}_{n-1}$, then Eq. (2.5-6) becomes

$$\dot{x}_n + a_n x_n + a_{n-1} x_{n-1} + \cdots + a_2 x_2 + a_1 x_1 = Ku$$

The phase-variable representation for this system is then

$$\dot{x}_1 = x_2$$
$$\dot{x}_2 = x_3$$
$$\cdots \cdots \qquad (2.5\text{-}7)$$
$$\dot{x}_{n-1} = x_n$$
$$\dot{x}_n = -a_1 x_1 - a_2 x_2 - \cdots - a_{n-1} x_{n-1} - a_n x_n + Ku$$

with

$$y = x_1 \qquad (2.5\text{-}8)$$

The matrices **A**, **b**, and **c** are then

$$\mathbf{A} = \begin{bmatrix} 0 & 1 & 0 & \cdots & 0 & 0 \\ 0 & 0 & 1 & \cdots & 0 & 0 \\ \cdot & \cdot & \cdot & \cdots & \cdot & \cdot \\ 0 & 0 & 0 & \cdots & 0 & 1 \\ -a_1 & -a_2 & -a_3 & \cdots & -a_{n-1} & -a_n \end{bmatrix}$$

$$\mathbf{b} = \begin{bmatrix} 0 \\ 0 \\ \cdot \\ \cdot \\ \cdot \\ 0 \\ K \end{bmatrix} \qquad \mathbf{c} = \begin{bmatrix} 1 \\ 0 \\ \cdot \\ \cdot \\ \cdot \\ 0 \end{bmatrix}$$

The block diagrams for the phase-variable representations of both the third-order example and the nth-order system are shown in Fig. 2.5-2. A simple examination of these block diagrams, the original transfer function or nth-order differential equations, and the phase-variable representation reveals the fact that any of these means of representation may be

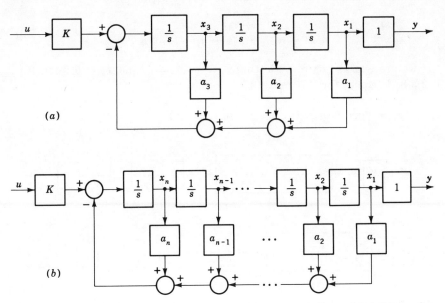

(a)

(b)

Fig. 2.5-2 Block diagrams for the phase-variable representation. (a) A third-order example; (b) an nth-order system.

determined from the other *by inspection*. This is very convenient in situations like that in Chap. 8, where it is desired to transfer one method of representation to the other easily. The reader familiar with analog-computer techniques will note the similarity of the phase-variable representation as illustrated by Fig. 2.5-2 with the direct programming method of simulating transfer functions.

An alternate block diagram for the phase-variable representation is shown in Fig. 2.5-3. This block-diagram form is suggested by a knowledge of the transfer function $G(s)$. Although the phase-variable equations are not so obvious in this alternate block diagram, we shall nevertheless find use for both forms of block diagram in the later chapters.

For the reader who has had little acquaintance with the block-diagram approach to control-system representation, it is pointed out that this development could just as easily have been based on a discussion of the differential equation (2.5-2) or (2.5-6). Since any set of linear simultaneous ordinary differential equations can be arranged as one nth-order equation, the approach from the point of view of either the block diagram or Eq. (2.5-2) or (2.5-6) is completely general and equivalent.

So far we have considered only the case where the transfer function $G(s)$ has no zeros. In order to include zeros in $G(s)$, it is necessary to modify the above approach slightly. To see why this is necessary, let us consider the same third-order example except with an added zero, so that

$$\frac{y(s)}{u(s)} = G(s) = \frac{K(c_2 s + c_1)}{s^3 + a_3 s^2 + a_2 s + a_1} \tag{2.5-9}$$

If we proceed as before by letting $x_1 = y$, $x_2 = \dot{y}$, and $x_3 = \ddot{y}$, then Eq. (2.5-3) becomes for this case

$$\dot{x}_3 + a_3 x_3 + a_2 x_2 + a_1 x_1 = K(c_2 \dot{u} + c_1 u)$$

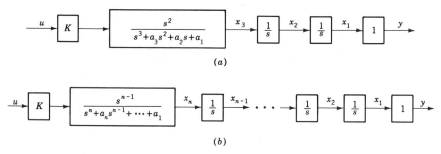

(a)

(b)

Fig. 2.5-3   Alternate block diagrams for the systems shown in Fig. 2.5-2.   (a) A third-order example; (b) an nth-order system.

The phase-variable representation of the plant equation as given by Eqs. (2.5-4) now contains a $\dot{u}$ term on the right-hand side, which violates the assumed form of Eq. (**Ab**).

In order to avoid this problem, let the transfer function $G(s)$ be divided into two parts in the following manner, as shown in Fig. 2.5-4,

$$G(s) = \frac{y(s)}{u(s)} = \frac{x_1(s)}{u(s)} \frac{y(s)}{x_1(s)}$$

where

$$\frac{x_1(s)}{u(s)} = \frac{K}{s^3 + a_3 s^2 + a_2 s + a_1}$$

and

$$\frac{y(s)}{x_1(s)} = c_2 s + c_1$$

The first transfer function, $x_1(s)/u(s)$, is identical to the original transfer function without the zero, and therefore its phase-variable representation is given by Eqs. (2.5-4). The second transfer function, $y(s)/x_1(s)$, however, indicates that y is no longer equal to just x_1 but is now

$$y(t) = c_2 \dot{x}_1(t) + c_1 x_1(t) = c_2 x_2(t) + c_1 x_1(t)$$

where the second expression is written by using the fact that $\dot{x}_1 = x_2$ since the system is in phase variables.

The complete phase-variable description of the system represented by the transfer function (2.5-9) is

$$\begin{bmatrix} \dot{x}_1 \\ \dot{x}_2 \\ \dot{x}_3 \end{bmatrix} = \begin{bmatrix} 0 & 1 & 0 \\ 0 & 0 & 1 \\ -a_1 & -a_2 & -a_3 \end{bmatrix} \begin{bmatrix} x_1 \\ x_2 \\ x_3 \end{bmatrix} + \begin{bmatrix} 0 \\ 0 \\ K \end{bmatrix} u$$

$$y = \begin{bmatrix} c_1 & c_2 & 0 \end{bmatrix} \begin{bmatrix} x_1 \\ x_2 \\ x_3 \end{bmatrix}$$

Fig. 2.5-4   Technique for handling a system with a zero.

A comparison of this result with the representation of the original system without the zero indicates that the only change made by the addition of the zero is in the output expression.

In a similar fashion we can show that the phase-variable representation of the general case where $G(s)$ has $m - 1$ zeros and n poles, $m \leq n$,

$$G(s) = \frac{K(c_m s^{m-1} + c_{m-1} s^{m-2} + \cdots + c_2 s + c_1)}{s^n + a_n s^{n-1} + a_{n-1} s^{n-2} + \cdots + a_2 s + a_1} \tag{2.5-10}$$

is

$$\begin{bmatrix} \dot{x}_1 \\ \dot{x}_2 \\ \cdots \\ \dot{x}_{n-1} \\ \dot{x}_n \end{bmatrix} = \begin{bmatrix} 0 & 1 & 0 & \cdots & 0 & 0 \\ 0 & 0 & 1 & \cdots & 0 & 0 \\ \cdots & & & & & \\ 0 & 0 & 0 & \cdots & 0 & 1 \\ -a_1 & -a_2 & -a_3 & \cdots & -a_{n-1} & -a_n \end{bmatrix} \begin{bmatrix} x_1 \\ x_2 \\ \cdots \\ x_{n-1} \\ x_n \end{bmatrix}$$

$$+ \begin{bmatrix} 0 \\ 0 \\ \cdots \\ 0 \\ K \end{bmatrix} u \tag{2.5-11}$$

$$y = [c_1 \quad c_2 \quad \cdots \quad c_m \quad 0 \quad \cdots \quad 0] \begin{bmatrix} x_1 \\ x_2 \\ \cdots \\ x_{n-1} \\ x_n \end{bmatrix} \tag{2.5-12}$$

Once again we see that the zeros affect only the output expression. The block diagrams of the phase-variable representation of the third-order example and the general nth-order system (Fig. 2.5-5) also illustrate this feature. We note, however, that the phase-variable representation is still easily determined by inspection from the transfer function and vice versa.

It should be noted that the specification of a separate gain term K in the transfer function (2.5-10) is somewhat artificial and arbitrary. For example, either K or c_m could be required to be unity without loss of generality. The general form is retained, however, for added flexibility.

Zeros may also be included by modifying the control vector **b** rather than the output vector **c**. In order to illustrate this technique, consider a simple second-order case

$$G(s) = \frac{K(c_2 s + c_1)}{s^2 + a_2 s + a_1} \tag{2.5-13}$$

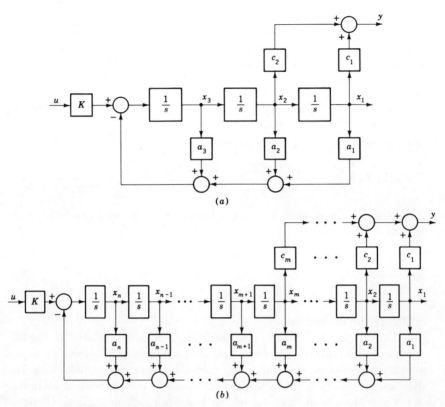

Fig. 2.5-5 Block diagrams for phase-variable representation. (*a*) A third-order example; (*b*) an *n*th-order system.

We wish to find a phase-variable representation of this system in the following form:

$$\begin{bmatrix} \dot{x}_1 \\ \dot{x}_2 \end{bmatrix} = \begin{bmatrix} 0 & 1 \\ -a_1 & -a_2 \end{bmatrix} \begin{bmatrix} x_1 \\ x_2 \end{bmatrix} + \begin{bmatrix} b_1 \\ b_2 \end{bmatrix} u \qquad (2.5\text{-}14)$$

$$y = \begin{bmatrix} 1 & 0 \end{bmatrix} \begin{bmatrix} x_1 \\ x_2 \end{bmatrix} \qquad (2.5\text{-}15)$$

Here we have retained the **A** and **c** matrices appropriate for the case without a zero but have chosen a general control vector. The problem is to determine the values of b_1 and b_2 such that this system represents the original transfer function. For example, if the zero were not present, we know that $b_1 = 0$ and $b_2 = K$ would be the correct answer.

In order to determine the correct values of b_1 and b_2, the uniqueness property of the transfer-function representation is used. More specifically, b_1 and b_2 are picked such that the transfer function associated with the phase-variable representation of Eqs. (2.5-14) and (2.5-15) is equal to the original transfer function of Eq. (2.5-13), i.e., we set

$$\mathbf{c}^T(s\mathbf{I} - \mathbf{A})^{-1}\mathbf{b} = G(s) \tag{2.5-16}$$

For the problem at hand this becomes

$$\begin{bmatrix} 1 & 0 \end{bmatrix} \begin{bmatrix} s & -1 \\ a_1 & s + a_2 \end{bmatrix}^{-1} \begin{bmatrix} b_1 \\ b_2 \end{bmatrix} = \frac{b_1 s + (b_1 a_2 + b_2)}{s^2 + a_2 s + a_1} = \frac{K(c_2 s + c_1)}{s^2 + a_2 s + a_1}$$

Equating like powers of s in the numerator of the two expressions, we obtain

$$b_1 = Kc_2 \qquad b_1 a_2 + b_2 = Kc_1$$

or

$$b_1 = Kc_2 \qquad b_2 = K(c_1 - a_2 c_2)$$

which is the desired result.

Unfortunately, the elements of **b** are not simply related to the elements of the transfer function, and therefore the phase-variable representation cannot be determined by inspection from the transfer function. Because of this fact, this alternate approach to the problem of including zeros is seldom used, and use of the first approach is implied whenever we refer to phase variables.

Although phase variables provide a simple means for representing a system in state-variable form as Eqs. (**Ab**) and (**c**), they do, however, have two disadvantages. First, the solution of the resulting n first-order differential equations is no simpler than the solution of the original nth-order equation. Hence, our state-variable representation is of no assistance in finding the time response of the system.

Second, phase variables are, in general, not real physical variables and therefore are not available for measurement or manipulation. If $G(s)$ has no zeros, the phase variables are equal to the output and its first $n - 1$ derivatives. Unfortunately, it is very difficult physically to take $n - 1$ derivatives if n is greater than 2 or 3; in the presence of noise it becomes impossible. (It is exactly for this reason that analog computers use integrators rather than differentiators.) If $G(s)$ has zeros, the phase variables bear little resemblance to real physical quantities in the system.

Thus, while the phase variables are simple to realize mathematically, they are not a practical set of state variables from a measurement or control point of view. It is shown in later chapters that for a large class of systems it is actually necessary to feed back not just the output but *all the state variables*. It is quite obvious that, from an engineering point of view, all the state variables must be real and measurable. This does not mean that phase variables are not useful and even valuable means of state-variable representation. We shall make extensive use of phase variables throughout Chap. 8, for example.

Before ending our discussion of phase variables, let us consider briefly the concepts of controllability and observability and their relation to the phase-variable representation of a system. It is not difficult to demonstrate that the phase-variable representation is always controllable and observable (see, for example, Exercise 2.4-1). Hence, phase variables may only be used to represent systems which are controllable and observable. In addition, it is possible to show (Kalman, 1963) that any controllable and observable system may always be represented in phase-variable form.

Exercises 2.5   *2.5-1.* Describe the following systems in phase variables.

(a) $G(s) = \dfrac{K}{s^2 + 2s + 1}$ (b) $G(s) = \dfrac{K(s + 1)}{s^2 + s + 1}$

(c) $G(s) = \dfrac{K(s + 2)}{s^3 + 2s^2 + s + 1}$

answers:

(a) $\dot{\mathbf{x}} = \begin{bmatrix} 0 & 1 \\ -1 & -2 \end{bmatrix} \mathbf{x} + \begin{bmatrix} 0 \\ K \end{bmatrix} u$ $y = x_1$

(b) $\dot{\mathbf{x}} = \begin{bmatrix} 0 & 1 \\ -1 & -1 \end{bmatrix} \mathbf{x} + \begin{bmatrix} 0 \\ K \end{bmatrix} u$ $y = x_1 + x_2$

(c) $\dot{\mathbf{x}} = \begin{bmatrix} 0 & 1 & 0 \\ 0 & 0 & 1 \\ -1 & -1 & -2 \end{bmatrix} \mathbf{x} + \begin{bmatrix} 0 \\ 0 \\ K \end{bmatrix} u$ $y = 2x_1 + x_2$

2.5-2. Find the transfer functions for the following systems.

(a) $\dot{\mathbf{x}} = \begin{bmatrix} 0 & 1 & 0 \\ 0 & 0 & 1 \\ -1 & -3 & -4 \end{bmatrix} \mathbf{x} + \begin{bmatrix} 0 \\ 0 \\ 10 \end{bmatrix} u$ $y = \begin{bmatrix} 1 & 0 & 0 \end{bmatrix} \mathbf{x}$

(b) $\dot{\mathbf{x}} = \begin{bmatrix} 0 & 1 & 0 \\ 0 & 0 & 1 \\ -9 & -3 & -1 \end{bmatrix} \mathbf{x} + \begin{bmatrix} 0 \\ 0 \\ K \end{bmatrix} u$ $y = \begin{bmatrix} 4 & 1 & 0 \end{bmatrix} \mathbf{x}$

answers:

(a) $G(s) = \dfrac{10}{s^3 + 4s^2 + 3s + 1}$

(b) $G(s) = \dfrac{K(s + 4)}{s^3 + s^2 + 3s + 9}$

2.6   Canonical variables

The canonical-variable, or normal-form, representation of a system often provides a convenient tool for the development of system properties because of the unique decoupled nature of the representation. By decoupled we refer to the fact that in normal form the n first-order equations are completely independent of each other. This decoupling feature also greatly simplifies the determination of the time response of the system.

We begin our discussion once again with the transfer-function representation of the system.

$$\frac{y(s)}{u(s)} = G(s) = \frac{K(c_m s^{m-1} + c_{m-1} s^{m-2} + \cdots + c_2 s + c_1)}{(s - \lambda_1)(s - \lambda_2)(s - \lambda_3) \cdots (s - \lambda_n)} \qquad m \le n$$

$$(2.6\text{-}1)$$

Here, however, the denominator of the transfer function has been written in factored form. The various values of λ_i are then the poles of the transfer function or equivalently the zeros of the denominator or *characteristic polynomial*,

$$\begin{aligned} \Delta(s) &= (s - \lambda_1)(s - \lambda_2) \cdots (s - \lambda_n) \\ &= s^n + a_n s^{n-1} + a_{n-1} s^{n-2} + \cdots + a_2 s + a_1 \end{aligned}$$

For simplicity, the poles are assumed to be distinct throughout this section. Although the normal-form representation may be extended to the case of multiple poles (Zadeh and Desoer, 1963), the added complexity is questionable since there are few practical systems which cannot be satisfactorily approximated by systems with distinct poles (Bellman, 1960). In addition, both the phase-variable and physical-variable representations may be applied directly to systems with multiple poles.

The first step in the development is to make a partial-fraction expansion of $G(s)$

$$\frac{y(s)}{u(s)} = G(s) = \frac{d_1}{s - \lambda_1} + \frac{d_2}{s - \lambda_2} + \frac{d_3}{s - \lambda_3} + \cdots + \frac{d_n}{s - \lambda_n}$$

$$(2.6\text{-}2)$$

This result may also be written as

$$\frac{y(s)}{u(s)} = G(s) = d_1 \frac{z_1(s)}{u(s)} + d_2 \frac{z_2(s)}{u(s)} + \cdots + d_n \frac{z_n(s)}{u(s)}$$

where

$$\frac{z_i(s)}{u(s)} = \frac{1}{s - \lambda_i} \qquad i = 1, 2, \ldots, n \tag{2.6-3}$$

and

$$y(s) = d_1 z_1(s) + d_2 z_2(s) + \cdots + d_n z_n(s) \tag{2.6-4}$$

In the time domain Eqs. (2.6-3) and (2.6-4) become

$$\dot{z}_i(t) = \lambda_i z_i(t) + u(t) \qquad i = 1, 2, \ldots, n$$
$$y(t) = d_1 z_1(t) + d_2 z_2(t) + \cdots + d_n z_n(t)$$

Using this result, we may now represent the system in Jordan normal form or more simply just *normal form* as

$$\dot{\mathbf{z}} = \mathbf{\Lambda}\mathbf{z} + \mathbf{b}^n u \tag{2.6-5}$$
$$y = \mathbf{c}^{nT}\mathbf{z} \tag{2.6-6}$$

where

$$\mathbf{\Lambda} = \begin{bmatrix} \lambda_1 & & & \mathbf{0} \\ & \lambda_2 & & \\ & & \cdots & \\ \mathbf{0} & & & \lambda_n \end{bmatrix} \qquad \mathbf{b}^n = \begin{bmatrix} 1 \\ 1 \\ \cdots \\ 1 \end{bmatrix} \qquad \text{and} \qquad \mathbf{c}^n = \begin{bmatrix} d_1 \\ d_2 \\ \cdots \\ d_n \end{bmatrix}$$

The state variables in this form are often referred to as *canonical variables*, although this term has also been used to describe phase variables (Kalman, 1963). Here the system matrix $\mathbf{A}$ takes on a particularly simple form as a diagonal matrix of the λ_i's. The elements of the $\mathbf{b}^n$ matrix, on the other hand, are all unity, and the elements of $\mathbf{c}^n$ are simply the residues at the respective poles.

A block diagram of the normal-form representation is shown in Fig. 2.6-1. This block diagram emphasizes the simple and decoupled nature of the normal-form representation. For example, the ith equation of Eq. (2.6-5) appears as

$$\dot{z}_i(t) = \lambda_i z_i(t) + u(t)$$

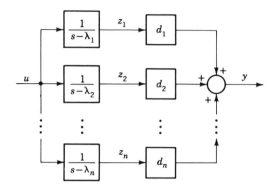

Fig. 2.6-1   Block diagram for the canonical-variable representation.

This equation may be solved for $z_i(t)$ independently of the other **z** coordinates.   Not only that, but the solution of the remaining $n - 1$ equations is of the same form as the solution of the ith equation.   This is an advantage of the normal-form representation.

Figure 2.6-1 also points out the similarity of the normal-form representation to the parallel programming technique of simulating a transfer function on an analog computer.   In fact, the close connection between the state-variable representation and the analog-computer simulation of the system is one of the strong points of the modern control methods.

Example 2.6-1   Let us represent the system described by the transfer function

$$\frac{y(s)}{u(s)} = G(s) = \frac{2(s + 3)}{(s + 1)(s + 2)}$$

in normal form.   Making a partial-fraction expansion of $G(s)$, we obtain

$$G(s) = \frac{4}{s + 1} + \frac{-2}{s + 2}$$

From this partial-fraction expansion the following relationships may be written directly:

$$\frac{z_1(s)}{u(s)} = \frac{1}{s + 1} \qquad \frac{z_2(s)}{u(s)} = \frac{1}{s + 2}$$

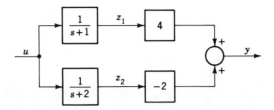

Fig. 2.6-2 Canonical-variable representation of a
second-order system.

and

$$y(s) = 4z_1(s) - 2z_2(s)$$

The normal-form representation is then

$$\begin{bmatrix} \dot{z}_1 \\ \dot{z}_2 \end{bmatrix} = \begin{bmatrix} -1 & 0 \\ 0 & -2 \end{bmatrix} \begin{bmatrix} z_1 \\ z_2 \end{bmatrix} + \begin{bmatrix} 1 \\ 1 \end{bmatrix} u$$

$$y = \begin{bmatrix} 4 & -2 \end{bmatrix} \begin{bmatrix} z_1 \\ z_2 \end{bmatrix}$$

Note that this representation could have been written directly from
the partial-fraction expansion of $G(s)$. A block-diagram representation of this system is shown in Fig. 2.6-2.

In Sec. 2.4 it is mentioned that the determinant of the matrix
$(s\mathbf{I} - \mathbf{A})$ is equal to the denominator polynomial of $G(s)$. By the use of
the normal-form representation it is easy to establish this fact. For this
case, the matrix $(s\mathbf{I} - \mathbf{A}) = (s\mathbf{I} - \mathbf{\Lambda})$ becomes

$$(s\mathbf{I} - \mathbf{\Lambda}) = \begin{bmatrix} s - \lambda_1 & & & 0 \\ & s - \lambda_2 & & \\ & & \ddots & \\ 0 & & & s - \lambda_n \end{bmatrix}$$

Then the determinant of $(s\mathbf{I} - \mathbf{\Lambda})$ is

$$\det \begin{bmatrix} s - \lambda_1 & & & 0 \\ & s - \lambda_2 & & \\ & & \ddots & \\ 0 & & & s - \lambda_n \end{bmatrix}$$
$$= (s - \lambda_1)(s - \lambda_2) \cdots (s - \lambda_n)$$
$$= \Delta(s)$$

which is exactly the denominator of $G(s)$, as predicted.

In matrix terminology the values of s which satisfy the *characteristic equation* of $\mathbf{A}$, namely,

$$\det{(s\mathbf{I} - \mathbf{A})} = 0$$

are referred to as the *eigenvalues* of the matrix $\mathbf{A}$. By the above development, we have shown that, at least in the case of the normal-form representation, the *eigenvalues of $\mathbf{A}$ are identical to the poles of $G(s)$*.

The reader has no doubt noticed that little use has been made of matrix manipulations. The vector-matrix notation has served simply as a convenient shorthand way of writing the system equations. For the remaining portion of this section, an alternate approach to the development of the normal form is presented which makes use of many of the matrix methods introduced in Sec. 2.3. This approach is based on a technique known as a *linear transformation of variables*.

As a vehicle for the discussion, consider the general nth-order linear system represented in state variables in the usual manner by Eqs. (**Ab**) and (**c**):

$$\dot{\mathbf{x}}(t) = \mathbf{A}\mathbf{x}(t) + \mathbf{b}u(t) \qquad\qquad\qquad (\mathbf{Ab})$$
$$y(t) = \mathbf{c}^T\mathbf{x}(t) \qquad\qquad\qquad (\mathbf{c})$$

Suppose now that a new set of variables $\mathbf{z}$ is introduced, where $\mathbf{x}$ and $\mathbf{z}$ are related by a *nonsingular matrix* $\mathbf{P}$ such that

$$\mathbf{x}(t) = \mathbf{P}\mathbf{z}(t) \qquad\qquad\qquad (2.6\text{-}7)$$

Here we see that the two sets of variables are *linearly* related by means of the transformation matrix $\mathbf{P}$.

In order to see how the system equations are affected by means of this transformation, we take the derivative of both sides of Eq. (2.6-7) to obtain

$$\dot{\mathbf{x}}(t) = \mathbf{P}\dot{\mathbf{z}}(t) \qquad\qquad\qquad (2.6\text{-}8)$$

The substitution of Eqs. (2.6-7) and (2.6-8) into Eqs. (**Ab**) and (**c**) yields

$$\mathbf{P}\dot{\mathbf{z}}(t) = \mathbf{A}\mathbf{P}\mathbf{z}(t) + \mathbf{b}u(t) \qquad y(t) = \mathbf{c}^T\mathbf{P}\mathbf{z}(t)$$

The first equation can be premultiplied on both sides by $\mathbf{P}^{-1}$ to obtain

$$\dot{\mathbf{z}} = \mathbf{P}^{-1}\mathbf{A}\mathbf{P}\mathbf{z}(t) + \mathbf{P}^{-1}\mathbf{b}u(t) \qquad y(t) = \mathbf{c}^T\mathbf{P}\mathbf{z}(t)$$

which may be written in the form

$$\dot{\mathbf{z}} = \mathbf{A}^*\mathbf{z} + \mathbf{b}^*u \tag{2.6-9}$$
$$y = \mathbf{c}^{*T}\mathbf{z} \tag{2.6-10}$$

where

$$\mathbf{A}^* = \mathbf{P}^{-1}\mathbf{A}\mathbf{P} \qquad \mathbf{b}^* = \mathbf{P}^{-1}\mathbf{b} \qquad \text{and} \qquad \mathbf{c}^* = \mathbf{P}^T\mathbf{c} \tag{2.6-11}$$

The multiplication by $\mathbf{P}^{-1}$ indicates the reason for the initial assumption that $\mathbf{P}$ is nonsingular, since in order to invert $\mathbf{P}$, it is necessary that $\mathbf{P}$ be nonsingular. Note, however, that $\mathbf{P}$ may be *any* nonsingular matrix. Thus a control system initially expressed by one set of state variables in the form (**Ab**) and (**c**) may be converted to an infinite number of alternate representations of the same form.

The linear transformation of the state-variable representations has two interesting and important properties:

(I) $\det (s\mathbf{I} - \mathbf{A}^*) = \det (s\mathbf{I} - \mathbf{A})$

(II) $\mathbf{c}^{*T}(s\mathbf{I} - \mathbf{A}^*)^{-1}\mathbf{b}^* = \mathbf{c}^T(s\mathbf{I} - \mathbf{A})^{-1}\mathbf{b}$

In order to establish the first property, we begin by replacing $\mathbf{A}^*$ by $\mathbf{P}^{-1}\mathbf{A}\mathbf{P}$, so that

$$\det (s\mathbf{I} - \mathbf{A}^*) = \det (s\mathbf{I} - \mathbf{P}^{-1}\mathbf{A}\mathbf{P}) \tag{2.6-12}$$

Since $\mathbf{P}^{-1}\mathbf{P} = \mathbf{I}$, Eq. (2.6-12) may be rewritten

$$\det (s\mathbf{I} - \mathbf{A}^*) = \det (s\mathbf{P}^{-1}\mathbf{P} - \mathbf{P}^{-1}\mathbf{A}\mathbf{P})$$
$$= \det [\mathbf{P}^{-1}(s\mathbf{I} - \mathbf{A})\mathbf{P}] \tag{2.6-13}$$

Since the determinant of a product is the product of the determinants, Eq. (2.6-13) becomes

$$\det (s\mathbf{I} - \mathbf{A}^*) = \det \mathbf{P}^{-1} \det (s\mathbf{I} - \mathbf{A}) \det \mathbf{P}$$

The determinant of a matrix is a scalar quantity, and therefore the determinants in the above expression may be rearranged so that

$$\det (s\mathbf{I} - \mathbf{A}^*) = \det \mathbf{P}^{-1} \det \mathbf{P} \det (s\mathbf{I} - \mathbf{A}) \tag{2.6-14}$$

Again making use of the fact that the product of determinants is the determinant of the product, we rewrite Eq. (2.6-14) as

$$
\det (s\mathbf{I} - \mathbf{A}^*) = \det (\mathbf{P}^{-1}\mathbf{P}) \det (s\mathbf{I} - \mathbf{A})
$$
$$
= \det (s\mathbf{I} - \mathbf{A}) \qquad (2.6\text{-}15)
$$

which is the result we wished to establish.

This property allows us to conclude that *the* det $(s\mathbf{I} - \mathbf{A})$ *and therefore the eigenvalues of the matrix* $\mathbf{A}$ *are invariant under any linear transformation* of variables. Since we have established in the case of canonic variables that det $(s\mathbf{I} - \mathbf{A}) = \Delta(s)$ and that the eigenvalues of $\mathbf{A}$ are equal to the poles of $G(s)$, these same properties must be true, as they are invariant, for any state-variable representation that may be found by a linear transformation of the normal form. But this is, in fact, every state-variable representation, and therefore we draw the following conclusions: for *any system representation of the form* $(\mathbf{Ab})$ *and* $(\mathbf{c})$, *the*

$$
\det (s\mathbf{I} - \mathbf{A}) = \Delta(s)
$$

and therefore the eigenvalues of $\mathbf{A}$ *are the poles of* $G(s)$. Since the eigenvalues of $\mathbf{A}$ are independent of which $\mathbf{A}$ matrix we use to represent the system, one usually speaks of the *eigenvalues of the system*, since they are an intrinsic property of the system and independent of the representation used.

It should be noted that although we have established the fact that

$$
\det (s\mathbf{I} - \mathbf{A}^*) = \det (s\mathbf{I} - \mathbf{A})
$$

this does *not* imply that

$$
(s\mathbf{I} - \mathbf{A}^*) = (s\mathbf{I} - \mathbf{A}) \qquad (2.6\text{-}16)
$$

In fact, if Eq. (2.6-16) were true, it would not be possible to prove property II, which is

$$
\text{(II)} \quad \mathbf{c}^{*T}(s\mathbf{I} - \mathbf{A}^*)^{-1}\mathbf{b}^* = \mathbf{c}^T(s\mathbf{I} - \mathbf{A})^{-1}\mathbf{b}
$$

In order to demonstrate this second property, we begin once again by substituting the definitions of Eqs. (2.6-11) into the expression to obtain

$$
\mathbf{c}^{*T}(s\mathbf{I} - \mathbf{A}^*)^{-1}\mathbf{b}^* = \mathbf{c}^T\mathbf{P}(s\mathbf{I} - \mathbf{P}^{-1}\mathbf{A}\mathbf{P})^{-1}\mathbf{P}^{-1}\mathbf{b}
$$

Taking the $\mathbf{P}$ and $\mathbf{P}^{-1}$ inside the inverse, we obtain

$$\mathbf{c}^{*T}(s\mathbf{I} - \mathbf{A}^*)^{-1}\mathbf{b}^* = \mathbf{c}^T(s\mathbf{P}\mathbf{P}^{-1} - \mathbf{A})^{-1}\mathbf{b} = \mathbf{c}^T(s\mathbf{I} - \mathbf{A})^{-1}\mathbf{b}$$

which is the desired result.

Since $\mathbf{c}^T(s\mathbf{I} - \mathbf{A})^{-1}\mathbf{b} = G(s)$, this property is nothing more than a statement that the transfer function associated with a state-variable representation is invariant under a linear transformation. This conclusion is simply a restatement of the uniqueness property of the transfer function.

Having investigated some of the properties of linear transformations, let us see how this technique can be used to develop the canonical-variable representation of systems. In particular, we wish to find a matrix $\mathbf{P}$ which transforms a general state-variable representation, $(\mathbf{Ab})$ and $(\mathbf{c})$, into the normal-form representation

$$\dot{\mathbf{z}} = \mathbf{\Lambda}\mathbf{z} + \mathbf{b}^n u \qquad (2.6\text{-}5)$$
$$y = \mathbf{c}^{nT}\mathbf{z} \qquad (2.6\text{-}6)$$

In terms of the transformation relations of Eqs. (2.6-11) this requirement is equivalent to the requirement that $\mathbf{P}$ satisfy the following equations:

$$\mathbf{P}^{-1}\mathbf{A}\mathbf{P} = \mathbf{\Lambda} \qquad (2.6\text{-}17)$$
$$\mathbf{P}^{-1}\mathbf{b} = \mathbf{b}^n \qquad (2.6\text{-}18)$$
$$\mathbf{P}^T\mathbf{c} = \mathbf{c}^n \qquad (2.6\text{-}19)$$

Since the elements of $\mathbf{\Lambda}$ are the poles of the transfer function $G(s)$ or, equivalently, the eigenvalues of $\mathbf{A}$, if $G(s)$ is known, the λ_i's and therefore $\mathbf{\Lambda}$ are known. The only unknown in the first two equations then is the matrix $\mathbf{P}$. In order to put these equations in a more convenient form, premultiply both sides of the equations by $\mathbf{P}$ to obtain

$$\mathbf{A}\mathbf{P} = \mathbf{P}\mathbf{\Lambda} \qquad (2.6\text{-}20)$$

and

$$\mathbf{b} = \mathbf{P}\mathbf{b}^n \qquad (2.6\text{-}21)$$

These two matrix equations generate a set of $n^2 + n$ linear equations in the elements of $\mathbf{P}$ which may be solved to determine $\mathbf{P}$.

Since there are only n^2 elements in $\mathbf{P}$, the reader may wonder how it is possible to satisfy $n^2 + n$ equations. The fact is that if the system is controllable, only n^2 of these $n^2 + n$ equations are linearly independent, and therefore the equations may always be satisfied. The reason that the system must be controllable can be understood if one considers the normal form. In the normal-form representation of Eqs. (2.6-5) and (2.6-6), it is easy to see that the system must be controllable since each state variable is decoupled and individually affected by the control u. Therefore in order to transform a system into this normal-form representation, it is necessary that the system be controllable.

By a similar argument it is possible to show that the system is observable if all the elements of $\mathbf{c}^n$, namely, $d_1, d_2, \ldots, d_n$, are nonzero. In fact, some authors (Gilbert, 1963) have used this approach as a definition of controllability and observability. This is done by taking any $\mathbf{P}$ matrix which satisfies Eq. (2.6-20) and then examining the resulting $\mathbf{b}^n$ and $\mathbf{c}^n$ vectors. If $\mathbf{b}^n$ and $\mathbf{c}^n$ contain only nonzero elements, the system is said to be controllable and observable.[1]

Since we have assumed that all the systems we shall deal with are controllable and observable, the requirement for controllability offers no problem. It is therefore always possible to solve Eqs. (2.6-20) and (2.6-21) to determine $\mathbf{P}$. The observability property may also be used to check the calculations by examining whether all the d_i's are nonzero, as they should be.

Example 2.6-2 In order to illustrate the above procedure for determining $\mathbf{P}$, let us consider once again the system of Example 2.6-1. Here we assume that the system is initially represented in phase-variable form rather than as a transfer function, so that

$$\begin{bmatrix} \dot{x}_1 \\ \dot{x}_2 \end{bmatrix} = \begin{bmatrix} 0 & 1 \\ -2 & -3 \end{bmatrix} \begin{bmatrix} x_1 \\ x_2 \end{bmatrix} + \begin{bmatrix} 0 \\ 2 \end{bmatrix} u$$

$$y = \begin{bmatrix} 3 & 1 \end{bmatrix} \begin{bmatrix} x_1 \\ x_2 \end{bmatrix}$$

Although the eigenvalues of the system, the poles of $G(s)$, are known, let us assume that they are unknown and calculate them from the characteristic equation of $\mathbf{A}$, which is

$$\det (s\mathbf{I} - \mathbf{A}) = \det \begin{bmatrix} s & -1 \\ 2 & s+3 \end{bmatrix} = s^2 + 3s + 2 = 0$$

---

[1] The reader is reminded that we have assumed that the eigenvalues are distinct. If this requirement is not satisfied, these statements must be modified.

The values of s which satisfy this equation are

$$s = -1 \quad \text{and} \quad s = -2$$

and therefore

$$\lambda_1 = -1 \quad \text{and} \quad \lambda_2 = -2$$

so that $\mathbf{\Lambda}$ becomes

$$\mathbf{\Lambda} = \begin{bmatrix} -1 & 0 \\ 0 & -2 \end{bmatrix}$$

The matrix $\mathbf{P}$ may now be found by the use of Eqs. (2.6-20) and (2.6-21), which are in this case

$$\begin{bmatrix} 0 & 1 \\ -2 & -3 \end{bmatrix} \begin{bmatrix} p_{11} & p_{12} \\ p_{21} & p_{22} \end{bmatrix} = \begin{bmatrix} p_{11} & p_{12} \\ p_{21} & p_{22} \end{bmatrix} \begin{bmatrix} -1 & 0 \\ 0 & -2 \end{bmatrix}$$

and

$$\begin{bmatrix} 0 \\ 2 \end{bmatrix} = \begin{bmatrix} p_{11} & p_{12} \\ p_{21} & p_{22} \end{bmatrix} \begin{bmatrix} 1 \\ 1 \end{bmatrix}$$

If these equations are expanded and the elements of the resulting matrices equated, the following six simultaneous equations result.

$$p_{21} = -p_{11} \qquad -2p_{11} - 3p_{21} = -p_{21}$$
$$p_{22} = -2p_{12} \qquad -2p_{12} - 3p_{22} = -2p_{22}$$
$$0 = p_{11} + p_{12} \qquad \quad 2 = p_{21} + p_{22}$$

The reader will immediately recognize that the first and second equations and the third and fourth equations are identical, and therefore there are only the four following equations to satisfy:

$$p_{21} = -p_{11} \qquad p_{22} = -2p_{12}$$
$$0 = p_{11} + p_{12} \qquad 2 = p_{21} + p_{22}$$

Simultaneously solving these four equations gives the following $\mathbf{P}$ matrix:

$$\mathbf{P} = \begin{bmatrix} 2 & -2 \\ -2 & 4 \end{bmatrix}$$

It is suggested that the reader verify that $\mathbf{P}$ satisfies Eqs. (2.6-17) and (2.6-18). We may now use Eq. (2.6-19) to determine $\mathbf{c}^n$.

$$\mathbf{P}^T\mathbf{c} = \begin{bmatrix} 2 & -2 \\ -2 & 4 \end{bmatrix} \begin{bmatrix} 3 \\ 1 \end{bmatrix} = \begin{bmatrix} 4 \\ -2 \end{bmatrix} = \mathbf{c}^n = \begin{bmatrix} d_1 \\ d_2 \end{bmatrix}$$

which is identical to the answer obtained in Example 2.6-1.

The reader may reasonably question why this elaborate linear-transformation approach to the canonical-variable representation has been developed, since it is possible to achieve the same result in an easier manner directly from the transfer function. There are several answers to this question. First, the linear-transformation technique is valuable in modern control concepts since it provides a procedure for relating two different sets of state variables. Second, the transfer function for a system may not be known if one has initially represented the system in state-variable form. Therefore rather than obtaining the transfer function and then representing the system in normal form, the linear-transformation technique allows us to transform the system to normal form directly. Third, it is often desirable to know the transformation matrix $\mathbf{P}$ even if the transfer function is known. This is the case whenever we wish to translate results obtained in normal form into another set of state variables.

Although the normal-form representation is valuable because of the simple decoupled nature of the resulting first-order equations, it does have two disadvantages. First, the normal form cannot be determined by inspection from the transfer function as phase variables can. This means that it is more difficult to relate the normal form and transfer functions than to relate phase variables and transfer functions.

Second, the canonical variables, like phase variables, are not real physical variables. This fact is perhaps most strikingly obvious if there are complex eigenvalues. In this case some of the canonical variables are also complex.

This means that $\mathbf{x}$ and $\mathbf{z}$ are related by a $\mathbf{P}$ matrix, some of the elements of which are complex. Therefore, in the physical system, or alternately on the block-diagram representation of the physical system, there is no set of real state variables that can be combined to form the canonical variables.

Exercises 2.6   *2.6-1.* For the systems shown below, express the equations of motion in (1) phase variables and (2) normal coordinates. Find the normal coordinates by linear transformation from the phase-variable representation and directly from the transfer function.

(a) $\quad G(s) = \dfrac{(s + 8)}{(s + 2)(s + 6)}$ $\qquad\qquad$ (b) $\quad G(s) = \dfrac{10(s + 4)}{s^3 + 3s^2 + 2s}$

answers:

(a) $\quad \dot{z} = \begin{bmatrix} -2 & 0 \\ 0 & -6 \end{bmatrix} z + \begin{bmatrix} 1 \\ 1 \end{bmatrix} u \qquad y = [3\tfrac{1}{2} \quad -\tfrac{1}{2}]z$

(b) $\quad \dot{z} = \begin{bmatrix} 0 & 0 & 0 \\ 0 & -1 & 0 \\ 0 & 0 & -2 \end{bmatrix} z + \begin{bmatrix} 1 \\ 1 \\ 1 \end{bmatrix} u \qquad y = [20 \quad -30 \quad 10]z$

2.6-2. The state-variable equations for a particular system are given below. Describe this system in canonical variables using the linear-transformation techniques. Draw a block diagram corresponding to the given equations and one corresponding to the canonical-form representation.

$$\dot{x} = \begin{bmatrix} 0 & 1 \\ -2 & -2 \end{bmatrix} x + \begin{bmatrix} 0 \\ 4 \end{bmatrix} u$$

$$y = [1 \quad 0]x$$

answer:

$$\dot{z} = \begin{bmatrix} -1 - j & 0 \\ 0 & -1 + j \end{bmatrix} z + \begin{bmatrix} 1 \\ 1 \end{bmatrix} u$$

$$y = [2j \quad -2j]z$$

2.7 Physical variables

The method of system representation in real physical-system variables is much more intuitive than the methods of the previous two sections. In fact, the reader may feel that this approach is so straightforward that it should not be called a method! The physical-system-variable representa-

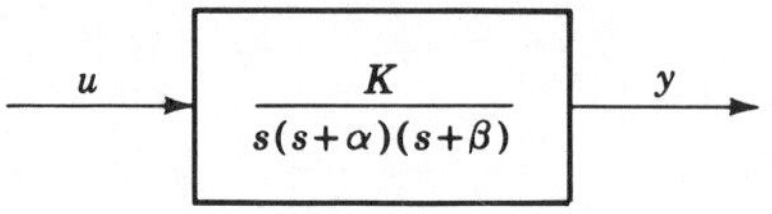

Fig. 2.7-1 Block diagram that can be represented by several state-variable forms.

tion is discussed separately here as a first step in emphasizing an outlook that is advocated throughout this book.

By way of introduction, let us start with the block-diagram approach used in the discussion of phase and canonic variables. Consider, for example, the rather specific block diagram of Fig. 2.7-1. One may think of this block diagram as originating from a simple position-control system containing a motor with electrical and mechanical time constants. This is not a unique interpretation by any means, as the block diagram may describe any other third-order system. In fact, that is the point. Because an overall block diagram is all that is given, one can only speculate about the physical origins of the example.

In order to realize several state-variable representations, the block diagram of Fig. 2.7-1 can be redrawn, as in Fig. 2.7-2a, b, or c. If this is done, as shown, so that each block contains only one pole, the state variables can be identified, and state-variable equations can be written directly. For Fig. 2.7-2b, for instance, the state-variable equations are

$$\dot{x}_1 = x_2$$
$$\dot{x}_2 = -\beta x_2 + \tfrac{1}{2}x_3$$
$$\dot{x}_3 = -\alpha x_3 + 2Ku$$
$$y = x_1$$

(a)

(b)

(c)

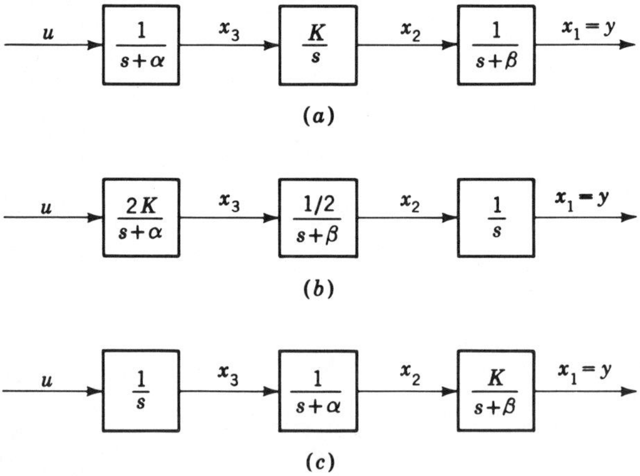

Fig. 2.7-2 Several sets of state variables from the same transfer function.

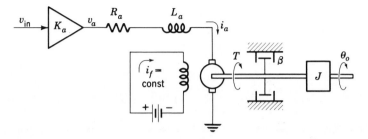

Fig. 2.7-3   Open-loop positioning system.

It is not possible to say whether or not these particular state variables have any physical meaning.

The obvious approach is to break the block diagram up in such a way that the physical-system variables can be identified. A more basic starting point is the governing equations themselves.

Let us assume that the block diagram of Fig. 2.7-1 actually does represent an open-loop positioning system, shown diagrammatically in Fig. 2.7-3. On the diagram physical-system variables and parameters are identified, where

θ_o = output position angle

v_{in} = input voltage

v_a = output voltage of linear amplifier

i_a = motor armature current

i_f = motor field current, assumed constant

K_a = gain of linear amplifier, assumed to have no significant time constants

R_a = resistance of armature winding

L_a = inductance of armature winding

J = inertial load

β = viscous-damping constant

K_T = torque constant of motor

K_v = back-emf constant of motor

The differential equations that govern the dynamics of the system are

$$J\ddot{\theta}_o + \beta\dot{\theta}_o = K_T i_a \tag{2.7-1}$$
$$L_a \dot{i}_a + R_a i_a = V_a - K_v \dot{\theta}_o \tag{2.7-2}$$

On the basis of these equations, the block diagram for this system can be drawn, as Fig. 2.7-4.

With all the system variables identified, it is a simple matter to choose physically meaningful state variables. The output θ_o is chosen as

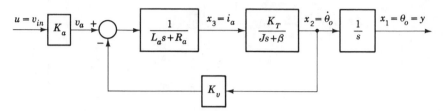

Fig. 2.7-4   Block-diagram representation of the control system of Fig. 2.7-3.

x_1 so that $y = x_1$, and the other choices are

$$x_2 = \dot{\theta}_o \quad . \quad x_3 = i_a \qquad u = v_{in} \tag{2.7-3}$$

In terms of the state variables defined in Eq. (2.7-3) the state equations may be written directly from Eqs. (2.7-1) and (2.7-2) or from Fig. 2.7-4.   First, from the definitions of x_1 and x_2, we have

$$\dot{x}_1 = x_2$$

Next, having substituted the definitions into Eq. (2.7-1), we obtain

$$J\ddot{x}_1 + \beta\dot{x}_1 = K_T x_3$$

Since $\dot{x}_1 = x_2$, this may be written as

$$J\dot{x}_2 + \beta x_2 = K_T x_3$$

or

$$\dot{x}_2 = -\frac{\beta}{J} x_2 + \frac{K_T}{J} x_3$$

Finally we use Eq. (2.7-2) to write

$$\dot{x}_3 = -\frac{R_a}{L_a} x_3 - \frac{K_v}{L_a} x_2 + \frac{K_a}{L_a} u$$

If these results are collected, the following physical-system representation is obtained:

$$\dot{x}_1 = x_2$$

$$\dot{x}_2 = -\frac{\beta}{J} x_2 + \frac{K_T}{J} x_3$$

$$\dot{x}_3 = -\frac{K_v}{L_a} x_2 - \frac{R_a}{L_a} x_3 + \frac{K_a}{L_a} u \tag{2.7-4}$$

$$y = x_1 \tag{2.7-5}$$

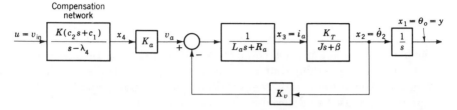

Fig. 2.7-5 Block diagram of Fig. 2.7-4 with a compensation network added.

These are the describing equations for the given positioning system that is pictured in Fig. 2.7-3 or equivalently represented by the block diagram of Fig. 2.7-4. Of course, Fig. 2.7-4 could be reduced to the overall system of Fig. 2.7-1. Obviously, physically meaningful state variables could not be chosen from that diagram.

One problem arises in the use of physical variables that does not occur in the other methods of system representation. It is introduced by zeros in $G(s)$. Each zero of $G(s)$ is always intimately related to a specific pole of $G(s)$. For example, if $G(s)$ includes a network, e.g., a lead or lag network, each of these networks introduces a zero. Physically this zero is associated with the pole of the network. If a lead or lag network is included in the position system that has been discussed in this section, the block diagram appears as in Fig. 2.7-5. Here the output of the compensation network is a physical variable, e.g., a voltage, and the relationship between u and x_4 is specified by the interconnecting block. In the time domain, the fourth state equation is

$$\dot{x}_4 = \lambda_4 x_4 + K c_2 \dot{u} + K c_1 u$$

Since $\dot{u}$ is involved on the right-hand side, this equation is not compatible with the form (**Ab**).

This problem was encountered before in the discussion of phase variables. There the means used to avoid the difficulty were a modification of either the output vector **c** or the control vector **b** (see Sec. 2.5). We have no such freedom in this case, since both the output and the control are unique and are defined by the physical system under study. If we wish to retain the use of real physical variables, we are not free to define alternate control or output expressions, no matter how convenient it might be. We do not meet this problem again until Chap. 9.

It has been implied throughout this chapter that the governing system differential equations and the block diagram convey the same information. They do, but only in an overall input-to-output sense. This example clearly demonstrates that a variety of system representations can be chosen from a block diagram, although many of these representations are not composed of physically real variables.

A better way to treat the topic of system representation is to ignore the block-diagram approach completely and simply write the state equations from the governing differential equations. That is the approach of Chap. 3, where use is made of the state function of Lagrange and Lagrange's equations are used to determine the state equations.

In this and the preceding two sections, we have discussed three different techniques for obtaining the state-variable representation of a system initially described by an overall input-output transfer function. These three methods are not the only means of accomplishing the desired result; in fact, there is an infinite variety of means, but the methods described here are the most common and effective. Let us summarize those results here for convenient reference.

First, phase variables afford a simple and direct means of translating the transfer-function information into a unique state-variable form. At the same time, they lack physical significance, particularly if the system has zeros, and they also offer little assistance in obtaining the time response.

Canonical variables, on the other hand, offer an indirect means of changing the transfer function into a unique state-variable representation. At the same time, however, the resulting system representation is in a simple decoupled form which facilitates an investigation of system properties and a determination of the time response. Once again, the state variables are not real physical variables and may, in fact, be complex quantities.

The use of the physical-system-variable representation, by its very essence, implies that the resulting state variables are real physical variables which can be measured and used for control purposes. By the very fact that this means of system representation is intimately related to the physical system, the approach no longer produces a unique form for the resulting state-variable representation. The same transfer function, for example, may generate two different representations if the physical system is different. The effort involved in determining this state-variable representation and its time response probably falls somewhere between the limits of the phase-variable and canonical-variable approaches.

Even though we reject the use of the phase variables and the canonical variables on physical grounds, this does not mean that we shall no longer have occasion to consider these particular coordinate frames. Because the mathematical characteristics of these sets of coordinates are so desirable, we shall continue to use them, as long as we realize that in the physical system we must ultimately deal with physical variables.

Exercises 2.7   *2.7-1.* For the system shown below find the equations of motion in the form (**Ab**) and (**c**). Use two different sets of variables, determined by breaking $G(s)$ into individual blocks, as indicated.

(a) $G(s) = \dfrac{2}{s+3}\dfrac{s+2}{s+1}\dfrac{1}{s}$ (b) $G(s) = \dfrac{2}{s}\dfrac{1}{s+1}\dfrac{s+2}{s+3}$

answers:

(a) $\dot{\mathbf{x}} = \begin{bmatrix} 0 & 1 & 0 \\ 0 & -1 & -1 \\ 0 & 0 & -3 \end{bmatrix} \mathbf{x} + \begin{bmatrix} 0 \\ 2 \\ 2 \end{bmatrix} u$ $y = x_1$

(b) $\dot{\mathbf{x}} = \begin{bmatrix} -3 & 1 & 1 \\ 0 & -1 & 1 \\ 0 & 0 & 0 \end{bmatrix} \mathbf{x} + \begin{bmatrix} 0 \\ 0 \\ 2 \end{bmatrix} u$ $y = x_1$

2.7-2. Find a block-diagram representation for the system shown in Fig. 2.7-6. Express the equations of motion in the form (**Ab**) and (**c**), with $x_1 = \theta_o$; $x_2 = e_t$, the tachometer voltage; and $x_3 = i_f$, the field current.

answer:

$$\dot{x}_1 = \frac{1}{K_T} x_2 \qquad \dot{x}_2 = -\frac{\beta}{J} x_2 + \frac{K_e K_T}{J} x_3$$

$$\dot{x}_3 = -\frac{1}{L_f} x_2 - \frac{R_f}{L_f} x_3 + \frac{K_a}{L_f} u$$

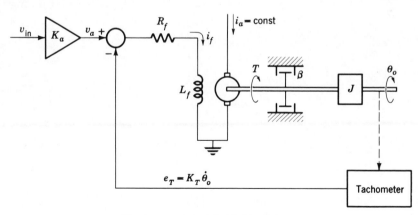

$K_e =$ torque constant, that is $T = K_e i_f$

Fig. 2.7-6   Exercise 2.7-2.

2.8   Representation of nonlinear systems

An advantage of time-domain techniques is that they can be directly extended to include time-varying, sampled-data, nonlinear systems, or a combination of both.   As an illustration of this feature, this section outlines how nonlinear-gain-type control systems can be represented in state-variable form.

Consider the block diagram of Fig. 2.8-1.   This may be thought of as a continuation of the example of the positioning system of Sec. 2.7. Here, however, the loop has been closed by assuming that the input u is equal to the negative of the output, $y = x_1$.   A further complication is that the amplifier is no longer assumed to be linear but is allowed to saturate, as indicated in Fig. 2.8-1.   The output of the amplifier is therefore

$$v_a = f(u) = f(-y) = f(-x_1)$$

Making the substitution of this nonlinear v_a for the quantity $K_a u$ in Eq. (2.7-4), we obtain the following state-variable representation of this nonlinear closed-loop position regulator:

$$\dot{x}_1 = x_2 \qquad \dot{x}_2 = -\frac{\beta}{J} x_2 + \frac{K_T}{J} x_3$$

$$\dot{x}_3 = -\frac{K_v}{L_a} x_2 - \frac{R_a}{L_a} x_3 + \frac{1}{L_a} f(-x_1) \qquad y = x_1$$

The phase-variable and canonical-variable representation may also be used for nonlinear systems.   Consider, for example, the general nth-order nonlinear-gain closed-loop system shown in Fig. 2.8-2.   The phase-

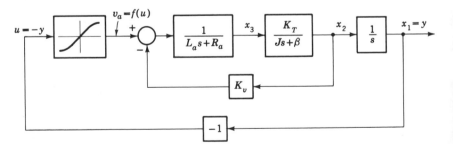

Fig. 2.8-1   Positioning system of Sec. 2.7 with the loop closed and a nonlinear amplifier.

variable description of this system is

$$\dot{x}_1 = x_2$$
$$\dot{x}_2 = x_3$$
$$\cdot \ \cdot \ \cdot \ \cdot \ \cdot$$
$$\dot{x}_{n-1} = x_n$$
$$\dot{x}_n = -a_1 x_1 - a_2 x_2 - \ \cdot \ \cdot \ \cdot \ - a_n x_n + K f(-y)$$

where

$$y = [c_1 \quad c_2 \quad \cdot \ \cdot \ \cdot \quad c_m \quad 0 \quad \cdot \ \cdot \ \cdot \quad 0]\mathbf{x}$$

Here $G(s)$ is given by

$$\frac{y(s)}{u(s)} = G(s) = \frac{K(c_m s^{m-1} + c_{m-1} s^{m-2} + \ \cdot \ \cdot \ \cdot \ + c_2 s + c_1)}{s^n + a_n s^{n-1} + \ \cdot \ \cdot \ \cdot \ + a_2 s + a_1}$$

In order to represent this nonlinear system in canonical variables, we begin, as before, by making a partial-fraction expansion of the transfer function of the linear portion of the system.

$$G(s) = \frac{d_1}{s - \lambda_1} + \frac{d_2}{s - \lambda_2} + \ \cdot \ \cdot \ \cdot \ + \frac{d_n}{s - \lambda_n}$$

When the same definition for the canonical variables as in Sec. 2.6 is used, the canonical-variable representation of the nonlinear-gain system is

$$\dot{z}_1 = \lambda_1 z_1 + f(-y)$$
$$\dot{z}_2 = \lambda_2 z_2 + f(-y)$$
$$\cdot \ \cdot \ \cdot \ \cdot \ \cdot \ \cdot \ \cdot \ \cdot \ \cdot \ \cdot \ \cdot \qquad \qquad (2.8\text{-}1)$$
$$\dot{z}_n = \lambda_n z_n + f(-y)$$

where

$$y = [d_1 \quad d_2 \quad \cdot \ \cdot \ \cdot \quad d_n]\mathbf{z}$$

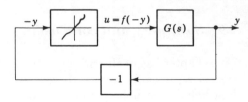

Fig. 2.8-2 General nth-order non-linear-gain closed-loop system.

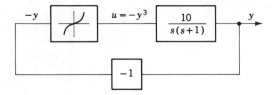

Fig. 2.8-3   Exercise 2.8-1.

This is a familiar form, but now u in each of the n equations has been replaced by $f(-y)$.   Since y is actually a linear combination of all the canonical variables, we see that in the nonlinear case the equations have not been decoupled.   Nonlinear-gain-type representations as in Eqs. (2.8-1) are referred to as being in *Lurie's canonical form.*

In this section, the state-variable representations of the preceding sections have been applied to the description of nonlinear-gain systems. This ability of the state-variable representation of systems to encompass nonlinear as well as time-varying systems is one of the strongest recommendations of the modern method.

In order to represent time-varying systems, it is only necessary to allow the matrices **A**, **B**, and **C** to become functions of time as

$$\dot{\mathbf{x}} = \mathbf{A}(t)\mathbf{x}(t) + \mathbf{B}(t)\mathbf{u}(t) \qquad \mathbf{y} = \mathbf{C}(t)\mathbf{x}(t)$$

Exercises 2.8   *2.8-1.*   Represent the nonlinear-gain system shown in Fig. 2.8-3 in (*a*) phase-variable form and (*b*) normal form.

answer:

$$(a) \quad \dot{\mathbf{x}} = \begin{bmatrix} 0 & 1 \\ 0 & -1 \end{bmatrix} \mathbf{x} + \begin{bmatrix} 0 \\ 10 \end{bmatrix} (-x_1)^3 \qquad y = x_1$$

$$(b) \quad \dot{\mathbf{z}} = \begin{bmatrix} 0 & 0 \\ 0 & -1 \end{bmatrix} \mathbf{z} + \begin{bmatrix} 1 \\ 1 \end{bmatrix} (-10z_1 + 10z_2)^3$$

$$y = \begin{bmatrix} 10 & -10 \end{bmatrix} \mathbf{z}$$

2.9   Summary and conclusion

This chapter has dealt with one aspect of problem formulation, namely, system representation in state-variable form.   The discussion has been based almost entirely upon the assumption that the control system being studied is known in the form of a block diagram. Admittedly, this is not a valid assumption in many cases. This procedure has been adopted purely as a means of transition from the familiar block-diagram representation in the frequency domain to the vector-matrix notation and first-order differential equations of the time domain.

Although the general linear transformation of variables has been discussed briefly, this chapter has emphasized three particular means of system description: description in phase variables, canonical variables, and physical-system variables. The phase variables prove to be the simplest to realize, while the canonical variables are the simplest to solve. Either of these coordinate frames may have particular state variables that are not measurable or real. The use of physical-system variables has been advocated, with a view toward the future requirement of feeding back all the state variables.

The following chapter presents a more general approach to the question of system representation in terms of physical-system variables by the use of the state function of Lagrange.

2.10 Problems

2.10-1. Show that $\mathbf{A}$ adj $\mathbf{A}$ = det $(\mathbf{A})\mathbf{I}$ and verify for

$$\mathbf{A} = \begin{bmatrix} 0 & -1 & -3 \\ 0 & 0 & 2 \\ -2 & 0 & -2 \end{bmatrix}$$

2.10-2. Show that $[(\mathbf{AB})^{-1}]^T = (\mathbf{A}^T)^{-1}(\mathbf{B}^T)^{-1}$ and verify for

$$\mathbf{A} = \begin{bmatrix} 1 & 1 \\ 2 & 1 \end{bmatrix} \quad \text{and} \quad \mathbf{B} = \begin{bmatrix} 1 & 2 \\ 0 & 4 \end{bmatrix}$$

2.10-3. Find the system representation $(\mathbf{AB})$ and $(\mathbf{c})$ for the block diagram of Fig. 2.10-1 using the variables indicated on the diagram. Discuss the controllability and observability of the system.

2.10-4. In the Ward-Leonard system shown in Fig. 2.10-2 the generator is driven at a constant speed, and the motor is excited by a constant current. The load torque T_L and the generator field voltage v_f are the system inputs, while the motor-shaft position θ_m is the output. Make assumptions that result in linear differential equations and draw a block diagram for the system showing θ_m, $\dot{\theta}_m$, e_g, v_f, and T_L. Express the system equations in the form $(\mathbf{AB})$ and $(\mathbf{c})$ using the above variables.

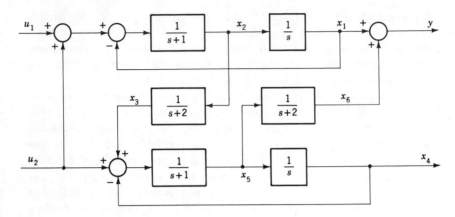

Fig. 2.10-1   Prob. 2.10-3.

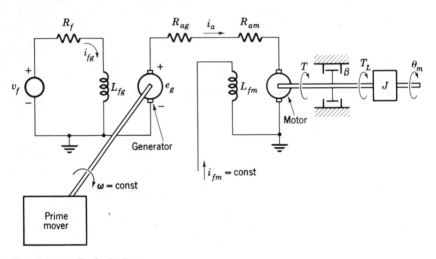

Fig. 2.10-2   Prob. 2.10-4.

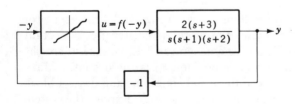

Fig. 2.10-3   Prob. 2.10-5.

2.10-5. Express the equations of motion in normal form for the nonlinear system shown in Fig. 2.10-3.

2.10-6. For the system given below represent the system in (*a*) phase variables, (*b*) canonical variables, and (*c*) physical variables, dividing the transfer function as shown. Find the transformation matrices relating each representation to the others. Verify in all cases that the transfer function is unique.

$$G(s) = \frac{10}{s+2} \frac{s+5}{s+1} \frac{1}{s}$$

2.10-7. Find the transfer function for the system given below (*a*) by means of Eq. (2.4-11) and (*b*) by block-diagram manipulations.

$$\dot{\mathbf{x}} = \begin{bmatrix} 0 & 1 & 1 \\ 0 & 2 & -1 \\ -1 & -2 & 0 \end{bmatrix} \mathbf{x} + \begin{bmatrix} 1 \\ 0 \\ 1 \end{bmatrix} u$$

$$y = [1 \quad 0 \quad 1]\mathbf{x}$$

2.10-8. For the system

$$\dot{\mathbf{x}} = \begin{bmatrix} 0 & 1 \\ -3 & -2 \end{bmatrix} \mathbf{x} + \begin{bmatrix} 0 \\ 1 \end{bmatrix} u$$

$$y = [1 \quad 1]\mathbf{x}$$

use the linear transformation

$$\mathbf{z} = \begin{bmatrix} 1 & 1 \\ 0 & 2 \end{bmatrix} \mathbf{x}$$

to find the system representation in terms of the **z** variables. Verify that

(*a*) $\det (s\mathbf{I} - \mathbf{A^*}) = \det (s\mathbf{I} - \mathbf{A})$
(*b*) $\mathbf{c}^{*T}(s\mathbf{I} - \mathbf{A^*})\mathbf{b^*} = \mathbf{c}^T(s\mathbf{I} - \mathbf{A})\mathbf{b}$

References

Bellman, R.: "Introduction to Matrix Analysis," McGraw-Hill Book Company, New York, 1960.

DeRusso, P. M., R. J. Roy, and C. M. Close: "State Variables for Engineers," John Wiley & Sons, Inc., New York, 1965.

Dorf, R. C.: "Time-domain Analysis and Design of Control Systems," Addison-Wesley Publishing Company, Inc., Reading, Mass., 1965.

Gilbert, E. G.: Controllability and Observability in Multi-variable Control Systems, *J. Soc. Ind. Appl. Math.*, ser. A, *Control*, vol. 1, no. 2, pp. 128–151, 1963.

Gupta, S. C.: "Transform and State Variable Methods in Linear Systems," John Wiley & Sons, Inc., New York, 1966.

Hohn, F. E.: "Elementary Matrix Algebra," The Macmillan Company, New York, 1958.

Huelsman, L. P.: "Circuits, Matrices, and Linear Vector Spaces," McGraw-Hill Book Company, New York, 1963.

Kalman, R. E., On the General Theory of Control Systems, "Proceedings IFAC Moscow Congress," vol. 1, pp. 481–492, Butterworth, Inc., Washington, D.C., 1960.

———: Mathematical Description of Linear Dynamical Systems, *J. Soc. Ind. Appl. Math.*, ser. A, *Control*, vol. 1, no. 2, pp. 152–192, 1963.

Korn, G. A., and T. M. Korn: "Mathematical Handbook for Scientists and Engineers," McGraw-Hill Book Company, New York, 1961.

Kreindler, E., and P. E. Sarachik: On the Concepts of Controllability and Observability of Linear Systems, *IEEE Trans. Autom. Control*, vol. AC-9, no. 2, pp. 129–136, April, 1964.

Nering, E. D.: "Linear Algebra and Matrix Theory," John Wiley & Sons, Inc., New York, 1963.

Zadeh, L. A., and C. A. Desoer: "Linear System Theory," McGraw-Hill Book Company, New York, 1963.

three system representation and the state function of lagrange

3.1 Introduction and outline of chapter

The previous chapter served to demonstrate a variety of means by which a conventional control system can be described in state-variable form. Each of the methods discussed for achieving such representation assumed that the given system was described in transfer-function form. The resulting variables may or may not have any physical meaning, although it was pointed out that physical variables can be chosen from the block diagram if care is exercised in their choice. If physical variables are to be chosen, however, more knowledge of the system must be available than just the transfer function.

In this chapter no recourse is made to the transfer function. As previously mentioned, the transfer function is not even a logical starting point. Physical systems just are not packaged in a black box with the transfer function painted on the outside. The transfer function was used in the previous chapter simply because it is so familiar and well understood.

This chapter is devoted to a systematic method of determining the governing differential equations, based on the lagrangian state function ℒ and Lagrange's equation. By way of introduction, the idea of the state function and the properties of state functions are mentioned. The generalized coordinates of classical mechanics are discussed in terms of the more familiar concepts of kinetic and potential energy and are related to the state variables of Chap. 2. The development of Lagrange's equation then proceeds from Newton's law. The student of classical mechanics may view the development here with some skepticism; however, the aim of this section is not to duplicate the comprehensive field of classical mechanics but only to take that portion which proves to be useful in automatic control.

While Lagrange's equation does not provide a complete and universal solution to the problem of system representation, it does prove to be valuable in a large number of control problems. In addition, and perhaps of equal importance, most of the modern optimal-control theory is closely patterned after the classical-mechanical formulation of Lagrange's equation. Hence the development of Lagrange's equation not only provides a valuable tool for system representation but also provides an introduction to the terminology and methodology of optimal-control theory.

The examples included in the later sections of this chapter involve electrical, mechanical, and electromechanical control systems. This is not meant to imply that the range of applicability of Lagrange's equations is restricted to systems in the above categories. Instead the presentation here is intentionally limited in breadth so that it may be probed in depth.

3.2   State function of Lagrange

In this section the basic concepts of the lagrangian formulation are introduced. In particular, attention is directed toward the kinetic- and potential-energy state functions and the notion of generalized coordinates. First, however, let us define more precisely the concept of a state function.

Definition 3.2-1   A *state function* is any scalar function of the state variables, and possibly time, whose value at any instant of time is completely determined by the values of the state variables at that instant and the time itself.

The complete dependence of the state function upon the state variables is of prime importance.   A state function, like the state itself, is independent of the path taken to reach a particular state.

In general a state function W may be written as $W(\mathbf{x},t)$, where $\mathbf{x}$ is actually $\mathbf{x}(t)$, so that $W(\mathbf{x},t)$ implies $W[\mathbf{x}(t),t]$.   The shorter notation is used for convenience.   Most of the state functions that we consider are not *explicit* functions of time, so that $W = W[\mathbf{x}(t)] = W(\mathbf{x})$.

If the state variables are chosen as physical-system variables, a state function defined in terms of these variables may then be closely associated with the physical realities of the system.   The close association between the state function and the physical system is particularly true for the state function that is discussed in this chapter, the lagrangian.   From the lagrangian of a given physical system the differential equations describing the dynamics of that system can be derived.   Knowledge of the describing differential equations implies knowledge of the motion of the system for all time; the differential equations need only be solved.   Thus, implicit in the lagrangian state function is the knowledge of the system behavior for all time.   As is shown in later chapters, two important contributions to modern control theory, the second method of Liapunov and the maximum   principle   of   Pontryagin,   are   also   based   upon   state functions.

State functions are not new; engineers and physicists have dealt with the state functions of potential and kinetic energy for many years.   For example, the kinetic energy of a body with a mass M and moving with a velocity v is given by $Mv^2/2$.

The engineer's familiarity with energy considerations is fortunate, since the lagrangian is composed solely of energy terms.   The *lagrangian* $\mathcal{L}(\mathbf{q},\dot{\mathbf{q}})$ is defined as the difference between the kinetic energy $\mathcal{J}(\mathbf{q},\dot{\mathbf{q}})$ and the potential energy $\mathcal{V}(\mathbf{q})$ of all energy-storage elements of the system so that

$$\mathcal{L}(\mathbf{q},\dot{\mathbf{q}}) = \mathcal{J}(\mathbf{q},\dot{\mathbf{q}}) - \mathcal{V}(\mathbf{q}) \tag{3.2-1}$$

Here $\mathbf{q}$ and $\dot{\mathbf{q}}$ are the generalized coordinates and velocities in which these energy terms are expressed.   The use of the term *generalized coordinates* is common in classical mechanics, as is the notation $\mathbf{q}$ and $\dot{\mathbf{q}}$.   These generalized coordinates are, as we shall see, closely related to the state variables of the previous chapter.   Associated with the ith energy-storage element of the system are the generalized coordinate and velocity q_i and

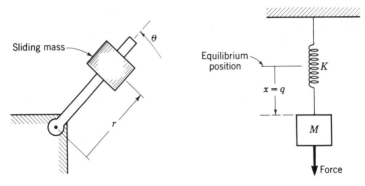

Fig. 3.2-1 The need for kinetic energy to depend on position as well as velocity.

Fig. 3.2-2 Spring-mass system in which the kinetic and potential energies are each a function of a single variable.

$\dot{q}_i$. The sense in which the term generalized is used becomes clear when problems other than those of mechanical translation are considered.

Some comment is perhaps appropriate concerning the functional dependencies indicated above of $\mathfrak{I}$ and $\mathcal{V}$ on $\mathbf{q}$ and $\dot{\mathbf{q}}$. Since kinetic energy, by its very nature, is related to energy storage due to motion, it is not surprising that $\mathfrak{I}(\mathbf{q},\dot{\mathbf{q}})$ depends on $\dot{\mathbf{q}}$. Similarly, since potential energy is associated with energy storage due to position, the dependence of $\mathcal{V}(\mathbf{q})$ on $\mathbf{q}$ is not surprising.

On the other hand, the need for the dependency of $\mathfrak{I}(\mathbf{q},\dot{\mathbf{q}})$ on $\mathbf{q}$ may not seem obvious. However, in many problems the kinetic energy is a function not only of velocity but also of position. Consider, for example, the system shown in Fig. 3.2-1. There we see that the kinetic energy is determined by not only the velocities $\dot{r}$ and $\dot{\theta}$ but also the position r.

In order to give the simplest interpretation to the concept of generalized coordinates and energy state functions, let us consider the special case where $\mathfrak{I}(\mathbf{q},\dot{\mathbf{q}})$ and $\mathcal{V}(\mathbf{q})$ each contain only one term and each is a function of only one variable. Perhaps the most familiar example of such a case is the spring-mass combination of Fig. 3.2-2. Here the kinetic energy of the mass is

$$\mathfrak{I}(q,\dot{q}) = \tfrac{1}{2}M\dot{x}^2$$

and the potential energy of the spring is

$$\mathcal{V}(q) = \tfrac{1}{2}Kx^2$$

In this example the generalized coordinate q is indeed a position coordinate x, and the generalized velocity $\dot{q}$ is also an actual velocity $\dot{x}$. For simplicity, x is measured from the equilibrium position of the mass so that we may neglect gravity. By the equilibrium position we mean the position that the mass will have if no force save gravity is applied. When gravity is not a factor, as in horizontal motion, the equilibrium position will be equal to the unstretched position of the spring. This assumption, which is made tacitly throughout this chapter, is indicated by the unspecified origin of the position variable x.

The expression for the kinetic energy[1] of the mass is determined from the integral formula

$$\mathfrak{I}(q,\dot{q}) = \int_0^{\dot{x}} (M\dot{x}')\, d\dot{x}' = \tfrac{1}{2}M\dot{x}^2 \tag{3.2-2}$$

where the quantity $M\dot{x}$ is recognized as the *momentum* of the mass. The primes are used to indicate the "dummy" integration variables. Similarly, the potential energy of the spring is given by

$$\mathcal{V}(q) = \int_0^{x} Kx'\, dx' = \tfrac{1}{2}Kx^2 \tag{3.2-3}$$

Here the quantity Kx is the *potential force*, i.e., the force necessary to maintain the spring at the position x.

These two integrals are nothing more than a statement of the fact that the *energy stored is equal to the energy input*. Since neither the spring (assumed ideal) nor the mass is able to dissipate energy, this is an obvious statement of fact. The kinetic energy stored in the motion of the mass, for example, is equal to the work that must have been done on the mass in order for it to have the velocity $\dot{x}$. The potential energy stored in the spring, on the other hand, is equal to the work done on the spring to stretch it by the amount x.

We are naturally interested in electrical as well as mechanical cases and in combinations of the two, i.e., in electromechanical control systems. Here we proceed by analogy in the simple case where the energies have one term, each a function of only one variable. By way of analogy, consider the following four second-order differential equations, which describe the mechanical and electrical systems of Fig. 3.2-3.

1. Mechanical translational: $M\ddot{x} + Kx = \text{force}$
2. Mechanical rotational: $J\ddot{\theta} + K\theta = \text{torque}$
3. Electrical series: $L\ddot{q} + \dfrac{1}{C}\,q = \text{voltage}$
4. Electrical parallel: $C\ddot{\lambda} + \dfrac{1}{L}\,\lambda = \text{current}$

[1] Often described as coenergy. See Meisel (1966) or White and Woodson (1959).

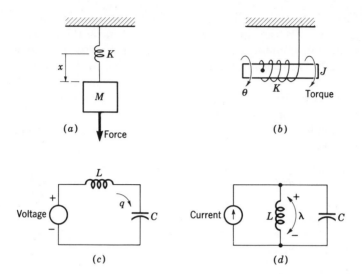

Fig. 3.2-3   Simple analog electrical and mechanical circuits. (*a*)
Mechanical translational; (*b*) mechanical rotational; (*c*)
electrical series; (*d*) electrical parallel.

In these equations the generalized coordinates are now x, θ, q, and λ,
where in the electrical equations q is the charge and λ is the flux linkage.
Clearly the generalized coordinates do not all indicate position. However,
each of the generalized coordinates does occupy the same physical location
in its particular equation. Simply by relating the different coefficients
and variables by their positions in these four equations, it is possible to
write the kinetic- and potential-energy terms associated with each of the
four physical systems of Fig. 3.2-3. Thus if the kinetic energy in the
mechanical example of Fig. 3.2-2 is $M\dot{x}^2/2$, then in the electrical case,
with charge as a coordinate, the kinetic energy must be $L\dot{q}^2/2$. Similarly,
with λ as a coordinate, the potential energy is $\lambda^2/2L$. Table 3.2-1 sum-
marizes these analogies for the four types of simple physical systems shown
in Fig. 3.2-3. It is only coincidence that the conventional symbol for
charge is q, the symbol used for the generalized coordinate.

It is interesting to note that the common electrical variables, current
$i = \dot{q}$ and voltage $v = \dot{\lambda}$, are generalized velocities rather than generalized
coordinates. If i and v are used as basic coordinates to describe the
corresponding circuits of Fig. 3.2-3, the resulting equations are no longer
differential equations but integrodifferential equations.

The energy expressions given in Table 3.2-1 can also be determined
by analogy through the use of the integral definitions given in Eqs. (3.2-2)
and (3.2-3). In the translational mechanical case, the basis for our

Table 3.2-1

Type of System	Generalized Coordinate q	Generalized Velocity $\dot{q}$	Kinetic Energy $\mathfrak{T}(q,\dot{q})$	Potential Energy $\mathfrak{V}(q)$	Generalized Momentum p	Potential Force f	Generalized Force $\mathfrak{F}$
Mechanical translational	Position x	Velocity $\dot{x} = v$	$\tfrac{1}{2}M\dot{x}^2$	$\tfrac{1}{2}Kx^2$	Momentum $M\dot{x}$	Force Kx	Force
Mechanical rotational	Angular position θ	Angular velocity $\dot{\theta} = \omega$	$\tfrac{1}{2}J\dot{\theta}^2$	$\tfrac{1}{2}K\theta^2$	Angular momentum $J\dot{\theta}$	Torque $K\theta$	Torque
Electrical series	Charge q	Current $\dot{q} = i$	$\tfrac{1}{2}L\dot{q}^2$	$\dfrac{1}{2C}q^2$	Flux linkage $L\dot{q}$	Voltage $\dfrac{1}{C}q$	Voltage
Electrical parallel	Flux linkage λ	Voltage $\dot{\lambda} = v$	$\tfrac{1}{2}C\dot{\lambda}^2$	$\dfrac{1}{2L}\lambda^2$	Charge $C\dot{\lambda}$	Current $\dfrac{1}{L}\lambda$	Current

analogy, the integrand of Eq. (3.2-2) is simply $M\ddot{x}$, the momentum, and in Eq. (3.2-3) the integrand is a potential force Kx.   If a generalized momentum is defined as p and a generalized potential force as f, then in terms of the generalized coordinates q and $\dot{q}$ the kinetic and potential energies of Eqs. (3.2-2) and (3.2-3) are

$$\mathfrak{I}(q,\dot{q}) = \int_0^{\dot{q}} p(q,\dot{q}')\,d\dot{q}' \tag{3.2-4}$$

$$\mathfrak{v}(q) = \int_0^q f(q')\,dq' \tag{3.2-5}$$

Here, as before, we are still considering only the case of a single energy term that is a function of one variable.

Our prime interest is not in cases as simple as those considered above. In general, the total energies may be made up of many terms, each of which may be a function of more than one variable.   Thus the integral definitions of the kinetic and potential energies of Eqs. (3.2-4) and (3.2-5) are only special cases of the more general definitions

$$\mathfrak{I}(\mathbf{q},\dot{\mathbf{q}}) = \int_0^{\dot{\mathbf{q}}} \mathbf{p}(\mathbf{q},\dot{\mathbf{q}}')^T\,d\dot{\mathbf{q}}' \tag{3.2-6}$$

$$\mathfrak{v}(\mathbf{q}) = \int_0^{\mathbf{q}} \mathbf{f}(\mathbf{q}')^T\,d\mathbf{q}' \tag{3.2-7}$$

These two defining equations are of sufficient importance and complexity to merit separate discussion.   Consider first Eq. (3.2-6), which in expanded form is

$$\mathfrak{I}(\mathbf{q},\dot{\mathbf{q}}) = \int_0^{\dot{\mathbf{q}}} \sum_{i=1}^N p_i(\mathbf{q},\dot{\mathbf{q}}')\,d\dot{q}_i' \tag{3.2-8}$$

where N is the number of generalized coordinates.

In Eqs. (3.2-6) and (3.2-8) the upper limit of integration is denoted as a vector.   This does not imply that the resulting kinetic energy $\mathfrak{I}(\mathbf{q},\dot{\mathbf{q}})$ is a vector quantity but rather that it is to be evaluated as a line integral from the origin to an arbitrary point $\dot{\mathbf{q}}$ in the generalized velocity space. The summation within the integral sign is intended to emphasize the physical basis from which $\mathfrak{I}$ is determined.   All kinetic-energy terms must be included before evaluating the line integral.

Since $\mathfrak{I}(\mathbf{q},\dot{\mathbf{q}})$ is a state function, the value of this line integral must be independent of the path of integration.   This is a basic property of a state function.   Because of this fact, the simplest path from 0 to $\dot{\mathbf{q}}$ may be used to evaluate the line integral.   One such path is to integrate first

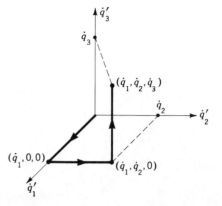

Fig. 3.2-4 Simple path of integration in a three-dimensional $\dot{\mathbf{q}}$ space.

along $\dot{q}_1'$, with the remaining $\dot{q}_i'$'s zero, then to integrate along $\dot{q}_2'$, with $\dot{q}_1' = \dot{q}_1$ and the remaining $\dot{q}_i'$'s zero, and so forth until the point $\dot{\mathbf{q}}$ is reached. Such a path of integration is indicated in Fig. 3.2-4 for $N = 3$. Thus in completely expanded form Eqs. (3.2-6) and (3.2-8) may be written as

$$\mathfrak{I}(\mathbf{q},\dot{\mathbf{q}}) = \int_0^{\dot{q}_1} p_1(\mathbf{q},\dot{q}_1',0, \ldots ,0)\, d\dot{q}_1' + \int_0^{\dot{q}_2} p_2(\mathbf{q},\dot{q}_1,\dot{q}_2',0, \ldots ,0)\, d\dot{q}_2'$$
$$+ \cdots + \int_0^{\dot{q}_N} p_N(\mathbf{q},\dot{q}_1, \ldots ,\dot{q}_{N-1},\dot{q}_N')\, d\dot{q}_N' \quad (3.2\text{-}9)$$

While any other path may be followed, this path often proves to be the easiest in practice.

The fact that the state function $\mathfrak{I}(\mathbf{q},\dot{\mathbf{q}})$ must be independent of the path of integration may be used to provide a simple check on the correct determination of the momentum vector $\mathbf{p}(\mathbf{q},\dot{\mathbf{q}})$. In standard texts on vector calculus (see Lass, 1950), it is shown that in order for a line integral of the form of Eq. (3.2-6) to be independent of the path of integration, it is necessary and sufficient that

$$\frac{\partial p_i(\mathbf{q},\dot{\mathbf{q}})}{\partial \dot{q}_j} = \frac{\partial p_j(\mathbf{q},\dot{\mathbf{q}})}{\partial \dot{q}_i} \qquad i,j = 1, \ldots , N \qquad (3.2\text{-}10)$$

Although $\mathbf{p}$ may be a function of $\mathbf{q}$, as well as $\dot{\mathbf{q}}$, partials with respect to $\mathbf{q}$ need not be considered, since the integration is taking place in the $\dot{\mathbf{q}}$ space. The partial derivatives of Eq. (3.2-10) may be used as an aid in checking the validity of $\mathbf{p}(\mathbf{q},\dot{\mathbf{q}})$. If these expressions are not satisfied, $\mathbf{p}$ must be invalid, since otherwise $\mathfrak{I}(\mathbf{q},\dot{\mathbf{q}})$ would not be independent of the path, which it must be. On the other hand, if the expressions are satisfied, one

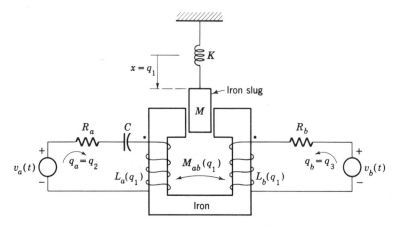

Fig. 3.2-5 A nontrivial electromechanical example.

cannot be certain that $\mathbf{p}$ is correct but only that it has the correct form for $\mathfrak{I}(\mathbf{q},\dot{\mathbf{q}})$ to be a state function.

In order to illustrate the use of Eq. (3.2-9) in a nontrivial example, let us consider the determination of the kinetic energy for the system shown in Fig. 3.2-5.   In this problem, an iron slug is suspended by a spring in the gap of a magnetic circuit.   The three generalized coordinates, q_a, q_b, and x, are indicated, where q_a is the charge flowing in the left circuit, q_b is the charge flowing in the right circuit, and x is the position of the mass measured from the equilibrium position of the mass as usual.

In order to be consistent with the notation used in the integral definition for $\mathfrak{I}(\mathbf{q},\dot{\mathbf{q}})$, let us make the following identification of the generalized coordinates:

$$q_1 = x \qquad q_2 = q_a \qquad \text{and} \qquad q_3 = q_b$$

Kinetic energy $\mathfrak{I}(\mathbf{q},\dot{\mathbf{q}})$ is concerned with the $\dot{\mathbf{q}}$ variables and the generalized momenta.   Consider the individual elements of the momentum vector $\mathbf{p}$. The momentum $p_1(\mathbf{q},\dot{\mathbf{q}})$ is associated with the q_1 coordinate and is therefore the momentum of the iron slug,

$$p_1(\mathbf{q},\dot{\mathbf{q}}) = M\dot{q}_1$$

The momentum $p_2(\mathbf{q},\dot{\mathbf{q}})$ is associated with the q_2 coordinate and is the electrical "momentum," or flux linkage, in the q_2 circuit.   The total flux linkage associated with q_2 is the sum of the self-inductance flux linkage $L_a\dot{q}_2$ and the mutual-inductance flux linkage $M_{ab}\dot{q}_3$.   Of course, both L_a

and M_{ab} are functions of the position of the iron mass, or $L_a = L_a(q_1)$, and $M_{ab} = M_{ab}(q_1)$. Thus $p_2(\mathbf{q},\dot{\mathbf{q}})$ is

$$p_2(\mathbf{q},\dot{\mathbf{q}}) = L_a(q_1)\dot{q}_2 + M_{ab}(q_1)\dot{q}_3$$

The momentum $p_3(\mathbf{q},\dot{\mathbf{q}})$ may be written in a similar fashion as

$$p_3(\mathbf{q},\dot{\mathbf{q}}) = L_b(q_1)\dot{q}_3 + M_{ab}(q_1)\dot{q}_2$$

The momentum vector $\mathbf{p}(\mathbf{q},\dot{\mathbf{q}})$ is now completely known as

$$\mathbf{p}(\mathbf{q},\dot{\mathbf{q}}) = \begin{bmatrix} M\dot{q}_1 \\ L_a(q_1)\dot{q}_2 + M_{ab}(q_1)\dot{q}_3 \\ L_b(q_1)\dot{q}_3 + M_{ab}(q_1)\dot{q}_2 \end{bmatrix}$$

It is easy to check that this momentum vector does satisfy Eq. (3.2-10), as it must. Now $\mathfrak{I}(\mathbf{q},\dot{\mathbf{q}})$ must be determined by line integration using Eq. (3.2-9) as

$$\mathfrak{I}(\mathbf{q},\dot{\mathbf{q}}) = \int_0^{\dot{q}_1} M\dot{q}_1' \, d\dot{q}_1' + \int_0^{\dot{q}_2} L_a(q_1)\dot{q}_2' \, d\dot{q}_2'$$
$$+ \int_0^{\dot{q}_3} [L_b(q_1)\dot{q}_3' + M_{ab}(q_1)\dot{q}_2] \, d\dot{q}_3' \quad (3.2\text{-}11)$$

or

$$\mathfrak{I}(\mathbf{q},\dot{\mathbf{q}}) = \tfrac{1}{2}M\dot{q}_1{}^2 + \tfrac{1}{2}L_a(q_1)\dot{q}_2{}^2 + \tfrac{1}{2}L_b(q_1)\dot{q}_3{}^2 + M_{ab}(q_1)\dot{q}_2\dot{q}_3$$
$$(3.2\text{-}12)$$

This example illustrates not only the determination of $\mathfrak{I}$ from $\mathbf{p}$ but a number of other points as well. The resulting kinetic energy has three terms which are functions of more than one variable. Such terms are common if there is coupling between electrical and mechanical coordinates. Here the coupling is not specifically described, as both self- and mutual-inductance terms are left as undefined functions of the position of the iron slug. In order to be able to determine the exact functional dependence of L_a on the position coordinate q_1, more detail must be given concerning the physical arrangements and dimensions of the electrical and mechanical elements that make up the system. This necessary attention to detail is always the case in the early stages of problem formulation, regardless of whether the Lagrange formulation is used or not. In addition, we note that $\mathfrak{I}$ is a function not only of $\dot{\mathbf{q}}$ but also of $\mathbf{q}$.

An implicit assumption made in this example is that no saturation takes place in any of the inductances. If saturation had been considered, the various self- and mutual inductances would have been functions of the currents as well as the position of the iron slug. The only complication that this adds is in the integration of $\mathbf{p}(\mathbf{q},\dot{\mathbf{q}})$ to form $\mathfrak{I}(\mathbf{q},\dot{\mathbf{q}})$. In integrating $\mathbf{p}$ according to Eq. (3.2-9), the inductance terms could not be taken outside the integral sign. The resulting $\mathfrak{I}$ corresponding to Eq. (3.2-12) would then be more complicated, but the basic approach is not changed.

Let us turn our attention next to the potential-energy state function defined by

$$\mathcal{V}(\mathbf{q}) = \int_0^{\mathbf{q}} \mathbf{f}(\mathbf{q}')^T \, d\mathbf{q}' \tag{3.2-7}$$

Here $\mathbf{f}$ is the potential force, and $d\mathbf{q}$ is a vector of differentials in the generalized coordinates $\mathbf{q}$. In expanded form Eq. (3.2-7) becomes

$$\mathcal{V}(\mathbf{q}) = \int_0^{\mathbf{q}} \sum_{i=1}^{N} f_i(\mathbf{q}') \, dq_i' \tag{3.2-13}$$

Once again, since $\mathcal{V}(\mathbf{q})$ is a state function, the line integral of Eq. (3.2-13) is independent of the path, and $\mathcal{V}(\mathbf{q})$ may be written as

$$\mathcal{V}(\mathbf{q}) = \int_0^{q_1} f_1(q_1',0, \ldots ,0) \, dq_1' + \int_0^{q_2} f_2(q_1,q_2',0, \ldots ,0) \, dq_2'$$
$$+ \cdots + \int_0^{q_N} f_N(q_1, \ldots ,q_{N-1},q_N') \, dq_N' \tag{3.2-14}$$

As a check on the formulation of $\mathbf{f}(\mathbf{q})$, equations analogous to Eq. (3.2-10) may be written as

$$\frac{\partial f_i(\mathbf{q})}{\partial q_j} = \frac{\partial f_j(\mathbf{q})}{\partial q_i} \tag{3.2-15}$$

In order to illustrate the use of Eq. (3.2-14), let us determine the potential energy for the example presented above. This example contains two potential-energy storage devices, the spring K and the capacitor C. In this example the generalized force terms are each a function of only one variable, so that $\mathbf{f}$ may be written immediately as

$$\mathbf{f}(\mathbf{q}) = \begin{bmatrix} Kq_1 \\ \dfrac{q_2}{C} \\ 0 \end{bmatrix}$$

The integral of Eq. (3.2-14) is then

$$\mathcal{V}(\mathbf{q}) = \int_0^{q_1} K q_1' \, dq_1' + \int_0^{q_2} \frac{1}{C} q_2' \, dq_2' = \frac{1}{2} K q_1{}^2 + \frac{1}{2C} q_2{}^2$$

There is an alternate way to view the relationship of $\mathbf{p}(\mathbf{q},\dot{\mathbf{q}})$ and $\mathbf{f}(\mathbf{q})$ with $\mathfrak{I}(\mathbf{q},\dot{\mathbf{q}})$ and $\mathcal{V}(\mathbf{q})$. If we assume that $\mathfrak{I}(\mathbf{q},\dot{\mathbf{q}})$ and $\mathcal{V}(\mathbf{q})$ are known and consider how $\mathbf{p}(\mathbf{q},\dot{\mathbf{q}})$ and $\mathbf{f}(\mathbf{q})$ may be determined, we find that $\mathbf{p}(\mathbf{q},\dot{\mathbf{q}})$ is simply

$$\mathbf{p}(\mathbf{q},\dot{\mathbf{q}}) = \begin{bmatrix} \dfrac{\partial \mathfrak{I}(\mathbf{q},\dot{\mathbf{q}})}{\partial \dot{q}_1} \\[2mm] \dfrac{\partial \mathfrak{I}(\mathbf{q},\dot{\mathbf{q}})}{\partial \dot{q}_2} \\[1mm] \cdot \\ \cdot \\ \cdot \\ \dfrac{\partial \mathfrak{I}(\mathbf{q},\dot{\mathbf{q}})}{\partial \dot{q}_N} \end{bmatrix} = \frac{\partial \mathfrak{I}(\mathbf{q},\dot{\mathbf{q}})}{\partial \dot{\mathbf{q}}} \tag{3.2-16}$$

while $\mathbf{f}(\mathbf{q})$ is

$$\mathbf{f}(\mathbf{q}) = \begin{bmatrix} \dfrac{\partial \mathcal{V}(\mathbf{q})}{\partial q_1} \\[2mm] \dfrac{\partial \mathcal{V}(\mathbf{q})}{\partial q_2} \\[1mm] \cdot \\ \cdot \\ \cdot \\ \dfrac{\partial \mathcal{V}(\mathbf{q})}{\partial q_N} \end{bmatrix} = \frac{\partial \mathcal{V}(\mathbf{q})}{\partial \mathbf{q}} \tag{3.2-17}$$

It is suggested that the reader verify these expressions for the example presented above. We shall make use of them in the next section.

Since the lagrangian $\mathcal{L}(\mathbf{q},\dot{\mathbf{q}})$ is defined as

$$\mathcal{L}(\mathbf{q},\dot{\mathbf{q}}) = \mathfrak{I}(\mathbf{q},\dot{\mathbf{q}}) - \mathcal{V}(\mathbf{q}) \tag{3.2-1}$$

the lagrangian is completely determined once the kinetic and potential energy are known. In the example presented above, the lagrangian is therefore

$$\mathcal{L}(\mathbf{q},\dot{\mathbf{q}}) = \tfrac{1}{2}M\dot{q}_1{}^2 + \tfrac{1}{2}L_a(q_1)\dot{q}_2{}^2 + \tfrac{1}{2}L_b(q_1)\dot{q}_3{}^2$$
$$+ M_{ab}(q_1)\dot{q}_2\dot{q}_3 - \tfrac{1}{2}Kq_1{}^2 - \frac{1}{2C}\,q_2{}^2$$

The lagrangian is also a state function, since it is composed only of state functions. Extensive use is made of the lagrangian state function in the following sections of this chapter.

Exercises 3.2 *3.2-1.* Find the kinetic- and potential-energy state function for the systems shown in Fig. 3.2-6. Use the coordinates indicated on the figure to express the answer.

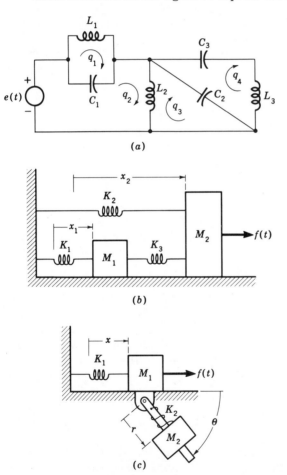

(a)

(b)

(c)

Fig. 3.2-6 Exercise 3.2-1.

answers:

(a) $\quad \mathfrak{I} = \frac{1}{2}L_1\dot{q}_1{}^2 + \frac{1}{2}L_2(\dot{q}_2 - \dot{q}_3)^2 + \frac{1}{2}L_3\dot{q}_4{}^2$

$\quad\quad \mathfrak{V} = \dfrac{1}{2C_1}(q_1 - q_2)^2 + \dfrac{1}{2C_2}(q_3 - q_4)^2 + \dfrac{1}{2C_3}q_4{}^2$

(b) $\quad \mathfrak{I} = \frac{1}{2}M_1\dot{x}_1{}^2 + \frac{1}{2}M_2\dot{x}_2{}^2$

$\quad\quad \mathfrak{V} = \frac{1}{2}K_1x_1{}^2 + \frac{1}{2}K_2x_2{}^2 + \frac{1}{2}K_3(x_1 - x_2)^2$

(c) $\quad \mathfrak{I} = \frac{1}{2}M_1\dot{x}^2 + \frac{1}{2}M_2(\dot{x}^2 + r\dot{\theta}^2 + \dot{r}^2 + 2\dot{r}\dot{x}\cos\theta - 2\dot{x}r\dot{\theta}\sin\theta)$

$\quad\quad \mathfrak{V} = \frac{1}{2}K_1x^2 + \frac{1}{2}K_2r^2$

3.2-2. Show that the kinetic- and potential-energy state functions for the system shown in Fig. 3.2-7 are

$$\mathfrak{I} = \frac{1}{2}M_1\dot{x}_1{}^2 + \frac{1}{2}M_2\dot{x}_2{}^2 + \frac{1}{2}L(x_2)\dot{q}^2$$

$$\mathfrak{V} = \frac{1}{2}K_1(x_1 - x_2)^2 + \frac{1}{2}K_2x_2{}^2 + \frac{1}{2C(x_1)}q^2$$

3.3 *Lagrange's equation and Newton's law*

Lagrange's equation provides a means of deriving the differential equations that govern the motion of a dynamic system. Partial- and total-differentiation operations on the lagrangian state function yield a set of N second-order ordinary differential equations in the coordinates **q** and **q̇**. In a trivial manner these second-order differential equations may be reduced to the desired state-variable form of first-order differential equations.

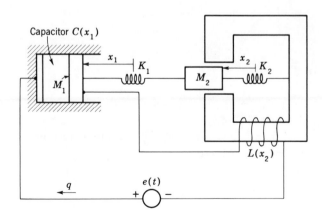

Fig. 3.2-7 Exercise 3.2-2.

The object of this section is to indicate in a rather heuristic way the origins and validity of Lagrange's equation. The derivation also serves to illustrate an important feature of Lagrange's equation, namely, that it is valid in any consistent set of generalized coordinates. The more elegant proof is based on Hamilton's principle and requires the use of the calculus of variations. This approach is discussed briefly in Chap. 6 after the necessary background in the calculus of variations has been presented. The remainder of the present chapter is devoted to examples, largely from the control area.

Consider a mechanical system made up of N particles of constant mass M_i, $i = 1, 2, \ldots, N$, which is described in cartesian coordinates $\mathbf{x}$. For simplicity, we assume that the particles move in a one-dimensional space and hence each particle has associated with it only one coordinate. If Newton's first law is applied to this system, we find that

$$\frac{d}{dt}[p_i(\dot{\mathbf{x}})] = F_i \qquad i = 1, 2, \ldots, N \tag{3.3-1}$$

where $p_i(\dot{\mathbf{x}}) = M_i \dot{x}_i$ is the momentum of the ith particle and F_i is the sum of the forces acting on the ith particle.

Let us suppose now that we wish to consider this same system in another coordinate system, the $\mathbf{q}$ coordinates. The transformation from $\mathbf{x}$ to $\mathbf{q}$ need not be linear, and we indicate this fact by the general notation

$$\mathbf{x} = \mathbf{x}(\mathbf{q}) \tag{3.3-2}$$

The time derivative of the old coordinates is then determined by the use of the "chain rule" of differentiation to be

$$\dot{\mathbf{x}} = \sum_{i=1}^{N} \frac{\partial \mathbf{x}(\mathbf{q})}{\partial q_i} \dot{q}_i = \dot{\mathbf{x}}(\mathbf{q}, \dot{\mathbf{q}}) \tag{3.3-3}$$

From this expression we see that the old velocities are functions not only of $\dot{\mathbf{q}}$ but also of $\mathbf{q}$.

The kinetic energy of the system may be written in terms of the cartesian coordinates $\mathbf{x}$ as

$$\Im(\dot{\mathbf{x}}) = \frac{1}{2} \sum_{i=1}^{N} M_i \dot{x}_i^2$$

It is clear, because of the functional dependence of $\dot{\mathbf{x}}$ on $\mathbf{q}$ and $\dot{\mathbf{q}}$, as indicated in Eq. (3.3-3), that $\mathfrak{I}$ is a function of $\mathbf{q}$ and $\dot{\mathbf{q}}$. Thus the partials of $\mathfrak{I}$ with respect to q_i and $\dot{q}_i$ may be formed, as

$$\frac{\partial \mathfrak{I}[\dot{\mathbf{x}}(\mathbf{q},\dot{\mathbf{q}})]}{\partial q_i} = \frac{\partial \mathfrak{I}}{\partial \dot{x}_1}\frac{\partial \dot{x}_1}{\partial q_i} + \frac{\partial \mathfrak{I}}{\partial \dot{x}_2}\frac{\partial \dot{x}_2}{\partial q_i} + \cdots + \frac{\partial \mathfrak{I}}{\partial \dot{x}_N}\frac{\partial \dot{x}_N}{\partial q_i} = \left(\frac{\partial \mathfrak{I}}{\partial \dot{\mathbf{x}}}\right)^T \frac{\partial \dot{\mathbf{x}}}{\partial q_i}$$

(3.3-4)

where

$$\frac{\partial \mathfrak{I}}{\partial \dot{\mathbf{x}}} = \begin{bmatrix} \dfrac{\partial \mathfrak{I}}{\partial \dot{x}_1} \\[6pt] \dfrac{\partial \mathfrak{I}}{\partial \dot{x}_2} \\[6pt] \cdot \\ \cdot \\ \cdot \\ \dfrac{\partial \mathfrak{I}}{\partial \dot{x}_N} \end{bmatrix} = \begin{bmatrix} M_1 \dot{x}_1 \\ M_2 \dot{x}_2 \\ \cdot \\ \cdot \\ \cdot \\ M_N \dot{x}_N \end{bmatrix} = \mathbf{p}(\dot{\mathbf{x}}) \tag{3.3-5}$$

The benefit of vector notation in Eq. (3.3-4) is obvious. In Eq. (3.3-5) the vector $\mathbf{p}$ is indicated as $\mathbf{p}(\dot{\mathbf{x}})$ to emphasize that this is a momentum vector in terms of the x-coordinate system rather than $\mathbf{q}$. Equation (3.3-4) may then be rewritten as

$$\frac{\partial \mathfrak{I}[\dot{\mathbf{x}}(\mathbf{q},\dot{\mathbf{q}})]}{\partial q_i} = \mathbf{p}(\dot{\mathbf{x}})^T \frac{\partial \dot{\mathbf{x}}}{\partial q_i} = \mathbf{p}(\dot{\mathbf{x}})^T \frac{d}{dt}\frac{\partial \mathbf{x}}{\partial q_i}$$

(3.3-6)

Here the last expression is obtained by interchanging the partial derivative with respect to q_i with the time derivative.

In a similar fashion the partial of $\mathfrak{I}(\dot{\mathbf{x}})$ with respect to the ith velocity variable $\dot{q}_i$ gives

$$\frac{\partial \mathfrak{I}[\dot{\mathbf{x}}(\mathbf{q},\dot{\mathbf{q}})]}{\partial \dot{q}_i} = \mathbf{p}(\dot{\mathbf{x}})^T \frac{\partial \dot{\mathbf{x}}}{\partial \dot{q}_i}$$

In order to put this result into a more convenient form, we observe that

$$\frac{\partial \dot{\mathbf{x}}}{\partial \dot{q}_i} = \frac{\partial}{\partial \dot{q}_i}\left(\sum_{j=1}^{N} \frac{\partial \mathbf{x}}{\partial q_j}\dot{q}_j\right) = \frac{\partial \mathbf{x}}{\partial q_i}$$

where the last reduction makes use of the fact that $\partial \dot{q}_j/\partial \dot{q}_i = 0$ unless $i = j$. Using this result, we can write $\partial \Im/\partial \dot{q}_i$ as

$$\frac{\partial \Im[\dot{\mathbf{x}}(\mathbf{q},\dot{\mathbf{q}})]}{\partial \dot{q}_i} = \mathbf{p}(\dot{\mathbf{x}})^T \frac{\partial \mathbf{x}}{\partial q_i} \tag{3.3-7}$$

As yet it is not clear what has been gained by the above manipulations. The goal becomes clearer if the total time derivative is taken of Eq. (3.3-7),

$$\frac{d}{dt} \frac{\partial \Im[\dot{\mathbf{x}}(\mathbf{q},\dot{\mathbf{q}})]}{\partial \dot{q}_i} = \left[\frac{d}{dt} \mathbf{p}(\dot{\mathbf{x}})\right]^T \frac{\partial \mathbf{x}}{\partial q_i} + \mathbf{p}(\dot{\mathbf{x}})^T \frac{d}{dt} \frac{\partial \mathbf{x}}{\partial q_i} \tag{3.3-8}$$

Note that the differentiation of the product yields two terms, the last of which is simply $\partial \Im/\partial q_i$. This term can be transferred to the left side, so that Eq. (3.3-8) reads

$$\frac{d}{dt} \frac{\partial \Im(\mathbf{q},\dot{\mathbf{q}})}{\partial \dot{q}_i} - \frac{\partial \Im(\mathbf{q},\dot{\mathbf{q}})}{\partial q_i} = \left[\frac{d}{dt} \mathbf{p}(\dot{\mathbf{x}})\right]^T \frac{\partial \mathbf{x}}{\partial q_i} \tag{3.3-9}$$

The manipulations are now nearly complete, and it is important to stress that all we have done is manipulate the kinetic-energy state function. As yet, no physical law has been called into consideration. Consider the right-hand side of Eq. (3.3-9). The bracketed quantity is simply the time rate of change of momentum, which, from Eq. (3.3-1), is equal to the force acting on the particle in question.

Therefore Eq. (3.3-9) becomes

$$\frac{d}{dt} \frac{\partial \Im(\mathbf{q},\dot{\mathbf{q}})}{\partial \dot{q}_i} - \frac{\partial \Im(\mathbf{q},\dot{\mathbf{q}})}{\partial q_i} = \sum_{j=1}^{N} F_j \frac{\partial x_j}{\partial q_i} \tag{3.3-10}$$

Now let us define

$$Q_i = \sum_{j=1}^{N} F_j \frac{\partial x_j}{\partial q_i}$$

as the force associated with the q_i coordinate so that Eq. (3.3-10) becomes

$$\frac{d}{dt} \frac{\partial \Im(\mathbf{q},\dot{\mathbf{q}})}{\partial \dot{q}_i} - \frac{\partial \Im(\mathbf{q},\dot{\mathbf{q}})}{\partial q_i} = Q_i \tag{3.3-11}$$

This is the most general form of Lagrange's equation. Since the coordinate q_i is completely general, we see that Lagrange's equation really corresponds to a set of N second-order differential equations describing the motion of our N particles. It is well to note that the ordinary differential equations produced by Lagrange's equation may very well be nonlinear. This is one of the benefits of the use of Lagrange's equation. If the system in question is nonlinear, this fact is made known in the early stages of problem formulation.

In the practical use of Lagrange's equation, one usually separates the Q_i's into three components in the following manner:

$$Q_i = -f_i - D_i + \mathfrak{F}_i \tag{3.3-12}$$

Here f_i is the potential force, D_i is the damping force, and $\mathfrak{F}_i$ is the applied force.

The potential force was discussed in detail in the previous section with regard to the potential-energy state function. In terms of the potential-energy function, f_i is given by

$$f_i = \frac{\partial \mathcal{U}(\mathbf{q})}{\partial q_i} \tag{3.3-13}$$

The negative sign precedes f_i in Eq. (3.3-12) because Q_i is the force acting on the mass, while f_i was defined as the force acting on the potential-energy storage device.

The damping force D_i includes the force from all dissipating elements associated with the q_i coordinate. The only type of damping that we consider here is viscous damping, for which D_i is given by

$$D_i = \beta_i \dot{q}_i$$

where β_i is the viscous-damping coefficient. This viscous-damping force is usually written in terms of another state function, the *Rayleigh dissipation function*

$$\mathfrak{D}(\dot{\mathbf{q}}) = \frac{1}{2} \sum_{j=1}^{N} \beta_j \dot{q}_j{}^2 \tag{3.3-14}$$

as

$$D_i = \frac{\partial \mathfrak{D}(\dot{\mathbf{q}})}{\partial \dot{q}_i} = \beta_i \dot{q}_i \tag{3.3-15}$$

The fact that the damping force opposes the motion of the system is indicated by the negative sign preceding D_i in Eq. (3.3-12).

The applied force $\mathfrak{F}_i$ includes all external forces which are associated with the q_i coordinate. These forces are defined as being positive when they act to increase the value of the coordinate. If Eqs. (3.3-12), (3.3-13), and (3.3-15) are substituted into Eq. (3.3-11), the practical form of Lagrange's equation becomes

$$\frac{d}{dt}\frac{\partial \mathfrak{I}(\mathbf{q},\dot{\mathbf{q}})}{\partial \dot{q}_i} - \frac{\partial \mathfrak{I}(\mathbf{q},\dot{\mathbf{q}})}{\partial q_i} = -\frac{\partial \mathfrak{V}(\mathbf{q})}{\partial q_i} - \frac{\partial \mathfrak{D}(\dot{\mathbf{q}})}{\partial \dot{q}_i} + \mathfrak{F}_i$$

or

$$\frac{d}{dt}\frac{\partial \mathfrak{I}(\mathbf{q},\dot{\mathbf{q}})}{\partial \dot{q}_i} - \frac{\partial \mathfrak{I}(\mathbf{q},\dot{\mathbf{q}})}{\partial q_i} + \frac{\partial \mathfrak{V}(\mathbf{q})}{\partial q_\iota} + \frac{\partial \mathfrak{D}(\dot{\mathbf{q}})}{\partial \dot{q}_i} = \mathfrak{F}_i$$

$$i = 1, 2, \ldots, N \quad (3.3\text{-}16)$$

This last equation is referred to as the *operational form* of Lagrange's equation and is of prime interest in Sec. 3.5.

By making use of the lagrangian state function, we can write this equation in a slightly more compact form. Since $\mathfrak{V}(\mathbf{q})$ is not a function of $\dot{\mathbf{q}}$, the partials of $\mathfrak{V}(\mathbf{q})$ with respect to $\dot{\mathbf{q}}$ are all zero, or, in other words,

$$\frac{\partial \mathfrak{V}(\mathbf{q})}{\partial \dot{q}_i} = 0 \qquad i = 1, 2, \ldots, N$$

Therefore we have

$$\frac{d}{dt}\frac{\partial \mathfrak{L}(\mathbf{q},\dot{\mathbf{q}})}{\partial \dot{q}_i} - \frac{\partial \mathfrak{L}(\mathbf{q},\dot{\mathbf{q}})}{\partial q_i} = \frac{d}{dt}\frac{\partial \mathfrak{I}(\mathbf{q},\dot{\mathbf{q}})}{\partial \dot{q}_i} - \frac{\partial \mathfrak{I}(\mathbf{q},\dot{\mathbf{q}})}{\partial q_i} + \frac{\partial \mathfrak{V}(\mathbf{q})}{\partial q_i}$$

If this result is substituted into Eq. (3.3-16), we obtain

$$\frac{d}{dt}\frac{\partial \mathfrak{L}(\mathbf{q},\dot{\mathbf{q}})}{\partial \dot{q}_i} - \frac{\partial \mathfrak{L}(\mathbf{q},\dot{\mathbf{q}})}{\partial q_i} + \frac{\partial \mathfrak{D}(\dot{\mathbf{q}})}{\partial \dot{q}_i} = \mathfrak{F}_i \qquad (3.3\text{-}17)$$

This last result takes on a particularly simple form in the case of unforced conservative systems. By *conservative* we mean that the system contains no dissipating elements, and therefore the damping force is zero. In this case Eq. (3.3-17) becomes

$$\frac{d}{dt}\frac{\partial \mathfrak{L}(\mathbf{q},\dot{\mathbf{q}})}{\partial \dot{q}_i} - \frac{\partial \mathfrak{L}(\mathbf{q},\dot{\mathbf{q}})}{\partial q_i} = 0 \qquad (3.3\text{-}18)$$

This equation, which represents the simplest form of Lagrange's equation, can be represented in an alternate manner by means of a result known as *Hamilton's equations*. In the hamiltonian formulation one uses the momentum **p** and the position **q** as basic variables rather than **q** and **q̇**, as used in the lagrangian formulation. In order to do this one must find the expression for **q̇** in terms of **q** and **p** as

$$\dot{\mathbf{q}} = \dot{\mathbf{q}}(\mathbf{q},\mathbf{p})$$

Then in terms of the **q** and **p** variables one defines the state function of Hamilton, the hamiltonian $\mathcal{K}$, as

$$\mathcal{K}(\mathbf{q},\mathbf{p}) = \mathbf{p}^T\dot{\mathbf{q}}(\mathbf{q},\mathbf{p}) - \mathcal{L}[\mathbf{q},\dot{\mathbf{q}}(\mathbf{q},\mathbf{p})] \tag{3.3-19}$$

The equations of motion are then given by Hamilton's equations as

$$\dot{p}_i = -\frac{\partial\mathcal{K}(\mathbf{q},\mathbf{p})}{\partial q_i} \qquad \dot{q}_i = \frac{\partial\mathcal{K}(\mathbf{q},\mathbf{p})}{\partial p_i} \tag{3.3-20}$$

Since Hamilton's equations directly yield first-order equations, it may appear at first glance that they are a more natural means of generating the state equations. This is not true. The application of Hamilton's equations to electrical networks, for example, yields results that are valid but not results that are identical to those produced from Kirchhoff's laws. This is due to the use of the unfamiliar momentum variable. A similar statement holds for mechanical systems: the results are not familiar to engineers. Lagrange's equations do produce familiar results, and hence they are preferred. In addition, it is rather difficult to modify Hamilton's equation to include nonconservative or forced systems.

Although the development of Lagrange's equation has been couched in terms of mechanical-system elements such as masses, dampers, and springs, it is evident that we may use the analogs discussed in the previous section to extend the result beyond the pure mechanical case. Then we think not in terms of mass but of a generalized mass, as J, L, or C, as well as M. Similarly, a generalized damping element is R or $1/R$, depending on the electrical coordinate involved, and a similar comment applies to generalized potential and applied forces. Thus we are able to treat not only mechanical systems but electrical or electromechanical systems as well. In fact, the reader may well wonder why we restrict the presentation this much. Surely thermal, acoustical, and optical systems, to mention only a few, could be treated in a similar fashion through the use of analogs. The presentation is restricted here to electromechanical systems to avoid the introduction of many new sets of coordinates that might only obscure the point.   The restriction is not due to a lack of generality in application of Lagrange's equation.

Before applying Lagrange's equation to several examples, let us examine more closely the problems of choosing the generalized coordinates.

3.4   *Generalized coordinates and constraints*

In the two preceding sections it was assumed that the generalized coordinates were known.   In the application of Lagrange's equation to practical problems, however, the first step is to select the generalized coordinates. Therefore let us examine more closely the procedure of selecting the generalized coordinates.   In order for Lagrange's equation to be valid, it is necessary that the generalized coordinates be *independent* and completely *unconstrained.*[1]

In order to illustrate more clearly the meaning of these requirements on the generalized coordinates, let us consider a system of N_u energy-storage elements—springs, masses, capacitors, and so forth.   If these elements are completely unrelated, it is necessary to specify N_u coordinates, $x_1, x_2, \ldots, x_{N_u}$, in order to describe the system.   In a practical system, however, they may not be unrelated, and one finds that there may exist many relations among the states of the elements.   Such relations are known as *constraints.*

Often these constraints take the form of either algebraic equations of the form

$$f(x_1, x_2, \ldots, x_{N_u}) = 0 \tag{3.4-1}$$

or *integrable* differential equations of the form

$$g(\dot{x}_1, \dot{x}_2, \ldots, \dot{x}_{N_u}, x_1, x_2, \ldots, x_{N_u}) = 0 \tag{3.4-2}$$

Constraints of this type are referred to as *holonomic constraints.*

Consider, for example, the simple spring-mass system shown in Fig. 3.4-1.   If the spring and the mass are unconnected, as in Fig. 3.4-1a, two coordinates, x_1 and x_2, are necessary to specify the complete state of the system.   When the spring and the mass are connected, as in Fig. 3.4-1b,

---

[1] The proof of this last statement is presented in Chap. 6 as part of the derivation of Lagrange's equation from the variational calculus.

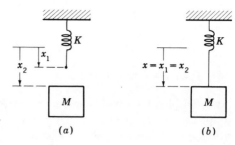

Fig. 3.4-1 Simple spring-mass system.

(*a*)   (*b*)

a holonomic constraint of the form

$$x_1 - x_2 = 0$$

is established between x_1 and x_2. This constraint can also be written as the integrable differential equation

$$\dot{x}_1 - \dot{x}_2 = 0$$

These two constraints are obviously equivalent.

Let the number of such holonomic constraints that the system has be equal to N_c. Then the difference

$$N = N_u - N_c \tag{3.4-3}$$

between the number of unconstrained coordinates and the number of constraints is known as the *degrees of freedom* of the system, and N is equal to the number of generalized coordinates needed to describe the system. In the above spring-mass problem of Fig. 3.4-1*b*, for example, we need one generalized coordinate, $x = x_1 = x_2$, since

$$N = N_u - N_c = 2 - 1 = 1$$

While this procedure indicates the number of generalized coordinates that are needed, it does not indicate how these coordinates are to be chosen. Any random selection of N coordinates is, in general, not adequate. One must be careful to ensure that the coordinates chosen are independent, i.e., that there exist no constraint relations among them. Although there are no hard and fast rules which dictate how to select the generalized coordinates, a little experience usually makes the selection reasonably obvious.

Constraints which cannot be expressed as either algebraic or integrable differential equations are known as *nonholonomic constraints*. In particular, one encounters two types of nonholonomic constraints in practical problems.

The first type is the *inequality constraint* of the form

$$f(x_1, \ldots ,x_{N_u}) \leq 0 \tag{3.4-4}$$

An example of a constrained coordinate is the restriction on the amount a spring can be stretched. If the displacement x is greater than some maximum value x_{max}, the elastic limit is exceeded, and the spring ceases to act as a spring; i.e., it no longer produces a potential force Kx. Therefore it is necessary that

$$x - x_{max} \leq 0$$

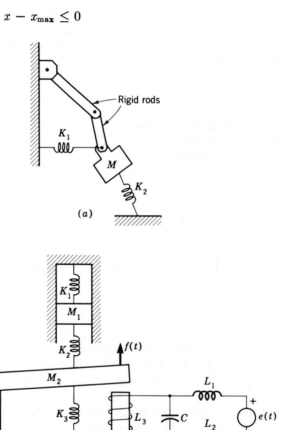

Fig. 3.4-2 Exercise 3.4-1.

All physical systems are subject to nonholonomic inequality constraints in one form or another.   Lagrange's equation applies only as long as these constraints are not violated.   More is said on this point in regard to the examples that follow.

The second type of nonholonomic constraint is the *nonintegrable* differential equation.   It is fortunate that this type of constraint rarely occurs in practical problems, since it is the most difficult constraint to handle.   In order to treat this type of constraint, it is almost always necessary to introduce the constraint by means of the method of undetermined Lagrange multipliers.   The method is developed in detail in Chap. 6 in relation to the optimal-control problem.   None of the examples of the next section contains any nonintegrable nonholonomic constraints.

Exercises 3.4   *3.4-1.*   Find the degrees of freedom of the two systems shown in Fig. 3.4-2 by assigning a coordinate to each energy-storage element and then writing all possible holonomic constraints.

answers:

(*a*) 3   (*b*) 4

3.4-2.   Show that the system shown in Fig. 3.4-3 has only three degrees of freedom even though there are ten energy-storage elements in the system.

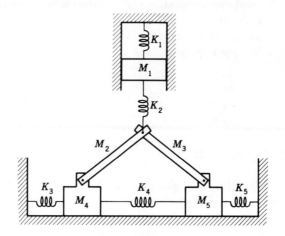

Fig. 3.4-3   Exercise 3.4-2.

3.5   Examples using Lagrange's equation

In this section Lagrange's equation is applied to several specific electrical, mechanical, and electromechanical examples. Before proceeding to these specific cases, however, it is well to recall the goal of this chapter, namely, system representation. We are ultimately interested in systems described by

$$\dot{\mathbf{x}} = \mathbf{A}\mathbf{x} + \mathbf{B}\mathbf{u} \tag{AB}$$

or the less general form of this equation, Eq. (**Ab**). But because Lagrange's equation is capable of generating nonlinear as well as linear equations, the form of our answer may well be

$$\dot{\mathbf{x}} = \mathbf{f}(\mathbf{x}, \mathbf{u})$$

where $\mathbf{f}(\mathbf{x}, \mathbf{u})$ is a general nonlinear function of the state variables and the control inputs. Since our immediate concern is only with system representation, the fact that the system may indeed be nonlinear is not important. That fact becomes important only when analysis or design of the system is attempted. Lagrange's equation gives no aid whatever in solving the ordinary differential equations that they generate. The subject of the solution of the resulting equations is a matter of analysis rather than problem formulation and is treated in the following chapters.

Since the use of Lagrange's equation normally generates a set of N second-order equations, it is necessary to convert these equations into the desired first-order form. This may be easily done by relating the generalized coordinate and velocity $\mathbf{q}$ and $\dot{\mathbf{q}}$ to the state variable $\mathbf{x}$ in the following manner:

$$
\begin{aligned}
x_1 &= q_1 \\
x_2 &= \dot{q}_1 \\
x_3 &= q_2 \\
&\ \cdot\ \cdot\ \cdot\ \cdot\ \cdot \\
x_{2N} &= \dot{q}_N
\end{aligned}
\tag{3.5-1}
$$

While this is the general procedure, in some cases application of Lagrange's equation yields only a first-order equation. This is the case, for example, in an electrical system which contains only resistance and inductance. When this occurs, either the associated generalized coordinate or velocity may be suppressed, and only one first-order state-variable equation is

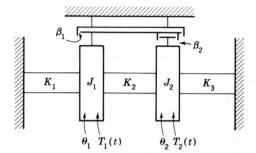

Fig. 3.5-1   Simple rotational system.

generated.   Therefore the number of state variables needed may vary from $2N$, if all the equations generated are second-order, to N, if all the equations generated are first-order.   We shall see both extremes in the examples which follow.

As a first example, consider the rotational mechanical system of Fig. 3.5-1.   The system consists of two flywheels with inertias J_1 and J_2 which are coupled together by means of a shaft with a torsional spring constant K_2.   The flywheels are also connected to the rigid wall by means of shafts with spring constants of K_1 and K_3.   In addition both flywheels are acted on by viscous-damping forces with coefficients β_1 and β_2 as well as by applied torques $T_1(t)$ and $T_2(t)$.   Note, however, that the inertia J_2 is subject to viscous-damping forces due only to the difference in velocity between J_1 and J_2.   In Fig. 3.5-1 the generalized coordinates are labeled θ_1 and θ_2, and the corresponding generalized velocities are $\dot{\theta}_1$ and $\dot{\theta}_2$.

It is assumed that the values of the system elements are constant and that the range of the variables is unrestricted.   Because the elements are constants, it is not necessary to integrate to determine $\mathfrak{I}(\mathbf{q},\dot{\mathbf{q}})$ and $\mathcal{V}(\mathbf{q})$.   They may be written down by inspection as

$$\mathfrak{I}(\mathbf{q},\dot{\mathbf{q}}) = \tfrac{1}{2}J_1\dot{\theta}_1{}^2 + \tfrac{1}{2}J_2\dot{\theta}_2{}^2$$
$$\mathcal{V}(\mathbf{q}) = \tfrac{1}{2}K_1\theta_1{}^2 + \tfrac{1}{2}K_2(\theta_1 - \theta_2)^2 + \tfrac{1}{2}K_3\theta_2{}^2$$
$$\mathfrak{D}(\dot{\mathbf{q}}) = \tfrac{1}{2}\beta_1\dot{\theta}_1{}^2 + \tfrac{1}{2}\beta_2(\dot{\theta}_1 - \dot{\theta}_2)^2$$

and

$$\mathfrak{F}_1(t) = T_1(t) \qquad \text{and} \qquad \mathfrak{F}_2(t) = T_2(t)$$

Let us derive first the equation pertaining to the generalized coordinate θ_1.   The bookkeeping is simplified if each term of the operational form of Lagrange's equation, Eq. (3.3-16), is evaluated separately, as

$$\frac{\partial \mathfrak{I}}{\partial \dot{\theta}_1} = J_1 \dot{\theta}_1 \quad \text{so that} \quad \frac{d}{dt} \frac{\partial \mathfrak{I}}{\partial \dot{\theta}_1} = J_1 \ddot{\theta}_1$$

$$\frac{\partial \mathfrak{I}}{\partial \theta_1} = 0 \quad \frac{\partial \mathfrak{V}}{\partial \theta_1} = K_1 \theta_1 + K_2(\theta_1 - \theta_2)$$

and

$$\frac{\partial \mathfrak{D}}{\partial \dot{\theta}_1} = \beta_1 \dot{\theta}_1 + \beta_2(\dot{\theta}_1 - \dot{\theta}_2)$$

If each term is now substituted into Eq. (3.3-16), the result is

$$J_1 \ddot{\theta}_1 + \beta_1 \dot{\theta}_1 + \beta_2(\dot{\theta}_1 - \dot{\theta}_2) + K_1 \theta_1 + K_2(\theta_1 - \theta_2) = T_1(t) \qquad (3.5\text{-}2)$$

This is one of the desired describing equations.   Note that if $\mathfrak{V}$ had been written with a term $K_2(\theta_2 - \theta_1)^2/2$ rather than $K_2(\theta_1 - \theta_2)^2/2$, the resulting equation, (3.5-2), would have been unchanged.

By a similar procedure, the second equation is

$$J_2 \ddot{\theta}_2 + \beta_2(\dot{\theta}_2 - \dot{\theta}_1) + K_2(\theta_2 - \theta_1) + K_3 \theta_2 = T_2(t)$$

These two equations can be put into state-variable form in terms of the more conventional $\mathbf{x}$ and $\mathbf{u}$ variables by defining

$$\begin{bmatrix} x_1 \\ x_2 \\ x_3 \\ x_4 \end{bmatrix} = \begin{bmatrix} \theta_1 \\ \dot{\theta}_1 \\ \theta_2 \\ \dot{\theta}_2 \end{bmatrix} \qquad \begin{bmatrix} u_1 \\ u_2 \end{bmatrix} = \begin{bmatrix} T_1 \\ T_2 \end{bmatrix}$$

The resulting four first-order equations are

$$\dot{x}_1 = x_2$$

$$\dot{x}_2 = \frac{1}{J_1}[-\beta_1 x_2 - \beta_2(x_2 - x_4) - K_1 x_1 - K_2(x_1 - x_3) + u_1(t)]$$

$$\dot{x}_3 = x_4 \qquad\qquad\qquad (3.5\text{-}3)$$

$$\dot{x}_4 = \frac{1}{J_2}[-\beta_2(x_4 - x_2) - K_2(x_3 - x_1) - K_3 x_3 + u_2(t)]$$

These equations are of the form (**AB**), with

$$\mathbf{A} = \begin{bmatrix} 0 & 1 & 0 & 0 \\ -\dfrac{K_1 + K_2}{J_1} & -\dfrac{\beta_1 + \beta_2}{J_1} & -\dfrac{K_2}{J_1} & \dfrac{\beta_2}{J_1} \\ 0 & 0 & 0 & 1 \\ \dfrac{K_2}{J_2} & \dfrac{\beta_2}{J_2} & -\dfrac{K_2 + K_3}{J_2} & -\dfrac{\beta_2}{J_2} \end{bmatrix}$$

$$\mathbf{B} = \begin{bmatrix} 0 & 0 \\ \dfrac{1}{J_1} & 0 \\ 0 & 0 \\ 0 & \dfrac{1}{J_2} \end{bmatrix}$$

It is interesting to observe that if the generalized coordinates are considered in sets of two, they are related by derivatives; i.e., they look like phase variables. In fact, for second-order systems, the phase variables and the generalized coordinates of Lagrange are often identical. The extension to third- and higher-order cases, however, does not naturally lead to higher derivatives as the phase variables would suggest.

As a second example, consider the electrical network of Fig. 3.5-2. The only unusual characteristic of this network is that the inductance L_1 is assumed to saturate, so that L_1 is actually $L_1 = L_1(\dot{q}_1)$, as indicated on the figure.

In the previous example the generalized coordinates θ_1 and θ_2 were chosen without discussion. Let us pay more attention to the selection of the generalized coordinates in this example. Because the applied force is in the form of a voltage, an examination of Table 3.2-1 indicates that the coordinates are charge q. The circuit contains three energy-storage elements, and we therefore expect three generalized coordinates. Three

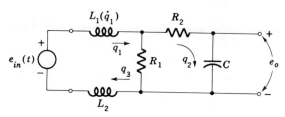

Fig. 3.5-2 Electrical network with three energy-storage elements.

coordinates are labeled on the figure as q_1, q_2, and q_3. One holonomic-constraint equation is immediately evident, since $q_1 = q_3$, or $q_1 - q_3 = 0$. Therefore there are only two generalized coordinates, which we may select as q_1 and q_2.

Because of the nonlinear element $L_1(\dot{q}_1)$, it is best to integrate the momentum vector to determine $\mathfrak{I}(\mathbf{q},\dot{\mathbf{q}})$. Here $\mathbf{p}(\mathbf{q},\dot{\mathbf{q}})$ is

$$\mathbf{p}(\mathbf{q},\dot{\mathbf{q}}) = \begin{bmatrix} L_1(\dot{q}_1)\dot{q}_1 + L_2\dot{q}_1 \\ 0 \end{bmatrix}$$

and

$$\mathfrak{I}(\mathbf{q},\dot{\mathbf{q}}) = \int_0^{\dot{q}_1} L_1(\dot{q}_1')\dot{q}_1' \, d\dot{q}_1' + \tfrac{1}{2}L_2\dot{q}_1{}^2$$

The other necessary state functions are written directly as

$$\mathcal{V}(\mathbf{q}) = \frac{1}{2C}\, q_2{}^2$$

$$\mathfrak{D}(\dot{\mathbf{q}}) = \tfrac{1}{2}R_1(\dot{q}_1 - \dot{q}_2)^2 + \tfrac{1}{2}R_2\dot{q}_2{}^2$$

and the only generalized force is

$$\mathfrak{F}_1 = e_{\text{in}}$$

The only possible source of difficulty in determining the equations of motion from the operational form of Lagrange's equations occurs in taking $\dfrac{d}{dt}\dfrac{\partial \mathfrak{I}}{\partial \dot{q}_1}$. This is done in two steps, as

$$\frac{\partial \mathfrak{I}}{\partial \dot{q}_1} = L_1(\dot{q}_1)\dot{q}_1 + L_2\dot{q}_1$$

$$\frac{d}{dt}\frac{\partial \mathfrak{I}}{\partial \dot{q}_1} = \left[L_1(\dot{q}_1) + \dot{q}_1\frac{\partial L_1(\dot{q}_1)}{\partial \dot{q}_1} + L_2 \right]\ddot{q}_1$$

If the remaining operations are performed, the two equations that result are

$$\left[L_1(\dot{q}_1) + \dot{q}_1\frac{\partial L_1(\dot{q}_1)}{\partial \dot{q}_1} + L_2 \right]\ddot{q}_1 + R_1(\dot{q}_1 - \dot{q}_2) = e_{\text{in}}$$

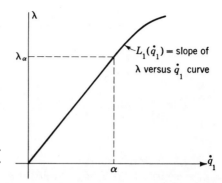

Fig. 3.5-3   Plot of flux linkages vs. current for the nonlinear inductance of Fig. 3.5-2.

and

$$(R_1 + R_2)\dot{q}_2 - R_1\dot{q}_1 + \frac{1}{C}q_2 = 0 \tag{3.5-4}$$

Also of interest is the fact that the output voltage is

$$e_o = \frac{1}{C}q_2$$

As expected, the resulting equations are nonlinear.

As yet the dependence of L_1 on $\dot{q}_1$ has not been specified. Assume that as the current $\dot{q}_1$ is changed, the flux linkages change as indicated in Fig. 3.5-3. The slope of this line is L_1. For all practical purposes the flux linkages increase linearly with current up to the point where $\dot{q}_1 = \alpha$. For $\dot{q}_1 < \alpha$, the inductance L_1 is a constant, and

$$\frac{\partial L_1(\dot{q}_1)}{\partial \dot{q}_1} = 0$$

For this range of $\dot{q}_1$, the system is therefore linear with the describing equations

$$(L_1 + L_2)\ddot{q}_1 + R_1(\dot{q}_1 - \dot{q}_2) = e_{\text{in}}$$

$$(R_1 + R_2)\dot{q}_2 - R_1\dot{q}_1 + \frac{1}{C}q_2 = 0$$

$$e_o = \frac{1}{C}q_2 \tag{3.5-5}$$

and we may discuss the transfer function of the system.

One approach to the problem of finding the first-order state-variable equations is to use this transfer function as we did in Chap. 2.   The transfer function of this linear system is easily found by taking the Laplace transform of Eq. (3.5-5),

$$\frac{e_o(s)}{e_{in}(s)} = \frac{R_1}{(R_1 + R_2)(L_1 + L_2)Cs^2 + (L_1 + L_2 + R_1R_2C)s + R_1}$$

$$(3.5\text{-}6)$$

Two first-order equations result from Eq. (3.5-6) by letting $x_1 = e_o$ and $\dot{x}_1 = x_2$ and identifying powers of s with the derivative, as done in Chap. 2.   The resulting variables are phase variables.

$$\dot{x}_1 = x_2$$

$$\dot{x}_2 = \frac{1}{(R_1 + R_2)(L_1 + L_2)C} [-R_1x_1 - (L_1 + L_2 + R_1R_2C)x_2 + R_1u]$$

and

$$y = x_1$$

where

$$y = e_o \quad \text{and} \quad u = e_{in}$$

An alternate and preferable approach is to proceed directly from Eq. (3.5-5).   Since q_1 does not appear in either of these equations, it need not be recognized as a meaningful state variable.   Also, $\ddot{q}_2$ does not appear in the second equation, and there is no need to consider $\dot{q}_2$ as a variable. Two possible state variables then are $\dot{q}_1$ and q_2.   The output e_o is simply related to q_2, and so we choose as our final state variables $x_1 = \dot{q}_1$ and $x_2 = q_2/C = e_o$.   After a small amount of manipulation the two resulting first-order equations are

$$\dot{x}_1 = \frac{1}{L_1 + L_2} \left(-\frac{R_1R_2x_1}{R_1 + R_2} - \frac{R_1x_2}{R_1 + R_2} + u \right)$$

$$\dot{x}_2 = \frac{R_1x_1}{C(R_1 + R_2)} - \frac{x_2}{C(R_1 + R_2)}$$

$$y = x_2$$

where

$$y = e_o \quad \text{and} \quad u = e_{in}$$

These state-variable equations are equivalent to specifying the transfer function and thus are equivalent to the phase-variable equations that result from Eq. (3.5-6). Obviously they are not equal and are equivalent only from an input-output point of view. The authors contend that the state variables chosen from the differential equations are the more natural system variables, and it is for this reason that the latter approach is preferred. In addition, if the system is nonlinear, the transfer function cannot be used, and one must proceed directly from Eq. (3.5-5).

It is interesting to note that while both of the above examples had two generalized coordinates, the first example results in a fourth-order system while the second example is only second-order. These results illustrate the statement made earlier in the section that the number of state variables could vary from N to $2N$. Note also in the second example that although the system is second-order, its natural lagrangian state variables are *not* phase variables.

As a final example, we consider the problem of the electrostatic gyroscope. One method of avoiding friction in a gyro is to do away with the bearings and suspend the inertial mass with an electrostatic field. If such a suspension is accomplished and the cavity in which the mass rotates is completely evacuated, both friction and viscous damping are essentially zero. Once started, the inertia continues to rotate the mass almost indefinitely.

The problem is to regulate the suspension of the inertial mass by means of an applied voltage $e(t)$. Let us consider a simplified one-dimensional problem for discussion purposes. In our example of Fig. 3.5-4 it is assumed that the inertia can move only in the vertical direction. The inertial mass is pictured as spherical, and the fixed top of the cavity is spherical as well. Means of electrically sensing rotor position provide a method for electrically grounding the rotor and at the same time provide a small amount of proportional support. This sensing circuit is ignored in our simplified example, and its effect is shown by grounding the inertial mass and assuming a linear support spring of constant K.

A variety of nonholonomic constraints exist for this problem, as for all real physical problems. Regardless of the polarity of $\dot{q}$, the inertial mass is drawn upward toward the fixed plate. This fact may not be obvious until the equations are written, but is nevertheless a fact. There is simply no way to move the mass downward with $e(t)$. If $e(t)$ decreases until it goes through zero, the negative values of current continue to force m in the upward direction. Thus $e(t)$, assumed positive here, is bounded away from zero, or

$$e(t) > 0$$

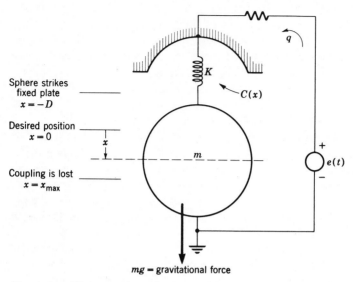

Fig. 3.5-4 Electrostatic gyroscope.

If the mass moves upward too far, it strikes the fixed plate; therefore

$$x \geq -D$$

On the other hand, if x becomes too positive, the coupling between the plates is lost; therefore

$$x \leq x_{\max}$$

The equations derived below are valid only if none of these constraints is violated.

The energy functions for our model may now be written, by inspection, from Fig. 3.5-4 as

$$\mathfrak{I} = \tfrac{1}{2}m\dot{x}^2$$

$$\mathfrak{V} = \tfrac{1}{2}Kx^2 + \frac{1}{2C(x)}\,q^2$$

Here $C(x)$ is the capacitance between the fixed plate and the inertial mass. If the radius of the sphere is large compared with the spacing, the plates are approximately parallel, and $C(x)$ is

$$C(x) = \frac{A\epsilon_o}{D + x}$$

where A is the area of the plate, ϵ_o is the dielectric constant, and D is the nominal spacing when $x = 0$.   The potential energy is therefore

$$\mathcal{U} = \tfrac{1}{2}Kx^2 + \frac{D + x}{2A\epsilon_o}q^2$$

The dissipation function and the applied forces are

$$\mathfrak{D} = \tfrac{1}{2}R\dot{q}^2$$

$$\mathfrak{F}_x = mg \quad \text{and} \quad \mathfrak{F}_q = e(t)$$

Notice that we have not bothered here to identify the variable x with the generalized coordinate notation q_1, $\dot{x}$ with $\dot{q}_1$, etc.   Such identification is a formalism that is soon bypassed as one becomes used to using Lagrange's equation.   Thus, to establish the equation corresponding to the x variable, we actually substitute into Lagrange's equations written as

$$\frac{d}{dt}\frac{\partial \mathfrak{I}}{\partial \dot{x}} - \frac{\partial \mathfrak{I}}{\partial x} + \frac{\partial \mathcal{U}}{\partial x} + \frac{\partial \mathfrak{D}}{\partial \dot{x}} = \mathfrak{F}_x$$

The result is

$$m\ddot{x} + Kx + \frac{q^2}{2\epsilon_o A} = mg$$

For q the resulting equation is

$$R\dot{q} + \frac{D + x}{\epsilon_o A}q = e(t)$$

If we let $x_1 = x$, $x_2 = \dot{x}$, and $x_3 = q$, the three state-variable equations become

$$\dot{x}_1 = x_2 \qquad \dot{x}_2 = -\frac{Kx_1}{m} - \frac{x_3{}^2}{2\epsilon_o A m} + g$$

$$\dot{x}_3 = -\frac{Dx_3}{\epsilon_o A R} - \frac{x_1 x_3}{\epsilon_o A R} + \frac{u}{R}$$

where $u(t) = e(t)$ and the output $y = x_1$.

We shall make use of this example later.

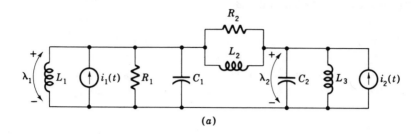

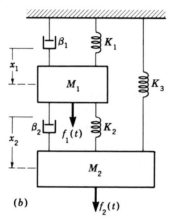

(b)

Fig. 3.5-5   Exercise 3.5-1.

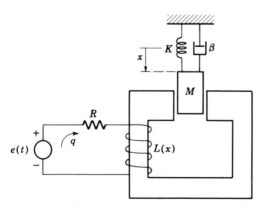

Fig. 3.5-6   Exercise 3.5-2.

Exercises 3.5   *3.5-1.* Show that the systems shown in Fig. 3.5-5 are the electrical and translational mechanical analogs of the first example of this section by finding the equations of motion of the two systems using Lagrange's equation.

3.5-2. Represent the system shown in Fig. 3.5-6 in state-variable form by using Lagrange's equation to find the equations of motion for the system and then letting $x_1 = x$, $x_2 = \dot{x}$, $x_3 = \dot{q}$, and $u(t) = e(t)$.

answers:

$$\dot{x}_1 = x_2$$

$$\dot{x}_2 = \frac{1}{M} \left[-Kx_1 + \frac{1}{2} \frac{\partial L(x_1)}{\partial x_1} x_3^2 - \beta x_2 \right]$$

$$\dot{x}_3 = \frac{1}{L(x_1)} \left[-Rx_3 + u(t) \right]$$

3.6   Summary and conclusion

This chapter has served to demonstrate how the state function of Lagrange and Lagrange's equation may be used as the basis of system representation for control engineers.   The resulting N second-order equations may be put into first-order form by trivial manipulations, so that the system representation is in the convenient modern form.

Enough examples have been worked in the chapter to indicate the power of the lagrangian approach for cases that are not so conventional as the simple position system.   Of course, in complicated problems the results are often nonlinear.   Since our principal interest throughout the book is in linear systems, methods of linearization are included as an early part of the next chapter.

The assumption in the chapters to follow is that the questions of problem formulation and system representation have now been answered. The next question is, "How does a system respond for particular inputs?" This is the question of analysis.   Chapters 4 and 5 deal with system analysis, based on the state-transition matrix and the state function of Liapunov.

3.7   Problems

3.7-1. Find the state-variable representation of the systems shown in Fig. 3.7-1.   Neglect the gravitational force.   Write and discuss all nonholonomic constraints in the systems.

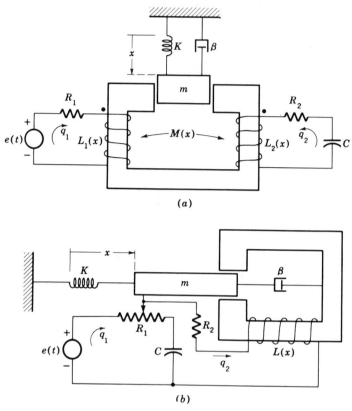

Fig. 3.7-1   Prob. 3.7-1.

3.7-2.   For the mechanical systems shown in Fig. 3.7-2

(a)   Find the state representation of the systems by using Lagrange's equation.

(b)   Find the transfer function $y(s)/u(s)$ for the systems if $y = x_1$ and $u = f(t)$.

(c)   Use the transfer function of part b to find a phase-variable representation for the system.

(d)   Find the linear transformation which relates the state-variable representations of parts a and c.

3.7-3.   Find the equations of motion for the system shown in Fig. 3.7-3 by means of Lagrange's equation.   List all nonholonomic constraints.

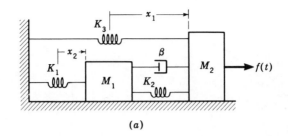

(a)

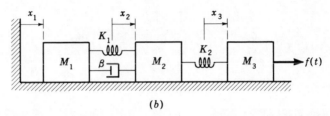

(b)

Fig. 3.7-2 Prob. 3.7-2.

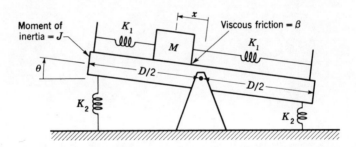

Fig. 3.7-3 Prob. 3.7-3.

3.7-4. For the electrical networks shown in Fig. 3.7-4

(a) Find the equations of motion using Kirchhoff's laws.
(b) Find the equations of motion using Lagrange's equation.

3.7-5. For the system shown in Fig. 3.7-5, find the degrees of freedom of the system by writing all possible holonomic constraints. Then determine the equations of motion for the system.

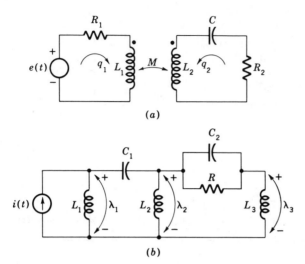

(a)

(b)

Fig. 3.7-4 Prob. 3.7-4.

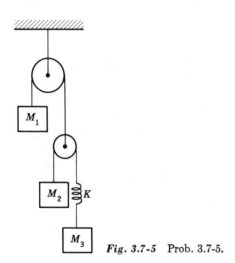

Fig. 3.7-5 Prob. 3.7-5.

3.7-6. Find the equation of motion of the double-pendulum system shown in Fig. 3.7-6.

3.7-7. Find the equations of motion for the systems given in Exercise 3.2-1.

3.7-8. Find the equations of motion for the system given in Exercise 3.2-2.

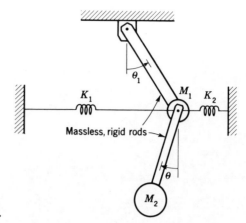

Fig. 3.7-6   Prob. 3.7-6.

References

Aseltine, J. A.: "Transform Method in Linear System Analysis," McGraw-Hill Book Company, New York, 1958.

Goldstein, H.: "Classical Mechanics," Addison-Wesley Publishing Company, Inc., Reading, Mass., 1950.

Lass, H.: "Vector and Tensor Analysis," McGraw-Hill Book Company, New York, 1950.

Meisel, J.: "Principles of Electromechanical Energy Conversion," McGraw-Hill Book Company, New York, 1966.

Seely, S.: "Electromechanical Energy Conversion," McGraw-Hill Book Company, New York, 1962.

White, D. C., and H. H. Woodson: "Electromechanical Energy Conversion," John Wiley & Sons, Inc., New York, 1959.

four   *time response of linear systems*

4.1   Introduction and outline of chapter

In the two preceding chapters the description of control systems in terms of state variables was introduced and developed by means of the state function of Lagrange. Here the basic concepts of the time response of systems are presented, while the next chapter discusses system stability in terms of the state function of Liapunov. These two chapters form the basic tools of analysis used in the remainder of the book.

Although our main concern is with linear systems, many of the procedures presented here can be applied more or less successfully to nonlinear systems. When this is the case, we shall make note of it.

Since the system equations obtained by the use of the Lagrange state function are generally nonlinear, a procedure for linearizing these equations is presented first. Once the system is represented by a set of first-order linear differential equations of the form (**AB**) and (**C**), the problem of obtaining the time response of the system in the case of both forced and unforced motion is considered. In this development the important notion of a state-transition matrix for a system is introduced. The state-transition matrix plays a role similar to the impulse-response function in the classic Laplace transform approach.

In order to obtain the time response of a system by the state-transition-matrix method, it is obviously necessary to know the state-transition matrix for the system. Several methods are examined for computing the state-transition matrix or its Laplace transform, the resolvent matrix. Each of the methods is shown to be more or less advantageous, depending on the experience of the investigator, the type of system, and the method of computation to be used.

As an illustration of the generality of the state-transition-matrix method, the method is applied to the analysis of sampled-data, time-varying, and nonlinear systems.

4.2   Linearization of the system equations

The previous chapter advocated the use of the state function of Lagrange as a means of obtaining the describing differential equations for electrical, mechanical, and electromechanical dynamic systems. It was pointed out that Lagrange's equation is equally applicable to systems whose describing equations are either linear or nonlinear. In general, as a result of the application of the state function of Lagrange, we are faced with a set of simultaneous nonlinear ordinary differential equations. These equations may be expressed as n first-order equations of the form

$$\dot{\mathbf{x}} = \mathbf{f}(\mathbf{x},\mathbf{u}) \tag{4.2-1}$$

Here although the vector function $\mathbf{f}(\mathbf{x},\mathbf{u})$ may be nonlinear, it is assumed to be continuously differentiable in all its arguments. Although this assumption of differentiability is more than sufficient to ensure that a solution exists, the problem of actually obtaining a solution remains. Unfortunately, no general solution is known for Eq. (4.2-1), nor is there any hope that such a general solution will be found. Since this book is concerned primarily with linear systems, we do not dwell on the solution of nonlinear differential equations but proceed to linearize these equations about some operating point. Our solutions are then valid only in a neighborhood of this point. Of course, if Eq. (4.2-1) is actually linear, no linearization is necessary, and the solution is valid everywhere. But in the general case this is not true, and our desire then is to find a linear system of the form

$$\dot{\mathbf{x}} = \mathbf{A}\mathbf{x} + \mathbf{B}\mathbf{u} \tag{AB}$$

which is a first-order or linear approximation of the nonlinear system (4.2-1) about some operating condition $\mathbf{x}^o$ and $\mathbf{u}^o$. It is assumed that for the conditions $\mathbf{x}^o$ and $\mathbf{u}^o$ the system is in equilibrium, that is,

$$\dot{\mathbf{x}} = \mathbf{f}(\mathbf{x}^o, \mathbf{u}^o) = 0$$

At equilibrium all the derivatives of the n state variables are zero. In fact, this is the definition of an equilibrium point.

Rather than begin with the general case of Eq. (4.2-1), let us look first at the analogous scalar equation

$$\dot{x} = f(x, u) \tag{4.2-2}$$

In order to linearize this system about some operating point it is first necessary to determine a compatible value of x and u for which such an operating point exists. This is done by setting $\dot{x}$ equal to zero, so that $f(x, u)$ equals zero. The solution of this equation determines one or more values for x^o and u^o. Equation (4.2-2) is linearized about this operating point by expanding $f(x, u)$ in a Taylor series about the point x^o and u^o, as

$$f(x, u) = f(x^o, u^o) + \frac{\partial f(x, u)}{\partial x}\bigg|_{\substack{x = x^o \\ u = u^o}} (x - x^o) + \frac{\partial f(x, u)}{\partial u}\bigg|_{\substack{x = x^o \\ u = u^o}} (u - u^o)$$
$$+ \text{ higher-order terms} \tag{4.2-3}$$

Now if changes in x and u from the operating condition x^o and u^o are designated as x^* and u^*, defined by

$$x^* = x - x^o \qquad u^* = u - u^o \tag{4.2-4}$$

then Eq. (4.2-3) may be written in terms of this new variable as

$$f(x, u) = f(x^o, u^o) + \frac{\partial f(x, u)}{\partial x}\bigg|_{\substack{x = x^o \\ u = u^o}} x^* + \frac{\partial f(x, u)}{\partial u}\bigg|_{\substack{x = x^o \\ u = u^o}} u^* + \cdots$$

Here $f(x^o, u^o)$ is zero, since x^o and u^o are assumed to be equilibrium conditions. In addition, since x^o and u^o are fixed, we see that $\dot{x} = \dot{x}^*$. Thus the first-order approximations of Eq. (4.2-2) may be written in terms of x^* and u^* as

$$\dot{x}^* = \frac{\partial f(x,u)}{\partial x}\bigg|_{\substack{x=x^\circ \\ u=u^\circ}} x^* + \frac{\partial f(x,u)}{\partial u}\bigg|_{\substack{x=x^\circ \\ u=u^\circ}} u^* \tag{4.2-5}$$

Equation (4.2-5) represents the complete linearization.

In the second-order case, the general form of Eq. (4.2-1) is

$$\begin{aligned} \dot{x}_1 &= f_1(x_1,x_2,u_1,u_2) \\ \dot{x}_2 &= f_2(x_1,x_2,u_1,u_2) \end{aligned} \tag{4.2-6}$$

and the linearization is about some point $x_1 = x_1^\circ$, $x_2 = x_2^\circ$, $u_1 = u_1^\circ$, and $u_2 = u_2^\circ$. Since f_1 and f_2 are each possible functions of four variables, partial derivatives with respect to each of these variables must appear in the linearized equations, that is, f_1 and f_2 must be expanded as a Taylor series in four variables. The resulting linearized equations for the second-order system of Eq. (4.2-6) are

$$\dot{x}_1^* = \frac{\partial f_1(\mathbf{x},\mathbf{u})}{\partial x_1}\bigg|_{\substack{\mathbf{x}=\mathbf{x}^\circ \\ \mathbf{u}=\mathbf{u}^\circ}} x_1^* + \frac{\partial f_1(\mathbf{x},\mathbf{u})}{\partial x_2}\bigg|_{\substack{\mathbf{x}=\mathbf{x}^\circ \\ \mathbf{u}=\mathbf{u}^\circ}} x_2^*$$

$$+ \frac{\partial f_1(\mathbf{x},\mathbf{u})}{\partial u_1}\bigg|_{\substack{\mathbf{x}=\mathbf{x}^\circ \\ \mathbf{u}=\mathbf{u}^\circ}} u_1^* + \frac{\partial f_1(\mathbf{x},\mathbf{u})}{\partial u_2}\bigg|_{\substack{\mathbf{x}=\mathbf{x}^\circ \\ \mathbf{u}=\mathbf{u}^\circ}} u_2^*$$

$$\dot{x}_2^* = \frac{\partial f_2(\mathbf{x},\mathbf{u})}{\partial x_2}\bigg|_{\substack{\mathbf{x}=\mathbf{x}^\circ \\ \mathbf{u}=\mathbf{u}^\circ}} x_1^* + \frac{\partial f_2(\mathbf{x},\mathbf{u})}{\partial x_2}\bigg|_{\substack{\mathbf{x}=\mathbf{x}^\circ \\ \mathbf{u}=\mathbf{u}^\circ}} x_2^*$$

$$+ \frac{\partial f_2(\mathbf{x},\mathbf{u})}{\partial u_1}\bigg|_{\substack{\mathbf{x}=\mathbf{x}^\circ \\ \mathbf{u}=\mathbf{u}^\circ}} u_1^* + \frac{\partial f_2(\mathbf{x},\mathbf{u})}{\partial u_2}\bigg|_{\substack{\mathbf{x}=\mathbf{x}^\circ \\ \mathbf{u}=\mathbf{u}^\circ}} u_2^* \tag{4.2-7}$$

If these two equations are written in the form $(\mathbf{AB})$, then $\mathbf{A}$ and $\mathbf{B}$ are seen to be

$$\mathbf{A} = \begin{bmatrix} \dfrac{\partial f_1(\mathbf{x},\mathbf{u})}{\partial x_1}\bigg|_{\substack{\mathbf{x}=\mathbf{x}^\circ \\ \mathbf{u}=\mathbf{u}^\circ}} & \dfrac{\partial f_1(\mathbf{x},\mathbf{u})}{\partial x_2}\bigg|_{\substack{\mathbf{x}=\mathbf{x}^\circ \\ \mathbf{u}=\mathbf{u}^\circ}} \\[3ex] \dfrac{\partial f_2(\mathbf{x},\mathbf{u})}{\partial x_1}\bigg|_{\substack{\mathbf{x}=\mathbf{x}^\circ \\ \mathbf{u}=\mathbf{u}^\circ}} & \dfrac{\partial f_2(\mathbf{x},\mathbf{u})}{\partial x_2}\bigg|_{\substack{\mathbf{x}=\mathbf{x}^\circ \\ \mathbf{u}=\mathbf{u}^\circ}} \end{bmatrix} \tag{4.2-8}$$

and

$$\mathbf{B} = \begin{bmatrix} \dfrac{\partial f_1(\mathbf{x},\mathbf{u})}{\partial u_1}\bigg|_{\substack{\mathbf{x}=\mathbf{x}^\circ \\ \mathbf{u}=\mathbf{u}^\circ}} & \dfrac{\partial f_1(\mathbf{x},\mathbf{u})}{\partial u_2}\bigg|_{\substack{\mathbf{x}=\mathbf{x}^\circ \\ \mathbf{u}=\mathbf{u}^\circ}} \\[3ex] \dfrac{\partial f_2(\mathbf{x},\mathbf{u})}{\partial u_1}\bigg|_{\substack{\mathbf{x}=\mathbf{x}^\circ \\ \mathbf{u}=\mathbf{u}^\circ}} & \dfrac{\partial f_2(\mathbf{x},\mathbf{u})}{\partial u_2}\bigg|_{\substack{\mathbf{x}=\mathbf{x}^\circ \\ \mathbf{u}=\mathbf{u}^\circ}} \end{bmatrix} \tag{4.2-9}$$

In each case the partials are evaluated at the equilibrium or operating point, and hence $\mathbf{A}$ and $\mathbf{B}$ are matrices with numbers as elements.

By completely analogous arguments the discussion may be extended from the first- and second-order cases to the nth-order case. In this general case the elements of the $\mathbf{A}$ and $\mathbf{B}$ matrices may be determined from the expressions

$$a_{ij} = \frac{\partial f_i(\mathbf{x},\mathbf{u})}{\partial x_j}\Bigg|_{\substack{\mathbf{x}=\mathbf{x}^o \\ \mathbf{u}=\mathbf{u}^o}} \tag{4.2-10}$$

and

$$b_{ij} = \frac{\partial f_i(\mathbf{x},\mathbf{u})}{\partial u_j}\Bigg|_{\substack{\mathbf{x}=\mathbf{x}^o \\ \mathbf{u}=\mathbf{u}^o}} \tag{4.2-11}$$

which the reader can easily see agree with the first- and second-order results.

Example 4.2-1 As an illustration of the above procedure, consider again the electrostatic gyro example presented in Sec. 3.5. There the system equations were found to be

$$\dot{x}_1 = x_2 \qquad \dot{x}_2 = -\frac{Kx_1}{m} - \frac{x_3{}^2}{2\epsilon_oAm} + g$$

$$\dot{x}_3 = -\frac{Dx_3}{\epsilon_oAR} - \frac{x_1x_3}{\epsilon_oAR} + \frac{u}{R}$$

The reader may recall that in the actual physical system x_1 is position, x_2 is velocity, and x_3 is charge. The control u is the applied voltage, and g is the gravitational force.

According to the procedure outlined above, it is first necessary to determine an equilibrium position (if one exists) by letting all the derivatives of the state variables go to zero. In terms of the operating points $\mathbf{x}^o$ and u^o, the equilibrium equations are

$$0 = x_2{}^o \qquad 0 = -\frac{Kx_1{}^o}{m} - \frac{(x_3{}^o)^2}{2\epsilon_oAm} + g$$

$$0 = -\frac{Dx_3{}^o}{\epsilon_oA} - \frac{x_1{}^ox_3{}^o}{\epsilon_oA} + u^o$$

Since this is a physically oriented example, we have some idea of the equilibrium conditions that are desirable in terms of gyro performance. It is desired to have the equilibrium position of the gyro rotor be such that it is stationary in the center of its housing, or x_1^o and x_2^o should equal zero. The applied voltage u^o must then be chosen to ensure that these conditions can be met. Under these assumptions the equilibrium equations are further reduced to

$$0 = -\frac{(x_3^o)^2}{2\epsilon_o A m} + g \quad \text{and} \quad 0 = -\frac{D x_3^o}{\epsilon_o A} + u^o$$

These two equations may be solved simultaneously to yield

$$u^o = D\sqrt{\frac{2mg}{\epsilon_o A}} \qquad x_3^o = \sqrt{2\epsilon_o A m g}$$

The important question that must be answered now is just how this system behaves in the presence of small disturbances in $u(t)$. Therefore the given equations must be linearized about this new operating point, or they must be expressed as Eq. (**Ab**). This is conveniently done by means of Eqs. (4.2-10) and (4.2-11) in terms of the starred quantities

$$u^* = u - u^o = u - D\sqrt{\frac{2mg}{\epsilon_o A}} \qquad x_1^* = x_1 - x_1^o = x_1$$

$$x_2^* = x_2 - x_2^o = x_2 \qquad x_3^* = x_3 - x_3^o = x_3 - \sqrt{2\epsilon_o A m g}$$

A is found to be

$$\mathbf{A} = \begin{bmatrix} 0 & 1 & 0 \\ -\dfrac{K}{m} & 0 & -\sqrt{\dfrac{2g}{\epsilon_o A m}} \\ -\sqrt{\dfrac{2mg}{\epsilon_o A R^2}} & 0 & -\dfrac{D}{\epsilon_o A R} \end{bmatrix}$$

where, for example, a_{23} is formed as

$$a_{23} = \frac{\partial f_2}{\partial x_3}\bigg|_{x^o, u^o} = -\frac{2x_3}{2\epsilon_o A m}\bigg|_{x_3 = \sqrt{2\epsilon_o A m g}} = -\sqrt{\frac{2g}{\epsilon_o A m}}$$

and

$$\mathbf{b} = \begin{bmatrix} 0 \\ 0 \\ 1 \\ \dfrac{1}{R} \end{bmatrix}$$

The resulting linearized equations are

$$\dot{x}_1^* = x_2^* \qquad \dot{x}_2^* = -\frac{K}{m}x_1^* - \sqrt{\frac{2g}{\epsilon_o A m}}\,x_3^*$$

$$\dot{x}_3^* = -\sqrt{\frac{2mg}{\epsilon_o A R^2}}\,x_1^* - \frac{D}{\epsilon_o A R}\,x_3^* + \frac{u^*}{R}$$

The coefficients of each of the x_i^* variables are now constants, and conventional methods may be used to determine the response for a given input $u(t)^*$.

Throughout this section no mention has been made of an output expression, Eq. **(C)**,

$$\mathbf{y} = \mathbf{Cx} \tag{C}$$

In general, one might assume that associated with Eq. (4.2-1) there is a nonlinear output expression, as

$$\mathbf{y} = \mathbf{g(x)} \tag{4.2-12}$$

Usually, however, this is not the case. When the nonlinear equations are generated by Lagrange's equation, which is the assumption made at the beginning of this section, the state variables are automatically physical-system variables. The outputs are usually one or more of these state variables, so that the output equation remains as Eq. **(C)**. If this is not the case, Eq. (4.2-12) may be linearized in exactly the same fashion as Eq. (4.2-1), with the result that

$$\mathbf{y} = \mathbf{Cx}^* \tag{4.2-13}$$

where

$$c_{ij} = \frac{\partial g_i(\mathbf{x})}{\partial x_j}\bigg|_{\mathbf{x}=\mathbf{x}^o} \tag{4.2-14}$$

One case where it is necessary to linearize the output expression occurs when the range of the output state variable is very large. This occurs in a nuclear reactor, for instance, where the power level may vary over six orders of magnitude. For control purposes it is convenient to use the log of the power level rather than the power level itself.

Exercises 4.2   *4.2-1.* Linearize the following systems about the origin:

(a) $\dot{x}_1 = x_1 x_2 + 3x_2 + u_1{}^2 + u_2$
     $\dot{x}_2 = 4x_1 + x_2 + x_1 u_2{}^2 + 2u_1$
(b) $\dot{x}_1 = x_1{}^2 - \sin 3x_2 + u_1{}^3 - u_2$
     $\dot{x}_2 = x_2 - u_1 + x_1 e^{-x_2}$

answers:

(a) $\dot{x}_1^* = 3x_2^* + u_2^*$ $\dot{x}_2^* = 4x_1^* + x_2^* + 2u_1^*$
(b) $\dot{x}_1^* = -3x_2^* - u_2^*$ $\dot{x}_2^* = x_1^* + x_2^* - u_1^*$

4.2-2. With $\mathbf{u}^o = \mathrm{col}\,(0, -1.5)$, show that the equilibrium point of the following system is $\mathbf{x}^o = \mathrm{col}\,(1, 0.5)$.

$$\dot{x}_1 = 4x_1 + 2x_2{}^2 + u_1 + 3u_2$$
$$\dot{x}_2 = x_1{}^3 + x_2 + 2u_1 + u_2$$

Linearize the equations about this operating point.

answer:

$$\dot{x}_1^* = 4x_1^* + 2x_2^* + u_1^* + 3u_2^*$$
$$\dot{x}_2^* = 3x_1^* + x_2^* + 2u_1^* + u_2^*$$

4.2-3. Show that the system

$$\dot{x}_1 = \tan^{-1} 2x_1 + x_2 - 2\sin x_2 - 4u_1 e^{-3u_2} + u_2{}^3$$
$$\dot{x}_2 = x_1{}^2 + 2x_2 e^{-u_1} - 3u_1 + u_2$$

when linearized about the origin is given by

$$\dot{x}_1^* = 2x_1^* - x_2^* - 4u_1^*   \qquad \dot{x}_2^* = 2x_2^* - 3u_1^* + u_2^*$$

4.3   *System response and the state-transition matrix*

In the remainder of the book, unless specifically noted, it is assumed that the equations we are dealing with are linear or that they have been linearized. In the case of equations that have been linearized, it is inconvenient to carry the starred notation, and in the future both linearized and linear equations are assumed to be described by (**AB**) and (**C**). We now turn our attention to the problem of obtaining the solution to this set of n first-order linear differential equations, (**AB**), repeated here for convenience:

$$\dot{x}(t) = \mathbf{A}x(t) + \mathbf{B}u(t) \qquad (\mathbf{AB})$$

The solution to (**AB**) involves the determination of the time response of all the state variables. This is the basic difference between the state-variable and transfer-function approaches to the problem of system response. In the transfer-function approach, emphasis is placed upon input-output relationships, and no attention is paid to the behavior of any of the variables that may exist internal to the system. The solution of (**AB**) in the time domain or in the frequency domain results in an exact knowledge of the behavior of all the state variables. Once $\mathbf{x}$ is known, $\mathbf{y}$ is also known.

The format of this section is similar to that of the last one. Instead of considering the general case at the outset, we begin by considering the analogous scalar equation

$$\dot{x}(t) = ax(t) + bu(t) \qquad (ab)$$

Since the unforced or homogeneous response plays an important role in the time-domain solution of Eq. (**AB**), we examine the unforced solutions of Eqs. (ab) and (**AB**) in order to introduce the important concept of the state-transition matrix for a system. A parallel development is made in the time and frequency domains.

4.3-1 Unforced response

In order to obtain the unforced response of the system (**AB**), that is, the time response of the homogeneous equation

$$\dot{x}(t) = \mathbf{A}x(t) \qquad (\mathbf{A})$$

where the forcing function $\mathbf{u}(t)$ has been set equal to 0, let us begin by considering the time response of the simple first-order scalar equation

$$\dot{x}(t) = ax(t) \qquad (a)$$

Although the solution of this equation may be written down by inspection as

$$x(t) = e^{at}x(0) \qquad (4.3\text{-}1)$$

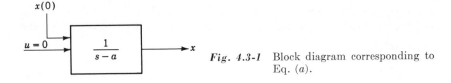

Fig. 4.3-1   Block diagram corresponding to Eq. (*a*).

for pedagogical reasons, let us solve Eq. (*a*) by Laplace transform methods. The Laplace transform of Eq. (*a*) is

$$sx(s) - x(0) = ax(s)$$

or

$$x(s) = \frac{x(0)}{s - a} = (s - a)^{-1}x(0) \tag{4.3-2}$$

The block diagram of Fig. 4.3-1 indicates that this simple first-order system is driven only by initial conditions, since here $u = 0$. The coefficients of $x(0)$ in Eqs. (4.3-1) and (4.3-2) are respectively e^{at} and $(s - a)^{-1}$. The term e^{at} is the inverse Laplace transform of $(s - a)^{-1}$ and is known as the impulse response or the weighting function of the system of Fig. 4.3-1.

   In attempting to determine the time response of the more complicated Eq. (**A**) by the use of time-domain methods, we are led by direct comparison with Eq. (4.3-1) to suspect that the solution should be of the form

$$\mathbf{x}(t) = e^{\mathbf{A}t}\mathbf{x}(0) \tag{4.3-3}$$

Although we might expect further that $e^{\mathbf{A}t}$ is somehow related to the impulse response of the system represented by the matrix **A**, some difficulty lies in interpreting the matrix function $e^{\mathbf{A}t}$. In order to do this, consider the power-series expansion of the function e^{at}, which may be considered as the definition of e^{at},

$$e^{at} = 1 + at + \frac{a^2}{2!}t^2 + \frac{a^3}{3!}t^3 + \cdots = \sum_{i=0}^{\infty} \frac{a^i}{i!}t^i$$

By analogy, let us define the matrix $e^{\mathbf{A}t}$ by a similar power series in the matrix **A** as

$$e^{\mathbf{A}t} = \mathbf{I} + \mathbf{A}t + \frac{\mathbf{A}^2}{2!}t^2 + \frac{\mathbf{A}^3}{3!}t^3 + \cdots = \sum_{i=0}^{\infty} \frac{\mathbf{A}^i}{i!}t^i \tag{4.3-4}$$

It is possible to show that this series converges absolutely for all finite t and uniformly in any finite interval (see Zadeh and Desoer, 1963).

It remains to be shown that our assumed solution, e^{At}, actually satisfies the given differential equation (A). If the expansion of e^{At} is substituted into Eq. (4.3-3), so that

$$\mathbf{x}(t) = \left[\mathbf{I} + \mathbf{A}t + \frac{\mathbf{A}^2}{2!} t^2 + \cdots \right] \mathbf{x}(0) \tag{4.3-5}$$

we see that the assumed solution does satisfy the initial conditions. In Eq. (4.3-5) for $t = 0$, all terms other than the first are zero, and

$$\mathbf{x}(0) = \mathbf{I}\mathbf{x}(0) = \mathbf{x}(0) \tag{4.3-6}$$

This is a hopeful sign, but to determine whether the assumed solution satisfies the differential equation, this assumed solution must be substituted into the differential equation (A). Differentiation of the series representation for e^{At} presents no problem, since all the elements of $\mathbf{A}$ are constant. Thus

$$\dot{\mathbf{x}}(t) = \frac{d}{dt} e^{At}\mathbf{x}(0) = \frac{d}{dt} \sum_{i=0}^{\infty} \frac{\mathbf{A}^i}{i!} t^i \mathbf{x}(0) = \left(\sum_{i=0}^{\infty} i \frac{\mathbf{A}^i}{i!} t^{i-1} \right) \mathbf{x}(0)$$

$$= \mathbf{A} \left(\sum_{i=0}^{\infty} \frac{\mathbf{A}^i}{i!} t^i \right) \mathbf{x}(0) \tag{4.3-7}$$

which we recognize as

$$\dot{\mathbf{x}}(t) = \mathbf{A}e^{At}\mathbf{x}(0) = \mathbf{A}\mathbf{x}(t) \tag{4.3-8}$$

Therefore Eq. (4.3-3) has been shown to be a solution of the differential equation (A).

Since a knowledge of the matrix e^{At} and the initial state of the system allows one to determine the state at *any* later time, the matrix e^{At} plays an important role in obtaining the time response of a system. Because of the key part that it plays in determining the transition of the system from one state to another, the matrix e^{At} has been termed the state-transition matrix (STM), usually written as $\mathbf{\Phi}(t)$, in which case Eq. (4.3-3) becomes

$$\mathbf{x}(t) = \mathbf{\Phi}(t)\mathbf{x}(0) \tag{4.3-9}$$

One might also consider $\mathbf{\Phi}(t)$ as a linear transformation of the initial state of the system into the state at time t. The significance of this interpretation of the STM is examined in more detail later.

Equation (4.3-4) may be considered as the time-domain matrix, and it indicates a manner in which this matrix may be calculated. The factor $\mathbf{A}^2$ in the third term of the series is just $[\mathbf{A}][\mathbf{A}]$, and once this multiplication has been made, the factor $\mathbf{A}^3$ in the fourth term may be determined by simply pre- or postmultiplying $\mathbf{A}^2$ by $\mathbf{A}$. This result may be used in calculating $\mathbf{A}^4$, etc. This procedure is feasible for low-order systems, although it is often impossible to recognize the resulting series expressions that go to make up the elements of the matrix $e^{\mathbf{A}t}$; that is, it is often not simple to express each element of $e^{\mathbf{A}t}$ in closed form. Alternate means of determining the state-transition matrix are indicated in the following sections.

An equivalent method of defining the STM is as the solution of the matrix differential equation

$$\dot{\mathbf{\Phi}}(t) = \mathbf{A}\mathbf{\Phi}(t) \tag{4.3-10}$$

with $\mathbf{\Phi}(0) = \mathbf{I}$. By a procedure similar to that presented above, it can be shown that the matrix $e^{\mathbf{A}t}$ satisfies this definition. The main motivation for the use of this definition is its direct extension to the more general case of time-varying systems (see Sec. 4.6).

Some properties of the STM which are of value later are summarized in Table 4.3-1. For comparison the similar properties of the function e^{at} are also listed. While there is a great deal of similarity between the two functions, the reader is cautioned not to extend the analogy too far. Although, in actuality, properties III and IV are simply special

Table 4.3-1   *Properties of the state transition matrix $e^{\mathbf{A}t}$ and the function e^{at}*

Property	$\mathbf{\Phi}(t) = e^{\mathbf{A}t}$	e^{at}
I	Nonsingular for all finite values of t	Nonzero for all finite values of t
II	$\mathbf{\Phi}(t_1)\mathbf{\Phi}(t_2) = \mathbf{\Phi}(t_1 + t_2)$	$e^{at_1}e^{at_2} = e^{a(t_1+t_2)}$
III	$\mathbf{\Phi}(t)^{-1} = \mathbf{\Phi}(-t)$	$(e^{at})^{-1} = e^{a(-t)}$
IV	$\mathbf{\Phi}(t)^n = \mathbf{\Phi}(nt)$	$(e^{at})^n = e^{a(nt)}$

cases of property II, they are used so frequently that they were listed separately for convenience and emphasis. The establishment of these properties is left to the reader (see Exercise 4.3-1).

As an illustration of how these properties may be used, let us consider next the form that Eq. (4.3-9) takes if the state of the system is known initially at $t = t_0 > 0$ rather than at $t = 0$. By analogy with the scalar case we are led to suspect that the answer should be

$$\mathbf{x}(t) = e^{\mathbf{A}(t-t_o)}\mathbf{x}(t_o) = \mathbf{\Phi}(t - t_o)\mathbf{x}(t_o) \tag{4.3-11}$$

To show that this is, in fact, the correct result, use Eq. (4.3-9) to write

$$\mathbf{x}(t_o) = \mathbf{\Phi}(t_o)\mathbf{x}(0) \tag{4.3-12}$$

Since, by property I, $\mathbf{\Phi}(t)$ is nonsingular, we obtain by premultiplying both sides of Eq. (4.3-12) by $\mathbf{\Phi}(t_o)^{-1}$

$$\mathbf{x}(0) = \mathbf{\Phi}(t_o)^{-1}\mathbf{x}(t_o)$$

Then using property III

$$\mathbf{x}(0) = \mathbf{\Phi}(-t_o)\mathbf{x}(t_o)$$

Substituting this result into Eq. (4.3-9), we obtain for $\mathbf{x}(t)$

$$\mathbf{x}(t) = \mathbf{\Phi}(t)\mathbf{\Phi}(-t_o)\mathbf{x}(t_o) = \mathbf{\Phi}(t - t_o)\mathbf{x}(t_o)$$

which is the desired result.

Before proceeding to the forced case, let us consider the solution of Eq. (**A**) by Laplace transform methods, much as Eq. (*a*) was solved by these methods. The solution requires taking the Laplace transform of a matrix and then an inverse Laplace transform finally to determine $\mathbf{x}(t)$. The Laplace transform or inverse transform of a matrix, denoted as $\mathcal{L}[\ \ ]$ and $\mathcal{L}^{-1}[\ \ ]$ respectively, is accomplished by performing the indicated operation on each element of the matrix. Therefore the Laplace transform of Eq. (**A**) is

$$s\mathbf{x}(s) - \mathbf{x}(0) = \mathbf{A}\mathbf{x}(s)$$
$$(s\mathbf{I} - \mathbf{A})\mathbf{x}(s) = \mathbf{x}(0)$$

and $\mathbf{x}(s)$ is obtained by premultiplying both sides of the above equation by $(s\mathbf{I} - \mathbf{A})^{-1}$ to obtain

$$\mathbf{x}(s) = (s\mathbf{I} - \mathbf{A})^{-1}\mathbf{x}(0) \tag{4.3-13}$$

which looks very similar to Eq. (4.3-2) in the analogous scalar case.   The time response $\mathbf{x}(t)$ is determined as

$$\mathbf{x}(t) = \mathcal{L}^{-1}[(s\mathbf{I} - \mathbf{A})^{-1}]\mathbf{x}(0)$$

This $\mathbf{x}(t)$ is the same as given in Eq. (4.3-3), and hence the STM is

$$e^{\mathbf{A}t} = \mathbf{\Phi}(t) = \mathcal{L}^{-1}[(s\mathbf{I} - \mathbf{A})^{-1}] \tag{4.3-14}$$

This is the basic frequency-domain definition of the STM.

The reader will remember that we encountered the matrix $(s\mathbf{I} - \mathbf{A})^{-1}$ in Chap. 2.   There we defined this matrix as $\mathbf{\Phi}(s)$, the resolvent matrix. In terms of this definition Eq. (4.3-13) becomes

$$\mathbf{x}(t) = \mathcal{L}^{-1}[\mathbf{\Phi}(s)]\mathbf{x}(0)$$

We see, therefore, that $\mathbf{\Phi}(s)$ is just the Laplace transform of the STM $\mathbf{\Phi}(t)$,

$$\mathbf{\Phi}(s) = \mathcal{L}[\mathbf{\Phi}(t)]$$

or similarly $\mathbf{\Phi}(t)$ is the inverse Laplace transform of $\mathbf{\Phi}(s)$,

$$\mathbf{\Phi}(t) = \mathcal{L}^{-1}[\mathbf{\Phi}(s)]$$

Example 4.3-1   Here the STM of the system described by the block diagram of Fig. 4.3-2 is determined by use of the time-domain equation (4.3-4) and the frequency-domain equation (4.3-14).   From the block diagram the two describing equations are

$$\dot{x}_1 = -x_1 + x_2$$
$$\dot{x}_2 = -2x_2 + u$$

so that the $\mathbf{A}$ matrix is

$$\mathbf{A} = \begin{bmatrix} -1 & 1 \\ 0 & -2 \end{bmatrix}$$

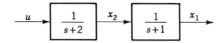

Fig. 4.3-2 Time-response example.

From Eq. (4.3-4) $e^{\mathbf{A}t}$ is

$$e^{\mathbf{A}t} = \mathbf{\Phi}(t) = \begin{bmatrix} 1 & 0 \\ 0 & 1 \end{bmatrix} + \begin{bmatrix} -1 & 1 \\ 0 & -2 \end{bmatrix} t + \begin{bmatrix} 1 & -3 \\ 0 & 4 \end{bmatrix} \frac{t^2}{2!}$$
$$+ \begin{bmatrix} -1 & 7 \\ 0 & -8 \end{bmatrix} \frac{t^3}{3!} + \cdots$$

or

$$\mathbf{\Phi}(t) = \begin{bmatrix} 1 - t + \dfrac{t^2}{2!} - \dfrac{t^3}{3!} + \cdots & 0 + t - \dfrac{3}{2!} t^2 + \dfrac{7}{3!} t^3 + \cdots \\ 0 & 1 - 2t + \dfrac{4t^2}{2!} - \dfrac{8t^3}{3!} + \cdots \end{bmatrix}$$

The terms ϕ_{11} and ϕ_{22} are easily recognized as the series expansions of e^{-t} and e^{-2t}, respectively, but it is somewhat more difficult to recognize the four terms in ϕ_{12} as the four leading terms of the series expansion of $e^{-t} - e^{-2t}$. This is, however, the case, and $\mathbf{\Phi}(t)$ is completely specified in closed form as

$$\mathbf{\Phi}(t) = \begin{bmatrix} e^{-t} & e^{-t} - e^{-2t} \\ 0 & e^{-2t} \end{bmatrix}$$

For any initial conditions with $u = 0$, $\mathbf{x}(t)$ is given by Eq. (4.3-3) as

$$\mathbf{x}(t) = e^{\mathbf{A}t}\mathbf{x}(0) = \mathbf{\Phi}(t)\mathbf{x}(0)$$

or

$$x_1(t) = e^{-t}x_1(0) + (e^{-t} - e^{-2t})x_2(0)$$

and

$$x_2(t) = x_2(0)e^{-2t}$$

The STM may be calculated in the frequency domain by the use of Eq. (4.3-14). The matrix $(s\mathbf{I} - \mathbf{A})$ is

$$(s\mathbf{I} - \mathbf{A}) = \begin{bmatrix} s & 0 \\ 0 & s \end{bmatrix} - \begin{bmatrix} -1 & 1 \\ 0 & -2 \end{bmatrix} = \begin{bmatrix} s + 1 & -1 \\ 0 & s + 2 \end{bmatrix}$$

Taking the inverse of this matrix, we obtain the resolvent matrix

$$\mathbf{\Phi}(s) = (s\mathbf{I} - \mathbf{A})^{-1} = \frac{1}{(s+1)(s+2)} \begin{bmatrix} s+2 & 1 \\ 0 & s+1 \end{bmatrix}$$

$$= \begin{bmatrix} \dfrac{1}{s+1} & \dfrac{1}{(s+1)(s+2)} \\ 0 & \dfrac{1}{s+2} \end{bmatrix}$$

Then using Eq. (4.3-14) we find the STM

$$\mathbf{\Phi}(t) = \mathcal{L}^{-1}[\mathbf{\Phi}(s)] = \begin{bmatrix} e^{-t} & e^{-t} - e^{-2t} \\ 0 & e^{-2t} \end{bmatrix}$$

Alternate methods of calculating the STM are described in Secs. 4.4 and 4.5.

4.3-2   Forced response

Although our concern here is for the solution of the vector equation (**AB**),

$$\dot{\mathbf{x}}(t) = \mathbf{A}\mathbf{x}(t) + \mathbf{B}\mathbf{u}(t) \tag{AB}$$

let us begin once again by examining the solution of the analogous scalar equation (*ab*),

$$\dot{x}(t) = ax(t) + bu(t) \tag{ab}$$

Figure 4.3-1 is again applicable, this time with u not equal to zero. If Eq. (*ab*) is transformed, $x(s)$ is found to be

$$x(s) = (s - a)^{-1}x(0) + (s - a)^{-1}bu(s)$$

If the inverse transform of $x(s)$ is taken, $x(t)$ may be expressed as either of the two following expressions:

$$x(t) = e^{at}x(0) + \mathcal{L}^{-1}[(s - a)^{-1}bu(s)] \tag{4.3-15}$$

$$\text{or} \quad x(t) = e^{at}x(0) + \int_0^t e^{a(t-\tau)}bu(\tau)\,d\tau \tag{4.3-16}$$

In Eq. (4.3-15) it is impossible to take the indicated inverse Laplace transform since $u(s)$ is unspecified. Equation (4.3-16) is the time-domain equivalent of Eq. (4.3-15) and expresses the fact that multiplication in the frequency domain appears as convolution in the time domain. Note that the convolution integral in Eq. (4.3-16) involves the system impulse response with the argument $t - \tau$.

From Eq. (4.3-16) we are led to expect that the solution to Eq. (**AB**) would be

$$
\begin{aligned}
\mathbf{x}(t) &= e^{\mathbf{A}t}\mathbf{x}(0) + \int_0^t e^{\mathbf{A}(t-\tau)}\mathbf{B}\mathbf{u}(\tau)\, d\tau \\
&= \mathbf{\Phi}(t)\mathbf{x}(0) + \int_0^t \mathbf{\Phi}(t-\tau)\mathbf{B}\mathbf{u}(\tau)\, d\tau
\end{aligned} \tag{4.3-17}
$$

This is, in fact, the correct solution, as can be seen by considering the derivative of $\mathbf{x}(t)$,

$$
\dot{\mathbf{x}}(t) = \dot{\mathbf{\Phi}}(t)\mathbf{x}(0) + \mathbf{\Phi}(0)\mathbf{B}\mathbf{u}(t) + \int_0^t \dot{\mathbf{\Phi}}(t-\tau)\mathbf{B}\mathbf{u}(\tau)\, d\tau \tag{4.3-18}
$$

By definition of $\mathbf{\Phi}(t)$, $\dot{\mathbf{\Phi}}(t) = \mathbf{A}\mathbf{\Phi}(t)$, and $\mathbf{\Phi}(0) = \mathbf{I}$. Hence Eq. (4.3-18) becomes

$$
\begin{aligned}
\dot{\mathbf{x}}(t) &= \mathbf{A}\mathbf{\Phi}(t)\mathbf{x}(0) + \mathbf{B}\mathbf{u}(t) + \mathbf{A}\int_0^t \mathbf{\Phi}(t-\tau)\mathbf{B}\mathbf{u}(\tau)\, d\tau \\
&= \mathbf{A}\left[\mathbf{\Phi}(t)\mathbf{x}(0) + \int_0^t \mathbf{\Phi}(t-\tau)\mathbf{B}\mathbf{u}(\tau)\, d\tau\right] + \mathbf{B}\mathbf{u}(t)
\end{aligned} \tag{4.3-19}
$$

Since by Eq. (4.3-17) the quantity in brackets is nothing more than $\mathbf{x}(t)$, we have

$$
\dot{\mathbf{x}}(t) = \mathbf{A}\mathbf{x}(t) + \mathbf{B}\mathbf{u}(t)
$$

and $\mathbf{x}(t)$ as given by Eq. (4.3-17) has been shown to be the solution of Eq. (**AB**).

Two comments on the above development are in order. First, demonstration that $\mathbf{x}(t)$ as given in Eq. (4.3-17) is a solution of (**AB**) required both the differentiation and the integration of a matrix. The reader is reminded that the application of these or any other linear operators to a matrix requires that the operation be applied to each element of the matrix. Second, note that a convolution integral again appears in the solution for $\mathbf{x}(t)$, much as in the scalar case. This fact leads us further to expect that the STM is closely related to some generalized impulse response as associated with the system described by the matrix $\mathbf{A}$.

Let us consider the evaluation of this convolution integral just a little further. The integrand is made up of an $n \times n$ $\boldsymbol{\Phi}$ matrix, an $n \times r$ $\mathbf{B}$ matrix, and an $r \times 1$ column vector $\mathbf{u}$. The resulting product is an $n \times 1$ vector, and the integration of one term of this column vector contributes to the solution of one of the state variables; i.e., there is one convolution integral to be evaluated for each state variable.

To obtain the time response to (**AB**) in the more general case where the initial state is given at $t = t_o$, we use Eq. (4.3-17) to write

$$\mathbf{x}(t_o) = \boldsymbol{\Phi}(t_o)\mathbf{x}(0) + \int_0^{t_o} \boldsymbol{\Phi}(t_o - \tau)\mathbf{B}\mathbf{u}(\tau) \, d\tau$$

Premultiplying both sides of this equation by $\boldsymbol{\Phi}(t_o)^{-1}$ and solving for $\mathbf{x}(0)$, we obtain

$$\begin{aligned}
\mathbf{x}(0) &= \boldsymbol{\Phi}(t_o)^{-1}\mathbf{x}(t_o) - \int_0^{t_o} \boldsymbol{\Phi}(t_o)^{-1}\boldsymbol{\Phi}(t_o - \tau)\mathbf{B}\mathbf{u}(\tau) \, d\tau \\
&= \boldsymbol{\Phi}(-t_o)\mathbf{x}(t_o) - \int_0^{t_o} \boldsymbol{\Phi}(-\tau)\mathbf{B}\mathbf{u}(\tau) \, d\tau
\end{aligned}$$

Substitute this result into Eq. (4.3-17) as

$$\begin{aligned}
\mathbf{x}(t) &= \boldsymbol{\Phi}(t) \left[\boldsymbol{\Phi}(-t_o)\mathbf{x}(t_o) - \int_0^{t_o} \boldsymbol{\Phi}(-\tau)\mathbf{B}\mathbf{u}(\tau) \, d\tau \right] \\
&\qquad\qquad\qquad\qquad + \int_0^t \boldsymbol{\Phi}(t - \tau)\mathbf{B}\mathbf{u}(\tau) \, d\tau \\
&= \boldsymbol{\Phi}(t - t_o)\mathbf{x}(t_o) - \int_0^{t_o} \boldsymbol{\Phi}(t - \tau)\mathbf{B}\mathbf{u}(\tau) \, d\tau \\
&\qquad\qquad\qquad\qquad + \int_0^t \boldsymbol{\Phi}(t - \tau)\mathbf{B}\mathbf{u}(\tau) \, d\tau
\end{aligned}$$

Then by combining the last two integrals we have the desired result

$$\mathbf{x}(t) = \boldsymbol{\Phi}(t - t_o)\mathbf{x}(t_o) + \int_{t_o}^t \boldsymbol{\Phi}(t - \tau)\mathbf{B}\mathbf{u}(\tau) \, d\tau \qquad (4.3\text{-}20)$$

From Eq. (4.3-20) the key role that the STM plays in determining the time response may be seen. We need know only three things to obtain the time response of any linear system:

1. The state at $t = t_o$, $\mathbf{x}(t_o)$
2. The input for $t > t_o$, that is, $\mathbf{u}(t)$, for $t > t_o$
3. The STM $\boldsymbol{\Phi}(t)$

Consideration of Eq. (4.3-20) also provides another interpretation of the STM. Assume that the system is initially at rest, that is, $\mathbf{x}(0) = 0$, and that the input is equal to a vector whose elements are each a unit impulse or Dirac delta function applied at $t = 0$, that is, $\mathbf{u}(t) = \boldsymbol{\delta}(t)$. Then from Eq. (4.3-20) the response $\mathbf{x}(t)$ is given by

$$\mathbf{x}(t) = \boldsymbol{\Phi}(t)\mathbf{B}\boldsymbol{\alpha}$$

where $\boldsymbol{\alpha}$ is an r-dimensional unit vector, that is, $\boldsymbol{\alpha}^T = (1,1, \ldots ,1)$. Again we see the close relationship between the STM and the impulse response of the system.

Before proceeding to an example, let us solve Eq. (**AB**) by transform methods to obtain a solution analogous to Eq. (4.3-15). The Laplace transform of Eq. (**AB**) is

$$s\mathbf{x}(s) - \mathbf{x}(0) = \mathbf{A}\mathbf{x}(s) + \mathbf{B}\mathbf{u}(s)$$

or

$$\mathbf{x}(s) = (s\mathbf{I} - \mathbf{A})^{-1}\mathbf{x}(0) + (s\mathbf{I} - \mathbf{A})^{-1}\mathbf{B}\mathbf{u}(s)$$

and $\mathbf{x}(t)$ is

$$\mathbf{x}(t) = \mathcal{L}^{-1}[(s\mathbf{I} - \mathbf{A})^{-1}]\mathbf{x}(0) + \mathcal{L}^{-1}[(s\mathbf{I} - \mathbf{A})^{-1}\mathbf{B}\mathbf{u}(s)] \qquad (4.3\text{-}21)$$

and the analogy is close indeed. Equation (4.3-20) may also be written in terms of $\boldsymbol{\Phi}(s)$ as

$$\mathbf{x}(t) = \mathcal{L}^{-1}[\boldsymbol{\Phi}(s)]\mathbf{x}(0) + \mathcal{L}^{-1}[\boldsymbol{\Phi}(s)\mathbf{B}\mathbf{u}(s)] \qquad (4.3\text{-}22)$$

Because of the importance of the STM and the resolvent matrix, the next two sections present several additional methods for obtaining these two matrices for a given system. However, let us first consider an example to illustrate how the above methods are used to determine the time response of a system.

Example 4.3-2   Obtain the time response of the system shown in Fig. 4.3-2 if $\mathbf{x}(0) = \text{col}\,(-1,0)$ and if $u(t) = 1$ for $t > 0$. For this system the describing differential equation is

$$\dot{\mathbf{x}} = \begin{bmatrix} -1 & 1 \\ 0 & -2 \end{bmatrix} \mathbf{x} + \begin{bmatrix} 0 \\ 1 \end{bmatrix} u(t)$$

The STM was found in Example 4.3-1 to be

$$\Phi(t) = \begin{bmatrix} e^{-t} & e^{-t} - e^{-2t} \\ 0 & e^{-2t} \end{bmatrix}$$

Therefore the time response of the system as given by Eq. (4.3-17) is

$$\mathbf{x}(t) = \begin{bmatrix} e^{-t} & e^{-t} - e^{-2t} \\ 0 & e^{-2t} \end{bmatrix} \begin{bmatrix} -1 \\ 0 \end{bmatrix}$$
$$+ \int_0^t \begin{bmatrix} e^{-(t-\tau)} & e^{-(t-\tau)} - e^{-2(t-\tau)} \\ 0 & e^{-2(t-\tau)} \end{bmatrix} \begin{bmatrix} 0 \\ 1 \end{bmatrix} d\tau$$

$$= \begin{bmatrix} -e^{-t} \\ 0 \end{bmatrix} + \int_0^t \begin{bmatrix} e^{-(t-\tau)} - e^{-2(t-\tau)} \\ e^{-2(t-\tau)} \end{bmatrix} d\tau$$

The convolution integral is easily evaluated in this simple case to give

$$\mathbf{x}(t) = \begin{bmatrix} -e^{-t} \\ 0 \end{bmatrix} + \begin{bmatrix} e^{-(t-\tau)} - \dfrac{e^{-2(t-\tau)}}{2} \\ \dfrac{e^{-2(t-\tau)}}{2} \end{bmatrix} \Bigg|_{\tau=0}^{\tau=t}$$

$$= \begin{bmatrix} \frac{1}{2} - 2e^{-t} + \dfrac{e^{-2t}}{2} \\ \frac{1}{2} - \dfrac{e^{-2t}}{2} \end{bmatrix}$$

and therefore

$$x_1(t) = \tfrac{1}{2} - 2e^{-t} + \tfrac{1}{2}e^{-2t}$$
$$x_2(t) = \tfrac{1}{2} - \tfrac{1}{2}e^{-2t}$$

With respect to the block diagram of Fig. 4.3-2, note that not only is $x_1(t)$ and therefore the output y known for all time, but so is the internal state variable $x_2(t)$. A plot of $x_1(t)$ and $x_2(t)$ appears in Fig. 4.3-3. Since t is unbounded, neither of these plots can be completely contained on a finite page. An alternate means of describing the behavior of the state of the system for all time is to plot x_1 versus x_2 on a state plane. This is done in Fig. 4.3-4, and the resulting curve is known as a *trajectory in state space*. In general, the solution to an nth-order system may be described in an n-dimensional state space. In practice the plotting of system response in state space is simple for $n = 2$; it is possible for $n = 3$; but

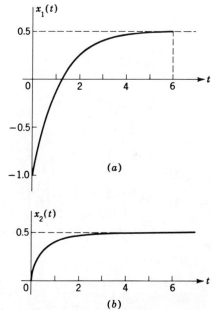

Fig. 4.3-3 Time response of Example 4.3-2. (*a*) $x_1(t)$ response; (*b*) $x_2(t)$ response.

it is geometrically impossible in our three-dimensional world for $n > 3$. Nevertheless, the concept of a trajectory in state space is important even for $n > 3$.

Exercises 4.3 *4.3-1.* Show that properties I to IV of Table 4.3-1 are true. In addition illustrate these properties using the STM

$$\Phi(t) = \begin{bmatrix} e^{-3t} & e^{-2t} - e^{-3t} \\ 0 & e^{-2t} \end{bmatrix}$$

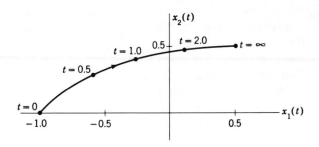

Fig. 4.3-4 The time response of Example 4.3-2 plotted as a trajectory in state space.

4.3-2.   Determine the time response of the systems whose STMs, initial conditions, forcing functions, and **B** matrices are

(a)
$$\Phi(t) = \begin{bmatrix} e^{-5t} & -e^{-2t} + e^{-5t} \\ 0 & e^{-2t} \end{bmatrix} \qquad \mathbf{x}(0) = \begin{bmatrix} 0 \\ 1 \end{bmatrix}$$

$$\mathbf{u}(t) = \begin{bmatrix} 3 \\ 1 \end{bmatrix} \qquad \mathbf{B} = \begin{bmatrix} 1 & 2 \\ 0 & -4 \end{bmatrix}$$

(b)
$$\Phi(t) = \begin{bmatrix} e^{-t} & 0 \\ e^{-t} - e^{-3t} & e^{-3t} \end{bmatrix} \qquad \mathbf{x}(0) = \begin{bmatrix} 2 \\ -1 \end{bmatrix}$$

$$u(t) = 2 \qquad \mathbf{b} = \begin{bmatrix} 1 \\ 0 \end{bmatrix}$$

Plot the response as a trajectory in state space.

answers:

(a) $\mathbf{x}(t) = \begin{bmatrix} 11/5 - 3e^{-2t} + 4/5 e^{-5t} \\ -2 + 3e^{-2t} \end{bmatrix}$

(b) $\mathbf{x}(t) = \begin{bmatrix} 2 \\ 4/3 - 7/3 e^{-3t} \end{bmatrix}$

4.4   A block-diagram approach to the resolvent matrix

The object of the previous section was to find the solution of Eq. (**AB**). In the time domain the solution was found in terms of the STM and a convolution integral involving this matrix.   The evaluation of the STM involved a series expansion of $e^{\mathbf{A}t}$, and even in the second-order example that was worked it was difficult to recognize the elements of $e^{\mathbf{A}t} = \Phi(t)$ in closed form.   In addition, n convolution integrals had to be evaluated, one for each state variable.   One of the advantages of the Laplace transform approach is the avoidance of the necessity of evaluation of convolution integrals.   The use of transform methods resulted in a solution of (**AB**) as Eq. (4.3-22).   This frequency-domain approach does not prove to be much better from a computational point of view, since finding the resolvent matrix requires a difficult matrix inversion.

Our difficulty in the last section lies in the fact that we are seeking to determine the STM solely from the matrix **A** and the definition of the STM.   Presumably we know much more about a physical system than just the matrix **A**.   For example, a problem statement in terms of either

Eq. (**AB**) or (**Ab**) indicates that the state variables have already been chosen, and, in fact, the problem is completely defined. Here it is assumed that we are in the earlier stages of problem formulation and that the state variables therefore have not yet been chosen. As possible choices of state variables we consider those variables which have already been discussed extensively in Chap. 2, namely, phase variables, normal coordinates, and the actual physical-system variables.

The reader will recall that in Chap. 2 it was pointed out that it is immaterial whether the system is described in terms of a transfer function, a block diagram, sets of simultaneous equations, an nth-order equation, or n first-order equations. The descriptions are equivalent, and given one of them, any other equivalent description can be obtained. In this section we take advantage of the fact that one transfer function may be represented by more than one block diagram, depending upon the choice of state variables. The basic assumption is that the physical system in question has been modeled in terms of differential equations and that these differential equations have been pictured in terms of a block diagram. As before, the ultimate goal is to determine the response of the system to a particular input **u**. For purposes of exposition, we restrict ourselves to consideration of Eq. (**Ab**), so that we have a single input–single output system with u a scalar rather than a vector. The solution to (**Ab**) and eventually to (**AB**) is found by frequency-domain methods in terms of the resolvent matrix.

In Sec. 4.3 the solution to Eq. (**A**) was found by transform methods to be Eq. (4.3-13), which is repeated as

$$\mathbf{x}(s) = \mathbf{\Phi}(s)\mathbf{x}(0) \tag{4.4-1}$$

In expanded form the ith equation of (4.4-1) is

$$x_i(s) = \phi_{i1}(s)x_1(0) + \phi_{i2}(s)x_2(0) + \cdots + \phi_{in}(s)x_n(0)$$

If all initial conditions are assumed to be zero except the initial condition on the jth variable, then

$$x_i(s) = \phi_{ij}(s)x_j(0) \tag{4.4-2}$$

If the value of the jth initial condition is unity, then $\phi_{ij}(s)$ is equal to $x_i(s)$.

Equation (4.4-2) is easily interpreted in terms of a block diagram. Assume that the given transfer function has been redrawn as a block diagram in such a way that each of the state variables is indicated. Identify the block whose output is the ith state variable as the ith block.

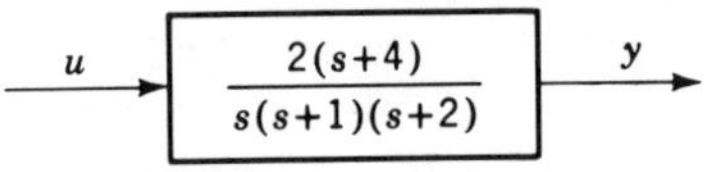

Fig. 4.4-1 The transfer function of the example.

Then the $\phi_{ij}(s)$ element of $\boldsymbol{\Phi}(s)$ may be determined by application of the following rule.

The element $\phi_{ij}(s)$ is equal to the Laplace transform of the ith state variable due to a unit initial condition applied at the input of the jth block, with all other initial conditions and inputs equal to zero.

This rule is simply a formalization of the results expressed in Eq. (4.4-2). All that remains to be done is to apply this rule in the various state-variable representations that have been dealt with in the past. This is most easily done in terms of a specific case, and it is assumed that the given system is specified by an open-loop transfer function $G(s)$, given as

$$G(s) = \frac{y(s)}{u(s)} = \frac{2(s + 4)}{s(s + 1)(s + 2)}$$

Figure 4.4-1 illustrates the example.

The phase-variable description of this plant is indicated by either Fig. 4.4-2a or b. Figure 4.4-2a may be realized from the nth-order equation associated with the given transfer function, and, alternately, the describing system equations may be written most easily from Fig. 4.4-2a. On the other hand, Fig. 4.4-2b, while it still describes the same system in phase variables, may be written directly from the transfer function. Determination of the resolvent matrix must be accomplished from Fig. 4.4-2a, even though Fig. 4.4-2b is an equally valid system representation in phase variables. The reason is associated with the idea that the elements of $\boldsymbol{\Phi}(s)$ represent impulse responses, since these elements appear in the convolution integral. The initial condition on x_j may be established at $t = 0$ by the application of an impulse of unit magnitude. It is necessary, of course, that this impulse affect only the x_j initial value and none of the others. In Fig. 4.4-2b, for example, if one attempts to establish the initial condition $x_3(0)$ by the application of an impulse to the left-hand-most block, the s in the numerator differentiates the impulse and a doublet appears at x_3. After integration, an impulse appears at x_2, and after a second integration, an initial condition appears at x_1. This is unwanted, and the block diagram of Fig. 4.4-2b cannot be used to determine the resolvent matrix.

Figure 4.4-2a is a phase-variable representation that is said to be in *elementary block-diagram* form. A block diagram is said to be in elementary form if the relations between all the states are indicated by

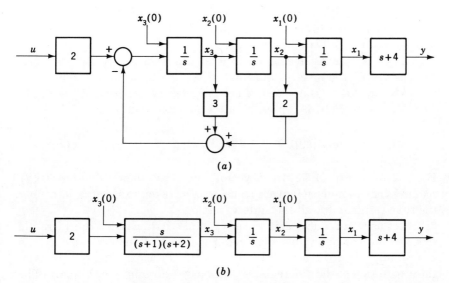

Fig. 4.4-2 Block diagrams of the phase-variable representation of the system of Fig. 4.4-1. (*a*) Direct approach; (*b*) transfer-function approach.

$1/s$ blocks. Phase variables are naturally in elementary form if the representation of Fig. 4.4-2*a* is chosen, rather than that of Fig. 4.4-2*b*. This problem is reworked later in both canonical variables and physical variables, and in the process the block diagrams for both these types of representation are shown in elementary form.

If we now apply an impulse input to the *j*th block in Fig. 4.4-2*a* and determine $x_i(s)$, this value of $x_i(s)$ is identical to $\phi_{ij}(s)$. If this is done systematically for the example of Fig. 4.4-2*a*, the resulting $\boldsymbol{\Phi}(s)$ is found to be

$$\boldsymbol{\Phi}(s) = \begin{bmatrix} \dfrac{1}{s} & \dfrac{s+3}{s(s+1)(s+2)} & \dfrac{1}{s(s+1)(s+2)} \\[3mm] 0 & \dfrac{s+3}{(s+1)(s+2)} & \dfrac{1}{(s+1)(s+2)} \\[3mm] 0 & \dfrac{-2}{(s+1)(s+2)} & \dfrac{s}{(s+1)(s+2)} \end{bmatrix} \qquad (4.4\text{-}3)$$

Here $\phi_{13}(s)$, for example, is determined from Fig. 4.4-2*a* by assuming that a unit initial condition is applied as $x_3(0)$, with all other initial conditions as zero, as well as $u = 0$. Then $x_1(s)$ is

$$x_1(s) = \frac{x_3(0)}{s(s+1)(s+2)} = \frac{1}{s(s+1)(s+2)}$$

Under these conditions $\phi_{13}(s) = x_1(s)$. That is, $\phi_{13}(s)$ is just the transfer function between $x_3(0)$ and x_1. In this way all the elements of $\Phi(s)$ are written down with little hesitation.

Thus far the resolvent matrix $\Phi(s)$ has been determined, and the STM is simply the inverse transform of $\Phi(s)$. As far as the solution of Eq. (**Ab**) or (**AB**) is concerned, it is not necessary ever to find the STM. The solution to (**AB**) is expressed in the previous section as

$$\mathbf{x}(t) = \mathcal{L}^{-1}[\Phi(s)]\mathbf{x}(0) + \mathcal{L}^{-1}[\Phi(s)\mathbf{B}\mathbf{u}(s)] \tag{4.3-22}$$

Each term of Eq. (4.3-22) is a vector, such that the evaluation of $\mathbf{x}(t)$ requires that $2n$ inverse Laplace transforms be taken to specify completely the time response for all the state variables.

Let us return once again to the example that has been considered in this section and determine the overall response of the system due to a step input. That is, $u(s) = 1/s$; find $y(t)$. Perhaps it is well to write the description of the differential-equation system from Fig. 4.4-2a. The equations are

$$\dot{x}_1 = x_2 \quad \dot{x}_2 = x_3$$
$$\dot{x}_3 = -3x_3 - 2x_2 + 2u \quad y(t) = 4x_1(t) + x_2(t)$$

$\Phi(s)$ is already known, and from the above equations, $\mathbf{b}$ is

$$\mathbf{b} = \begin{bmatrix} 0 \\ 0 \\ 2 \end{bmatrix}$$

For this problem the expanded form of $\mathbf{x}(s)$ with zero initial conditions is

$$\begin{bmatrix} x_1(s) \\ x_2(s) \\ x_3(s) \end{bmatrix} = \begin{bmatrix} \dfrac{1}{s} & \dfrac{s+3}{s(s+1)(s+2)} & \dfrac{1}{s(s+1)(s+2)} \\ 0 & \dfrac{s+3}{(s+1)(s+2)} & \dfrac{1}{(s+1)(s+2)} \\ 0 & \dfrac{-2}{(s+1)(s+2)} & \dfrac{s}{(s+1)(s+2)} \end{bmatrix} \begin{bmatrix} 0 \\ 0 \\ 2 \end{bmatrix} \dfrac{1}{s}$$

so that

$$x_1(s) = \frac{2}{s^2(s+1)(s+2)} \qquad x_2(s) = \frac{2}{s(s+1)(s+2)}$$

and

$$y(s) = 4x_1(s) + x_2(s) = \frac{2(s+4)}{s^2(s+1)(s+2)} \qquad (4.4\text{-}4)$$

This $y(s)$ is the same as might have been written down immediately from the given transfer function, $G(s) = y(s)/u(s)$. Nothing profound has been accomplished here, other than the completion of an example to increase the reader's confidence in the methods being discussed.

Figure 4.4-3 represents the block-diagram representation of the given transfer function in normal coordinates and in what are assumed to be the real physical variables. For the normal-coordinate system $\Phi(s)$ is

$$\Phi(s) = \begin{bmatrix} \dfrac{1}{s} & 0 & 0 \\[2mm] 0 & \dfrac{1}{s+1} & 0 \\[2mm] 0 & 0 & \dfrac{1}{s+2} \end{bmatrix}$$

and $y(s) = 4z_1(s) - 6z_2(s) + 2z_3(s)$, and $u(s)$ is, as before, $1/s$, while **b** is

$$\mathbf{b} = \begin{bmatrix} 1 \\ 1 \\ 1 \end{bmatrix}$$

The reader may assure himself that the resulting $y(s)$ is as given previously by Eq. (4.4-4). The reason why the example was originally worked with zero initial conditions is now clear. If an initial condition had been given on any of the phase variables, the **P** matrix relating **x** and **z** would have to be known to translate this initial condition to the **z** space. This would only have obscured the problem and made the comparision of results more difficult. For systems with simple poles, $\Phi(s)$ always has this diagonal form, which considerably simplifies the determination of $\mathbf{x}(t)$ and $y(t)$.

From Fig. 4.4-3b the resolvent matrix for the system described in physical variables is

$$\Phi(s) = \begin{bmatrix} \dfrac{1}{s} & \dfrac{1}{s(s+1)} & \dfrac{2}{s(s+1)(s+2)} \\[2mm] 0 & \dfrac{1}{s+1} & \dfrac{2}{(s+1)(s+2)} \\[2mm] 0 & 0 & \dfrac{1}{s+2} \end{bmatrix}$$

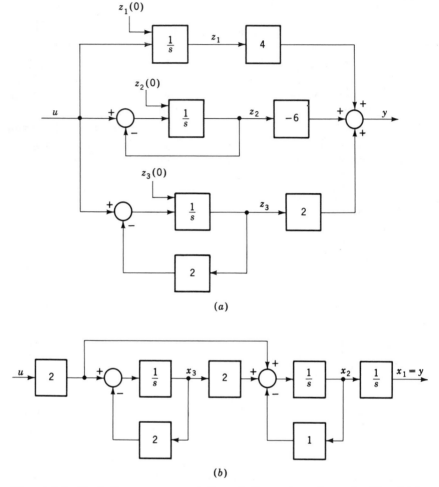

Fig. 4.4-3   Block-diagram representation of the system shown in Fig. 4.4-1. (*a*) Normal coordinates; (*b*) physical variables.

Real system variables have the advantage that answers in terms of the state variables have meaning in terms of physical quantities. This same knowledge may be obtained if the problem is worked in other variable systems but not without a linear change of variables.

This section has illustrated a convenient method of determining the resolvent matrix from a given block diagram, regardless of the choice of state variables. Of course, from the resolvent matrix, the STM can be determined. Often, however, this may not be necessary, particularly in the case when one is interested only in the time response of one or more of the state variables. Then the time response may be determined from Eq. (4.3-22) by taking the required inverse transforms. In fact, it should be obvious from the examples presented that the resolvent matrix is just a systematic method of writing down the transfer functions that relate the impulse responses of the system.

The more general case concerned with Eq. (**AB**) is handled in the same way. The only complication occurs because the order of the systems and number of inputs and outputs are increased. Otherwise the concepts are identical to those that apply in the scalar case.

Exercises 4.4   *4.4-1.*   Find the STM for the systems whose **A** matrices are given below by making use of the method of this section to find the resolvent matrix first.

(a) $\begin{bmatrix} 1 & -2 \\ 4 & -5 \end{bmatrix}$ (b) $\begin{bmatrix} 0 & 1 \\ -2 & -3 \end{bmatrix}$ (c) $\begin{bmatrix} -4 & 2 \\ -2 & 1 \end{bmatrix}$

(d) $\begin{bmatrix} 0 & 5 \\ 0 & -4 \end{bmatrix}$

answers:

(a) $\begin{bmatrix} 2e^{-t} - e^{-3t} & -e^{-t} + e^{-3t} \\ 2e^{-t} - 2e^{-3t} & -e^{-t} + 2e^{-3t} \end{bmatrix}$

(b) $\begin{bmatrix} 2e^{-t} - e^{-2t} & e^{-t} - e^{-2t} \\ -2e^{-t} + 2e^{-2t} & -e^{-t} + 2e^{-2t} \end{bmatrix}$

(c) $\begin{bmatrix} -\frac{1}{3} + \frac{4}{3}e^{-3t} & \frac{2}{3} - \frac{2}{3}e^{-3t} \\ -\frac{2}{3} + \frac{2}{3}e^{-3t} & \frac{4}{3} - \frac{1}{3}e^{-3t} \end{bmatrix}$

(d) $\begin{bmatrix} 1 & \frac{5}{4} - \frac{5}{4}e^{-4t} \\ 0 & e^{-4t} \end{bmatrix}$

4.4-2.   Plot the output response vs. time and the time response as a trajectory in state space for the unforced systems whose **A** matrices are given below. The initial state for all cases is $\mathbf{x}(0) = \text{col }(2,2)$ and the output is equal to x_1.

(a) $\mathbf{A} = \begin{bmatrix} 0 & 1 \\ -6 & -5 \end{bmatrix}$ (b) $\mathbf{A} = \begin{bmatrix} 0 & 1 \\ -25 & 6 \end{bmatrix}$

(c) $\mathbf{A} = \begin{bmatrix} 0 & 1 \\ -9 & 0 \end{bmatrix}$

4.5   Sylvester's expansion theorem

In a modern control book it would be impossible to leave the discussion of the STM without at least mentioning a digital-computer approach. The determination of $\Phi(t)$ from the definition of the series expansion of $e^{\mathbf{A}t}$ according to Eq. (4.3-4) is a possible computer approach, assuming that t remains small. A closed-form solution, however, is much more desirable. Sylvester's expansion theorem provides a convenient method for calculating the STM in closed form using strictly numerical processes in the time domain. Although the proof of Sylvester's expansion theorem is not especially difficult, it requires more matrix theory than is provided in Chap. 2; the proof is therefore omitted here, and the reader is referred either to DeRusso et al. (1965) or Zadeh and Desoer (1963).

The following statement of Sylvester's expansion theorem applies when $\mathbf{A}$ has n distinct eigenvalues.

Theorem 4.5-1   Sylvester's expansion theorem If $f(\mathbf{A})$ is a polynomial function of $\mathbf{A}$, as

$$f(\mathbf{A}) = \sum_{k=0}^{\infty} c_k \mathbf{A}^k \qquad (4.5\text{-}1)$$

then $f(\mathbf{A})$ may be expressed as

$$f(\mathbf{A}) = \sum_{i=1}^{n} f(\lambda_i) \mathbf{F}_i \qquad (4.5\text{-}2)$$

where the λ_i's are the eigenvalues of $\mathbf{A}$ and

$$\mathbf{F}_i = \prod_{\substack{j=1 \\ j \neq i}}^{n} \frac{\mathbf{A} - \lambda_j \mathbf{I}}{\lambda_i - \lambda_j} \qquad (4.5\text{-}3)$$

In determining the STM we are interested in the function $f(\mathbf{A}) = e^{\mathbf{A}t}$. Since $e^{\mathbf{A}t}$ is expressible in terms of a power series as Eq. (4.3-4), $\Phi(t)$ is of the form of Eq. (4.5-1). Thus Sylvester's expansion theorem applies, and $\Phi(t)$ is given from Eq. (4.5-2) as

$$\Phi(t) = e^{\mathbf{A}t} = \sum_{i=1}^{n} e^{\lambda_i t} \mathbf{F}_i \qquad (4.5\text{-}4)$$

It should be noted that in order to apply this method we need know only the eigenvalues of $\mathbf{A}$, and hence this technique is applicable regardless of what state-variable representation is chosen. The complete procedure is presented in Table 4.5-1.

Table 4.5-1	Outline of the Sylvester Expansion Theorem Procedure for Determining the STM
Step 1	Determine the n eigenvalues of the matrix $\mathbf{A}$
Step 2	Find the n $\mathbf{F}_i$'s from the expression $$\mathbf{F}_i = \prod_{\substack{j=1 \\ j \neq i}}^{n} \frac{\mathbf{A} - \lambda_j\mathbf{I}}{\lambda_i - \lambda_j} \qquad (4.5\text{-}3)$$
Step 3	Determine the STM from the relation $$\mathbf{\Phi}(t) = \sum_{i=1}^{n} e^{\lambda_i t}\mathbf{F}_i \qquad (4.5\text{-}4)$$

From Eq. (4.5-4) it is seen that each element of the STM is of the form

$$\phi_{ij}(t) = a_1 e^{\lambda_1 t} + a_2 e^{\lambda_2 t} + \cdots + a_n e^{\lambda_n t} = \sum_{k=1}^{n} a_k e^{\lambda_k t}$$

It must be emphasized that we have assumed distinct eigenvalues.

Example 4.5-1 In order to illustrate the above procedure for computing the STM, let us consider the system

$$\dot{\mathbf{x}}(t) = \begin{bmatrix} -1 & 1 \\ 0 & -2 \end{bmatrix} \mathbf{x}(t)$$

The characteristic equation for this system is found from the $\det(\lambda\mathbf{I} - \mathbf{A})$ to be

$$\lambda^2 + 3\lambda + 2 = 0$$

and hence the eigenvalues of the system are

$$\lambda_1 = -1 \qquad \lambda_2 = -2$$

The two matrices $\mathbf{F}_1$ and $\mathbf{F}_2$ are

$$\mathbf{F}_1 = \frac{\mathbf{A} - (\lambda_2)\mathbf{I}}{\lambda_1 - \lambda_2} = \frac{\mathbf{A} + 2\mathbf{I}}{-1 - (-2)} = \begin{bmatrix} 1 & 1 \\ 0 & 0 \end{bmatrix}$$

$$\mathbf{F}_2 = \frac{\mathbf{A} - (\lambda_1)\mathbf{I}}{\lambda_2 - \lambda_1} = \frac{\mathbf{A} + \mathbf{I}}{-2 - (-1)} = \begin{bmatrix} 0 & -1 \\ 0 & +1 \end{bmatrix}$$

Then $\boldsymbol{\Phi}(t)$ is determined by means of Eq. (4.5-4) as

$$\boldsymbol{\Phi}(t) = e^{\lambda_1 t}\mathbf{F}_1 + e^{\lambda_2 t}\mathbf{F}_2$$
$$= e^{-t}\begin{bmatrix} 1 & 1 \\ 0 & 0 \end{bmatrix} + e^{-2t}\begin{bmatrix} 0 & -1 \\ 0 & 1 \end{bmatrix} = \begin{bmatrix} e^{-t} & e^{-t} - e^{-2t} \\ 0 & e^{-2t} \end{bmatrix}$$

Since the computation of the $\mathbf{F}$ matrices is a completely numerical process, the method is well suited for determining the STM in closed form by means of a digital computer. On the other hand, the computations involved in determining both the $\mathbf{F}$ matrices and finally $\boldsymbol{\Phi}(t)$ are relatively simple. Hence the method is reasonably well suited to manual computation at least for low-order systems. For high-order systems none of the methods provides an easy solution.

This method may be extended to the case of multiple eigenvalues, although it becomes considerably more complicated (see, for example, Zadeh and Desoer, 1963, appendix D). As was pointed out previously, for practical calculations there is little need to be concerned with this problem.

Exercise 4.5   *4.5-1.* In the previous section the STM for the system whose transfer function is given below was determined by block-diagram manipulations for the system represented in phase variables, normal coordinates, and physical-system variables.

$$G(s) = \frac{2(s + 4)}{s(s + 1)(s + 2)}$$

Use Sylvester's expansion theorem to show that the various $\boldsymbol{\Phi}(s)$ matrices corresponding to these particular choices of state variables were determined correctly in Sec. 4.4.

4.6 Additional applications of the state transition matrix

As an illustration of the generality of the STM method for obtaining time response, in this section we show how the method may be extended to sampled-data systems. In addition we show how approximate solutions of time-varying and nonlinear systems may also be obtained using the STM method.

4.6-1 Sampled-data systems

Before applying the STM method to sampled-data systems, it is necessary to introduce the concept of sampling. For simplicity we shall restrict our development to the simplest and most widely used form of sampling, called *conventional sampling*. It should be noted, however, that almost any form of sampling may be handled by the approach presented below. This is, in fact, one of the most useful features of this approach.

By conventional sampling of a time function $f(t)$, we mean the process of measuring or sampling the value of $f(t)$ at equally spaced values of time, 0, T, $2T$, $3T$, . . . , called *sampling times* and then maintaining this value until the next sampling time. The result of this procedure is illustrated in Fig. 4.6-1, where both the original and the sampled function are shown. There the sampled function $f_s(t)$ is seen to be piecewise constant with points of discontinuity at the sampling times. The value of the sampled function between two sampling times nT and $(n + 1)T$ is given by $f(nT)$. Hence the time function $f_s(t)$ may be expressed mathematically as

$$f_s(t) = f(nT) \quad \begin{array}{l} \text{for } nT \leq t < (n + 1)T \\ n = 0, 1, 2, \ldots \end{array} \tag{4.6-1}$$

It should be noted that the above process can be implemented by the use of any one of several physical devices. In simple control systems, the analog sample-hold circuit is often employed (Korn and Korn, 1964). In more complicated systems with a digital computer in the loop, the computer output is passed through a digital-to-analog converter and held until the next computer output appears. In an analog-to-digital converter, the opposite takes place; i.e., a continuous signal is sampled and converted into a digital signal, which is held until the next sample. The solution of differential equations on a digital computer normally involves some sampling procedure.

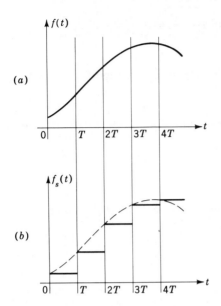

Fig. 4.6-1 (a) Original time function; (b) sampled time function.

Let us consider the time response of the system

$$\dot{\mathbf{x}}(t) = \mathbf{A}\mathbf{x}(t) + \mathbf{B}\mathbf{u}(t) \tag{AB}$$

if the control signal $\mathbf{u}(t)$ is subjected to such a sampling process. By a direct application of Eq. (4.3-17) the time response is

$$\mathbf{x}(t) = \boldsymbol{\Phi}(t)\mathbf{x}(0) + \int_0^t \boldsymbol{\Phi}(t - \tau)\mathbf{B}\mathbf{u}_s(\tau)\,d\tau \tag{4.6-2}$$

where $\mathbf{u}_s(t)$ is the sampled input. Since

$$\mathbf{u}_s(t) = \mathbf{u}(nT) \quad \begin{array}{l} \text{for } nT \le t < (n+1)T \\ n = 0,\ 1,\ 2,\ \ldots \end{array} \tag{4.6-3}$$

Eq. (4.6-2) becomes

$$\mathbf{x}(t) = \boldsymbol{\Phi}(t)\mathbf{x}(0) + \sum_{j=0}^{n-1} \left[\int_{jT}^{(j+1)T} \boldsymbol{\Phi}(t - \tau)\mathbf{B}\mathbf{u}(jT)\,d\tau \right]$$
$$+ \int_{nT}^{t} \boldsymbol{\Phi}(t - \tau)\mathbf{B}\mathbf{u}(nT)\,d\tau \tag{4.6-4}$$

or

$$\mathbf{x}(t) = \boldsymbol{\Phi}(t)\mathbf{x}(0) + \boldsymbol{\Phi}(t) \sum_{j=0}^{n-1} \left[\int_{jT}^{(j+1)T} \boldsymbol{\Phi}(-\tau)\mathbf{B} \, d\tau \, \mathbf{u}(jT) \right]$$

$$+ \int_{nT}^{t} \boldsymbol{\Phi}(t-\tau)\mathbf{B}\mathbf{u}(nT) \, d\tau \qquad \text{for } nT \leq t \leq (n+1)T \quad (4.6\text{-}5)$$

$$n = 0, 1, 2, \ldots$$

For notational convenience let us define

$$\boldsymbol{\zeta} = \sum_{j=0}^{n-1} \left[\int_{jT}^{(j+1)T} \boldsymbol{\Phi}(-\tau)\mathbf{B} \, d\tau \, \mathbf{u}(jT) \right] \qquad (4.6\text{-}6)$$

Equation (4.6-5) then becomes

$$\mathbf{x}(t) = \boldsymbol{\Phi}(t)\mathbf{x}(0) + \boldsymbol{\Phi}(t)\boldsymbol{\zeta} + \int_{nT}^{t} \boldsymbol{\Phi}(t-\tau)\mathbf{B}\mathbf{u}(nT) \, d\tau \qquad (4.6\text{-}7)$$

In many cases one is interested only in the values of the state at the sampling times.   In such a situation one would like to be able to obtain the values of the state at the sampling time without obtaining the continuous time response.   In order to show how this may be done, let us use Eq. (4.6-7) to determine the state at $t = nT$ and $(n+1)T$.

$$\mathbf{x}(nT) = \boldsymbol{\Phi}(nT)\mathbf{x}(0) + \boldsymbol{\Phi}(nT)\boldsymbol{\zeta} \qquad (4.6\text{-}8)$$

and

$$\mathbf{x}(\overline{n+1}T) = \boldsymbol{\Phi}(\overline{n+1}T)\mathbf{x}(0) + \boldsymbol{\Phi}(\overline{n+1}T)\boldsymbol{\zeta}$$

$$+ \int_{nT}^{(n+1)T} \boldsymbol{\Phi}(\overline{n+1}T - \tau)\mathbf{B}\mathbf{u}(nT) \, d\tau \quad (4.6\text{-}9)$$

If we now solve Eq. (4.6-8) for $x(0)$, we obtain

$$\mathbf{x}(0) = \boldsymbol{\Phi}(-nT)\mathbf{x}(nT) - \boldsymbol{\zeta}$$

Then substituting this result into Eq. (4.6-9) gives

$$\mathbf{x}(\overline{n+1}T) = \boldsymbol{\Phi}(T)\mathbf{x}(nT) + \int_{nT}^{(n+1)T} \boldsymbol{\Phi}(\overline{n+1}T - \tau)\mathbf{B}\mathbf{u}(nT) \, d\tau$$

$$(4.6\text{-}10)$$

If we make the substitution

$$\tau = (n + 1)T - \lambda$$

Eq. (4.6-10) becomes

$$\mathbf{x}(\overline{n + 1}T) = \mathbf{\Phi}(T)\mathbf{x}(nT) + \left[\int_0^T \mathbf{\Phi}(\lambda)\mathbf{B} \, d\lambda \right] \mathbf{u}(nT) \qquad (4.6\text{-}11)$$

Now let us define

$$\mathbf{D} = \int_0^T \mathbf{\Phi}(\lambda)\mathbf{B} \, d\lambda \qquad (4.6\text{-}12)$$

Note that this is a constant matrix.   In terms of this definition, $\mathbf{x}(\overline{n + 1}T)$ becomes

$$\mathbf{x}(\overline{n + 1}T) = \mathbf{\Phi}(T)\mathbf{x}(nT) + \mathbf{D}\mathbf{u}(nT) \qquad (4.6\text{-}13)$$

This equation forms an algebraic recursion relation which may be used to obtain the time response at the sampling times and hence the time response of the sampled system.   If, in addition to the sampled response, it is desired to obtain the continuous time response in between any two sampling times, Eq. (4.6-8) may be substituted into Eq. (4.6-7) to obtain

$$\mathbf{x}(t) = \mathbf{\Phi}(t - nT)\mathbf{x}(nT) + \int_{nT}^t \mathbf{\Phi}(t - \tau)\mathbf{B}\mathbf{u}(nT) \, d\tau \qquad (4.6\text{-}14)$$

This is a very useful feature of this time-domain approach to sampled systems.

Another useful feature of this approach is the ability to handle systems with quantizers.   Then $\mathbf{u}_s(nT)$ does not equal the value of $\mathbf{u}$ at the time nT but can be determined easily by a look-up procedure, as specified by the quantizer.

Example 4.6-1   As an illustration of the above procedure, consider the system shown in Fig. 4.6-2, where the input is sampled at $t = 0, 1, 2, \ldots$, that is, $T = 1$ sec.   Let us use Eq. (4.6-13) to find the time response for $t = 1$ and 2 if the system is initially at rest, $\mathbf{x}(0) = 0$, and is subject to a unit step at $t = 0$, that is, $u(t) = 1$ for $t \geq 0$.

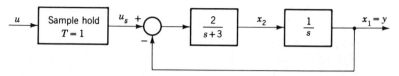

Fig. 4.6-2 Sampled-data example.

From Fig. 4.6-2 we write the system equations directly as

$$\dot{\mathbf{x}}(t) = \mathbf{A}\mathbf{x}(t) + \mathbf{b}u_s(t)$$

where

$$\mathbf{A} = \begin{bmatrix} 0 & 1 \\ -2 & -3 \end{bmatrix} \quad \text{and} \quad \mathbf{b} = \begin{bmatrix} 0 \\ 2 \end{bmatrix}$$

The STM is found to be

$$\mathbf{\Phi}(t) = e^{\mathbf{A}t} = \begin{bmatrix} 2e^{-t} - e^{-2t} & e^{-t} - e^{-2t} \\ -2e^{-t} + 2e^{-2t} & -e^{-t} + 2e^{-2t} \end{bmatrix}$$

in which case

$$\mathbf{\Phi}(T) = \mathbf{\Phi}(1) = \begin{bmatrix} 0.600 & 0.233 \\ -0.466 & -0.100 \end{bmatrix}$$

Now using Eq. (4.6-12), we determine the matrix **D**. (Since **D** has only one column, it is written as a vector **d**.)

$$\mathbf{d} = \int_0^1 \begin{bmatrix} 2e^{-\lambda} - e^{-2\lambda} & e^{-\lambda} - e^{-2\lambda} \\ -2e^{-\lambda} + 2e^{-2\lambda} & -e^{-\lambda} + 2e^{-2\lambda} \end{bmatrix} \begin{bmatrix} 0 \\ 2 \end{bmatrix} d\lambda = \begin{bmatrix} 0.400 \\ 0.466 \end{bmatrix}$$

Since $u(t)$ is a unit step, $u(0) = u(1) = u(2) = \cdots = 1$. Then $x(1)$ may be determined by the use of Eq. (4.6-13).

$$\mathbf{x}(1) = \begin{bmatrix} 0.600 & 0.233 \\ -0.466 & -0.100 \end{bmatrix} \begin{bmatrix} 0 \\ 0 \end{bmatrix} + \begin{bmatrix} 0.400 \\ 0.466 \end{bmatrix} (1) = \begin{bmatrix} 0.400 \\ 0.466 \end{bmatrix}$$

and $\mathbf{x}(2)$ is

$$\mathbf{x}(2) = \begin{bmatrix} 0.600 & 0.233 \\ -0.466 & -0.100 \end{bmatrix} \begin{bmatrix} 0.400 \\ 0.466 \end{bmatrix} + \begin{bmatrix} 0.400 \\ 0.466 \end{bmatrix} (1) = \begin{bmatrix} 0.749 \\ 0.233 \end{bmatrix}$$

In a similar fashion, $x(3)$, $x(4)$, . . . can be determined. If it is desired to obtain the continuous response between any two sampling times, we simply use the value of x at the first sampling time and then apply Eq. (4.6-14).

4.6-2 Time-varying systems

As another illustration of the STM method, let us consider briefly the time response of the linear time-varying system

$$\dot{x}(t) = A(t)x(t) + B(t)u(t) \qquad (4.6\text{-}15)$$

where $A(t)$ and $B(t)$ are $n \times n$ and $n \times r$ matrices of continuous scalar functions of t respectively. As before, $x(t)$ is the state vector while $u(t)$ is the input vector.

As in Sec. 4.3, we define the STM as a solution to the matrix differential equation (4.3-10). In the more general case $\Phi(t,t_o)$ satisfies

$$\dot{\Phi}(t,t_o) = A(t)\Phi(t,t_o) \qquad (4.6\text{-}16)$$

with the initial condition

$$\Phi(t_o,t_o) = I \qquad (4.6\text{-}17)$$

Then the solution of Eq. (4.6-15) is given by

$$x(t) = \Phi(t,t_o)x(t_o) + \int_{t_o}^{t} \Phi(t,\tau)B(\tau)u(\tau)\,d\tau \qquad (4.6\text{-}18)$$

This solution may be verified by direct substitution using Eqs. (4.6-16) and (4.6-17). The reader is warned not to extend from the scalar case to write

$$\Phi(t,t_o) = \exp \int_{t_o}^{t} A(\tau)\,d\tau$$

This result is correct in the vector case only for special classes of systems.

There is only one major problem with the above procedure: it is generally impossible to obtain the STM except numerically on a digital computer. This is due to the fact that Eq. (4.6-16) represents a time-varying equation for which no general method of solution is known. Because of this problem, the usefulness of this procedure is somewhat less than in the case of time-invariant systems.

However, use of the sampling process presented in the previous section provides a method of obtaining an approximate solution for the above system. In this case, however, rather than sampling the input or the state of the system, we apply the sampling process to the time-varying system. By this sampling process, the system time variations become piecewise constant and hence piecewise time-invariant. It should be emphasized, however, that no actual physical sampling takes place, as in a sampled-data system. Here the sampling is simply an artifice used to determine an approximate solution.

During the intervals when the sampled system is time-invariant the STM method of Sec. 4.3 may be used to obtain the time response. If we then use the final state in one interval as the initial state in the next, we can find the complete time response. During each interval it is generally necessary to recompute the STM for the system.

This method works as long as the time variations of the systems are slow compared with the sampling rate. Just how fast to make the sampling in order to obtain a reasonably good approximation of the time response can perhaps best be answered by simply sampling faster and checking the effect on the response. When the effect becomes negligible, the sampling rate is fast enough.

Unfortunately, this method has the undesirable result of accumulating error. If the terminal state of the first interval is incorrect, this error propagates through the response.

4.6-3 Nonlinear systems

The sampling procedure presented in Sec. 4.6-1 may also be used to obtain the approximate response of nonlinear systems. In this case we sample both the input and state and then linearize the system during each interval about these sampled conditions. Having linearized the system using the method of Sec. 4.2, we can once again apply the STM procedures of Sec. 4.3 to determine the response in that interval. Only one minor modification must be made in the procedures as presented. Since, in general, we are not linearizing about an equilibrium state, the linearized equations include a constant term; hence

$$\dot{\mathbf{x}}(t) = \mathbf{A}\mathbf{x}(t) + \mathbf{B}\mathbf{u}(t) + \mathbf{f}(\mathbf{x}^o, \mathbf{u}^o) \qquad (4.6\text{-}19)$$

The time response then takes the form

$$\mathbf{x}(t) = \mathbf{\Phi}(t - t_o)\mathbf{x}(t_o) + \int_{t_o}^{t} \mathbf{\Phi}(t - \tau)\mathbf{B}\mathbf{u}(\tau)\, d\tau + \mathbf{f}(\mathbf{x}^o, \mathbf{u}^o)(t - t_o)$$
$$(4.6\text{-}20)$$

Once again by using the terminal state of one interval as the initial state of the next, we can obtain the complete response. The comments above concerning the quality of the approximation and the problem of accumulating error apply equally well to this problem.

It should be obvious that this procedure can also be extended to time-varying nonlinear systems by simply sampling the system in addition to the input and state. The approach presented here for obtaining the time response of nonlinear and time-varying systems is certainly not the best numerical technique for accomplishing this result. The method was not presented for this reason but rather to illustrate the generality of the STM procedure to time-response determination.

Exercises 4.6   *4.6-1.* Given the following state-transition and system matrices, verify the equation

$$\dot{\Phi}(t) = A(t)\Phi(t)$$

(a) $$\Phi(t) = \frac{1}{2}\begin{bmatrix} -e^{7t} + 3e^{5t} & -3e^{7t} + 3e^{5t} \\ e^{-t} - e^{-3t} & 3e^{-t} - e^{-3t} \end{bmatrix}$$

$$A(t) = \begin{bmatrix} 4 & -3e^{8t} \\ e^{-8t} & 0 \end{bmatrix}$$

(b) $$\Phi(t) = \begin{bmatrix} e^{(a-1)t}\cos t & e^{-t}\sin t \\ -e^{(a-1)t}\sin t & e^{-t}\cos t \end{bmatrix}$$

$$A(t) = \begin{bmatrix} -1 + a\cos^2 t & 1 - a\sin t\cos t \\ -1 - a\sin t\cos t & -1 + a\sin^2 t \end{bmatrix}$$

4.6-2. Assuming that the input is sampled at $t = 0$, 1, and 2 sec, find the time response at $t = 1$ and 2 sec for the system given below. Compare these values with those obtained in the continuous case.

$$\dot{x} = \begin{bmatrix} 0 & 5 \\ 0 & -1 \end{bmatrix} x + \begin{bmatrix} 0 \\ 1 \end{bmatrix} u$$

$$y = x_1 \qquad x(0) = \text{col }(0,1) \qquad u(t) = t$$

answer:

$$x(1) = \text{col }(3.16, 0.368) \qquad x(2) = \text{col }(6.16, 0.767)$$

4.7   Summary and conclusion

In this chapter we have introduced the STM method of determining the time response of linear systems described by a set of first-order differential equations. In addition to showing how the time response could be obtained, the concept of interpreting the response as a trajectory in state space was presented in order to lend greater physical meaning to the time response.

As an illustration of the generality of the STM method, the method was applied to sampled-data, time-varying, and nonlinear systems.

The time-response method of this chapter and the stability concepts of the next chapter form the basic analytic tools for the design chapters which follow. Whereas the time response gives a complete picture of the behavior of the system, the work involved in obtaining the time response is excessive for all but trivial systems. This is particularly true in the design case, where one is attempting to pick either the form of the system or some of the parameters of the system.

Hence, as an engineering compromise between information received and computational labor required, one is willing to settle for less than the knowledge of the complete behavior. As a first step, one usually concerns oneself simply with ensuring that the system is stable. This topic is treated in the next chapter through the use of the state function of Liapunov.

4.8 Problems

4.8-1. Find the time response using the STM approach and the classical Laplace transform technique for the following system represented in

(*a*) Phase variables
(*b*) Canonical variables
(*c*) Any other set of state variables

Let $u(t) = e^{-2t}$ and $\mathbf{x}(0) = \text{col}\ (1,0,-1)$.

$$\frac{y(s)}{u(s)} = \frac{1}{s(s+1)(s+2)}$$

4.8-2. Using the generalized coordinates shown in Fig. 4.8-1, determine the time response for each of the systems. Do this by

(*a*) Writing the differential equations of motion of the system using Lagrange's equations
(*b*) Linearizing the system about the origin
(*c*) Solving the resulting equations using the STM method

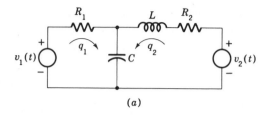

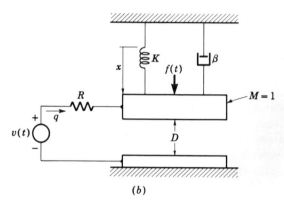

Fig. 4.8-1   Prob. 4.8-2.   (a) $R_1 = 1$, $L = 1$, $C = 1$,
$R_2 = 2$; $v_1(t) = te^{-2t}$, and $v_2(t) = 3 \cos t$;
(b) $R = 1$, $K = 2$, $\beta = 3$, $D = 1$; $v(t) =$
$\sin 3t$, $f(t) = 3e^{-t}$.

Assume that all systems are initially at the origin; that is, $\mathbf{x}(0) = 0$.

4.8-3.   Given the system

$$\dot{\mathbf{x}} = \begin{bmatrix} -3 & 0 \\ 2 & -1 \end{bmatrix} \mathbf{x} + \begin{bmatrix} 3 & 0 \\ 3 & 2 \end{bmatrix} \mathbf{u}$$

find $\mathbf{u}(t)$ to give the following time response:

$$x_1(t) = 6(1 - e^{-t})$$
$$x_2(t) = 3e^{-3t} - 2e^{-4t} + 6(1 - e^{-t})$$

Discuss the situation in which **B** is singular.

4.8-4.   For the system given by

$$\dot{\mathbf{x}} = \begin{bmatrix} -1 & 0 \\ 3 & -1 \end{bmatrix} \mathbf{x} + \begin{bmatrix} 1 \\ 0 \end{bmatrix} u$$
$$y = [1 \quad 0]\mathbf{x}$$

with $\mathbf{x}(0) = \text{col }(2,0)$ and $u(t) = 1$, determine and plot x_1 and x_2 as functions of time. Notice that the magnitude of x_2 may become large in a system of this sort without giving any indication of this to an observer of only y. This is comparable with classical feedback systems, in which only the output variable is fed back.

4.8-5. Obtain the approximate time response of the unforced system of Exercise 4.6-2 at $t = 0.1$, 0.2, and 0.3 sec. Do this by applying the sampling process at $t = 0$, 0.1, and 0.2 sec to the time-varying system. Let $\mathbf{x}(0) = \text{col }(-1,1)$. Compare the answer with the exact solution.

4.8-6. Obtain the approximate time response at $t = 0.1$, 0.2, and 0.3 sec for the system in Exercise 4.2-1a. Do this by sampling both the input and state and then linearizing the system during each interval about these sampled conditions. Let $\mathbf{u}(t) = \text{col }(\cos 2t, 4e^{-t})$, $\mathbf{x}(0) = \text{col }(2,-1)$.

References

Buck, R. C.: "Advanced Calculus," McGraw-Hill Book Company, New York, 1958.

DeRusso, P. M., R. J. Roy, and C. M. Close: "State Variables for Engineers," John Wiley & Sons, Inc., New York, 1965.

Dorf, R. C.: "Time-domain Analysis and Design of Control Systems," Addison-Wesley Publishing Company, Inc., Reading, Mass., 1965.

Gupta, S. C.: "Transform and State Variable Methods in Linear Systems," John Wiley & Sons, Inc., New York, 1966.

Korn, G. A., and T. M. Korn: "Electronic Analog and Hybrid Computers," McGraw-Hill Book Company, New York, 1964.

Zadeh, L. A., and C. A. Desoer: "Linear System Theory," McGraw-Hill Book Company, New York, 1963.

five

stability and the state function of Liapunov

5.1 Introduction and outline of chapter

In this chapter the stability of linear systems is studied through the use of the state function of Liapunov $V(\mathbf{x})$ and the second method of Liapunov. This is the first of two state functions of modern control theory to be introduced in this book. In Chap. 3 potential- and kinetic-energy and lagrangian state functions were introduced. As is shown later, the Liapunov state function is simply a generalization of the total energy $\mathfrak{I} + \mathfrak{V}$ and is therefore closely related to classical mechanics. In the following chapters we introduce the state function of Pontryagin H and show how it is related to the Liapunov state function.

The stability information obtained in this chapter can be thought of as the least information that we need to know about a system. In other words, if we are to know anything about a system, we must first know that it is stable. This is to be contrasted with the time-response information determined by the STM method of the previous chapter, which is the most information that can be obtained about a system. Somewhere between these two extremes lies a practical design area, in which one requires, in addition to system stability, a knowledge of system behavior which is less than the complete time response.

We begin this chapter with a discussion of the concepts of definiteness of scalar functions and a special class of scalar functions known as quadratic forms. This is followed by definitions of various types of system stability and theorems which may be used to establish the applicable type of stability. These concepts are then applied to the study of the stability of linear systems.

As a brief introduction to the design procedures of the following chapters, a technique for using the state function of Liapunov to estimate transient behavior is presented next.

One of the main reasons for the introduction of stability through the state function and second method of Liapunov is that while it is no more difficult to apply in the linear case than classical procedures, the second method can be directly extended to the analysis of nonlinear and sampled-data systems. Although the emphasis in this book is on the analysis and design of linear systems, as an illustration of the generality of the techniques of this chapter, their application to nonlinear systems is discussed briefly.

5.2   Definiteness and quadratic forms

For convenience in discussing the stability definitions and theorems in the following sections, the concept of definiteness of a scalar function is introduced in this section. In addition, an important class of scalar functions known as the quadratic form is discussed.

The concept of the sign definiteness of a scalar function of a scalar variable is well known. For example, one says that a function $f(x)$ is positive (negative) on an interval $a \leq x \leq b$ if $f(x) > 0$ (<0). Or if $f(x) \geq 0$ (≤ 0) for $a \leq x \leq b$, we usually say that the function is non-negative (nonpositive) on the interval $[a,b]$.

The concept of the definiteness of a scalar function of a vector or n-dimensional variable $\mathbf{x}$ is simply an extension of the above idea. In this case the sign definiteness of the function is referred to some n-dimensional region.   Because of the manner in which these scalar functions are used later, sign definiteness is defined with respect to a spherical region about the origin.   Such a spherical region can be written compactly as $\|\mathbf{x}\| \leq K$, where $\|\mathbf{x}\|$ is the euclidean norm of $\mathbf{x}$ given by

$$\|\mathbf{x}\| = (x_1{}^2 + x_2{}^2 + \cdots + x_n{}^2)^{\frac{1}{2}} \tag{5.2-1}$$

and K is a positive constant equal to the radius of the region.

> **Definition 5.2-1   Positive (negative) definite**   A scalar function $V(\mathbf{x})$ is positive (negative) or, more commonly, *positive (negative) definite* if at all nonzero points $\mathbf{x}$ in the spherical region $\|\mathbf{x}\| \leq K$ the values of $V(\mathbf{x})$ are positive (negative), that is, $V(\mathbf{x}) > 0\ (<0)$, and if $V(0) = 0$.

If we relax the requirement that $V(\mathbf{x})$ be strictly positive (negative), then $V(\mathbf{x})$ is said to be *positive (negative) semidefinite.*

> **Definition 5.2-2   Positive (negative) semidefinite**   A scalar function $V(\mathbf{x})$ is positive (negative) semidefinite if for all $\mathbf{x}$, such that $\|\mathbf{x}\| \leq K$, $V(\mathbf{x}) \geq 0\ (\leq 0)$ and if $V(0) = 0$.

In the semidefinite case, $V(\mathbf{x})$ is allowed to equal zero for values of $\mathbf{x} \neq 0$.   If in the above definitions K may be made arbitrarily large, the definitions hold in the whole space and are said to be global.   This is the case with almost all the scalar functions to be discussed in the following developments.

It should be noted that some scalar functions do not fall into either of the above categories, regardless of how small K is chosen.   Such functions are referred to as being indefinite.

> **Definition 5.2-3   Indefinite**   A scalar function $V(\mathbf{x})$ is indefinite if $V(\mathbf{x})$ assumes both positive and negative values within the region $\|\mathbf{x}\| \leq K$ no matter how small K is made.

A few examples serve to clarify these definitions.   The function

$$V(\mathbf{x}) = \|\mathbf{x}\|^2 = x_1{}^2 + x_2{}^2 + \cdots + x_n{}^2$$

is positive definite, while the function

$$V(\mathbf{x}) = x_1{}^2 + x_2{}^2$$

on the other hand, is positive definite if the system is second-order. It is only semidefinite if the system is of higher order, since for $x_1 = x_2 = 0$, $V(x)$ is zero independent of $x_3, x_4, \ldots$. On the other hand, the function

$$V(x) = (x_1 + x_2)^2$$

is semidefinite even for second-order systems, since if $x_1 = -x_2$, $V(x)$ is zero even though x is not equal to zero. The function

$$V(x) = x_1 + x_2$$

is obviously indefinite regardless of the order of the system.

One class of scalar functions which plays a particularly important role in this and the following chapters is a *quadratic form*. In this case $V(x)$ may be written in the form

$$V(x) = x^T R x \tag{5.2-2}$$

where R is a constant matrix. Equation (5.2-2) may be written in expanded form as

$$V(x) = [x_1 \quad x_2 \quad \cdots \quad x_n] \begin{bmatrix} r_{11} & r_{12} & \cdots & r_{1n} \\ r_{21} & r_{22} & \cdots & r_{2n} \\ \vdots & & & \vdots \\ r_{n1} & r_{n2} & \cdots & r_{nn} \end{bmatrix} \begin{bmatrix} x_1 \\ x_2 \\ \vdots \\ x_n \end{bmatrix} \tag{5.2-3}$$

or

$$V(x) = r_{11}x_1^2 + (r_{12} + r_{21})x_1x_2 + \cdots + (r_{1n} + r_{n1})x_1x_n \\ + r_{22}x_2^2 + (r_{23} + r_{32})x_2x_3 + \cdots + r_{nn}x_n^2 \tag{5.2-4}$$

Usually if $V(x)$ is a quadratic form, the definiteness of $V(x)$ is attributed to R. Hence one speaks, for example, of a positive definite matrix.

Any scalar function which contains only second-order terms in x, that is, which is homogeneous of degree 2 in x, may be written as a quadratic form. In fact, the quadratic form takes its name from the quadratic nature of each of its terms. Consider, for example, the scalar function

$$V(x) = 2x_1^2 + 2x_1x_2 + 4x_2^2 + 5x_3^2 - 4x_1x_3$$

This function is of the form of Eq. (5.2-4) and hence is a quadratic form.

By the notation of Eq. (5.2-2), **R** is

$$\mathbf{R} = \begin{bmatrix} 2 & 1 & -2 \\ 1 & 4 & 0 \\ -2 & 0 & 5 \end{bmatrix} \tag{5.2-5}$$

It should be noted that we can always assume that **R** is symmetric. If this assumption is not valid, we need consider only the symmetric portion of **R**. In order to show this fact we observe first that

$$\mathbf{x}^T\mathbf{R}^T\mathbf{x} = \mathbf{x}^T\mathbf{R}\mathbf{x} \tag{5.2-6}$$

which can be shown by writing out the matrix products involved, as in Eq. (5.2-4). Next we write **R** as the sum of a symmetric and skew-symmetric matrix (see Sec. 2.3),

$$\mathbf{R} = \mathbf{R}_s + \mathbf{R}_{sk}$$

where

$$\mathbf{R}_s = \frac{\mathbf{R} + \mathbf{R}^T}{2} \qquad \mathbf{R}_{sk} = \frac{\mathbf{R} - \mathbf{R}^T}{2} \tag{5.2-7}$$

The quadratic form $\mathbf{x}^T\mathbf{R}\mathbf{x}$ then becomes

$$\mathbf{x}^T\mathbf{R}\mathbf{x} = \mathbf{x}^T\mathbf{R}_s\mathbf{x} + \mathbf{x}^T\mathbf{R}_{sk}\mathbf{x} \tag{5.2-8}$$

By the use of Eqs. (5.2-6) and (5.2-7) the second term is zero, since

$$\mathbf{x}^T\mathbf{R}_{sk}\mathbf{x} = \frac{\mathbf{x}^T\mathbf{R}\mathbf{x} - \mathbf{x}^T\mathbf{R}^T\mathbf{x}}{2} = \frac{\mathbf{x}^T\mathbf{R}\mathbf{x} - \mathbf{x}^T\mathbf{R}\mathbf{x}}{2} = 0$$

Equation (5.2-8) then becomes

$$\mathbf{x}^T\mathbf{R}\mathbf{x} = \mathbf{x}^T\mathbf{R}_s\mathbf{x} \tag{5.2-9}$$

and it is seen that only the symmetric portion of **R** is of importance. We shall therefore tacitly assume in the future that **R** is symmetric.

The usual means of determining the definiteness of a quadratic form is through the application of *Sylvester's theorem* (this should not be confused with Sylvester's expansion theorem presented in Sec. 4.5):

Theorem 5.2-1   Sylvester's theorem   In order that a quadratic form (5.2-2) be positive definite, it is necessary and sufficient that each of the quantities

$$\det [r_{11}], \det \begin{bmatrix} r_{11} & r_{12} \\ r_{12} & r_{22} \end{bmatrix}, \det \begin{bmatrix} r_{11} & r_{12} & r_{13} \\ r_{12} & r_{22} & r_{23} \\ r_{13} & r_{23} & r_{33} \end{bmatrix}, \dots, \det (\mathbf{R})$$

(5.2-10)

be positive.

If any of the above determinants fails to be positive by being zero, the function is only semidefinite.   A matrix $\mathbf{R}$ is negative definite or semidefinite if the matrix $-\mathbf{R}$ is positive definite or semidefinite.   It should be noted that the definiteness of a quadratic form is global.

Example 5.2-1   As an illustration of the application of Sylvester's theorem, let us consider the $\mathbf{R}$ matrix given by Eq. (5.2-5).   Here

$$\det [r_{11}] = \det [2] = 2 > 0$$

$$\det \begin{bmatrix} r_{11} & r_{12} \\ r_{12} & r_{22} \end{bmatrix} = \det \begin{bmatrix} 2 & 1 \\ 1 & 4 \end{bmatrix} = 7 > 0$$

and

$$\det \begin{bmatrix} r_{11} & r_{12} & r_{13} \\ r_{12} & r_{22} & r_{23} \\ r_{13} & r_{23} & r_{33} \end{bmatrix} = \det \begin{bmatrix} 2 & 1 & -2 \\ 1 & 4 & 0 \\ -2 & 0 & 5 \end{bmatrix} = 19 > 0$$

Since all these quantities are positive, we conclude that the quadratic form (5.2-5) is positive definite.

Note that in the special case where $\mathbf{R}$ is a diagonal matrix, $V(\mathbf{x})$ is positive (negative) definite if $r_{ii} > 0$ (<0) for $i = 1, 2, \dots, n$; positive (negative) semidefinite if $r_{ii} \geq 0$ (≤ 0) for any i; and indefinite if $r_{ii} > 0$ for some i and $r_{jj} < 0$ for some $j \neq i$.

Closely related to the concept of definiteness is the concept of a simple closed surface or curve.   A surface is *simple* if it does not intersect itself and *closed* if it intersects all paths that lead from the origin to infinity.   The reader is reminded that we are centering our attention about the origin, and hence the definition of closeness with regard to the origin is of primary importance here.

A simple closed surface is topologically equivalent to the surface of an n-dimensional sphere about the origin. In other words, a simple closed surface can be thought of as a hollow rubber ball, with the origin on the inside, which has been distorted by pushing or stretching various segments of its surface.

It can be shown (Letov, 1961) that if a scalar function $V(\mathbf{x})$ is positive definite and is, in addition, radially unbounded, then the set of all points $\mathbf{x}$ such that $V(\mathbf{x}) = K$, a positive constant, is a simple closed surface. In addition, the surface $V(\mathbf{x}) = K_1$ lies entirely inside the surface $V(\mathbf{x}) = K_2$ whenever $K_1 < K_2$. By radially unbounded we mean that the value of $V(\mathbf{x})$ approaches infinity as the norm of $\mathbf{x}$ goes to infinity, or $V(\mathbf{x}) \to \infty$ as $\|\mathbf{x}\| \to \infty$.

As an illustration of the above concepts, consider once again the quadratic form of Eq. (5.2-2). We can easily see that if $V(\mathbf{x})$ is positive definite, it is also radially unbounded, since $V(\mathbf{x})$ can be made as large as desired by letting $\|\mathbf{x}\| \to \infty$. Hence the surface $V(\mathbf{x}) = \mathbf{x}^T\mathbf{R}\mathbf{x} = K$ corresponds to a simple closed surface which is an n-dimensional hyperellipsoid. The major axes may or may not be aligned with the coordinate axes.

Example 5.2-2 As a specific example, let us consider a second-order case so that the resulting closed curves can be easily illustrated. Let the matrix $\mathbf{R}$ be given by

$$\mathbf{R} = \begin{bmatrix} 1 & 1 \\ 1 & 4 \end{bmatrix}$$

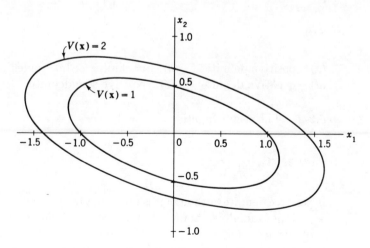

Fig. 5.2-1 Surfaces of constant $V(\mathbf{x})$ for $V(\mathbf{x}) = \mathbf{x}^T\mathbf{R}\mathbf{x}$.

in which case $V(\mathbf{x})$ is

$$V(\mathbf{x}) = \mathbf{x}^T \mathbf{R} \mathbf{x} = x_1{}^2 + 2x_1 x_2 + 4x_2{}^2$$

By an application of Sylvester's theorem $V(\mathbf{x})$ is shown to be positive definite, and since $V(\mathbf{x})$ is a quadratic form, it is also radially unbounded. In Fig. 5.2-1 the closed curves corresponding to $V(\mathbf{x}) = 1$ and $V(\mathbf{x}) = 2$ are shown.

The concept of simple closed surfaces is discussed further in Sec. 5.4 with regard to the geometric interpretation of stability theorems. First, however, we introduce some definitions of stability.

Exercises 5.2   *5.2-1*.   Determine the definiteness of the following quadratic forms.

(a) $V(\mathbf{x}) = x_1{}^2 + 4x_1 x_2 + 5x_2{}^2 + 2x_2 x_3 + x_3{}^2$

(b) $V(\mathbf{x}) = \mathbf{x}^T \mathbf{R} \mathbf{x}$ and $\mathbf{R} = \begin{bmatrix} 1 & 7 \\ 0 & 3 \end{bmatrix}$

(c) $V(\mathbf{x}) = -x_1{}^2 + 6x_1 x_2 - 4x_2{}^2 - x_3{}^2$
(d) $V(\mathbf{x}) = -x_1{}^2 + 2x_1 x_2 - 4x_2{}^2 - x_3{}^2$

(e) $V(\mathbf{x}) = \mathbf{x}^T \mathbf{R} \mathbf{x}$ and $\mathbf{R} = \begin{bmatrix} 1 & 1 & 1 \\ 1 & 2 & 0 \\ 1 & 0 & 2 \end{bmatrix}$

answers:

(a)   positive definite   (b)   indefinite   (c)   indefinite
(d)   negative definite   (e)   positive semidefinite

5.2-2.   The scalar function

$$V(\mathbf{x}) = x_1{}^2 + \frac{x_2{}^2}{1 + x_2{}^2}$$

is positive definite, although it is not a quadratic form. In addition, $V(\mathbf{x})$ is not radially unbounded, since $V(\mathbf{x}) \to 1$ along the line $x_1 = 0$. Plot surfaces of $V(\mathbf{x})$ equal to $\frac{1}{2}$, 1, and 2, and note that $V(\mathbf{x})$ does not represent a closed surface in all $x_1 x_2$ space.

5.3   *Definitions of stability*

The concept of the stability of a linear autonomous system is basic to all classical control engineering.   There it is assumed that the system is completely described in terms of a transfer function or that the system is completely controllable and observable.   Such a system is said to be stable if "its output in response to every bounded input remains bounded" (Bower and Schultheiss, 1958).   From this definition it is possible to establish as a necessary and sufficient condition for stability that the system weighting function or impulse response must be absolutely integrable from zero to infinity, that is,

$$\int_0^\infty |w(t)|\, dt \text{ is finite} \tag{5.3-1}$$

The weighting function is simply the inverse Laplace transform of the system transfer function.   From this result it can be shown that it is necessary and sufficient for a system to be stable that all its poles or eigenvalues have negative real parts.

In an equivalent manner one might assume either of these results as a definition of stability and then develop the other result and the above definition as necessary and sufficient conditions.   Hence the three items play completely equivalent roles in the concept of stability.

While the above concepts are entirely adequate for the study of linear autonomous systems, they are not sufficient for nonlinear systems, since weighting functions and eigenvalues are meaningless in that case. On the other hand, the more basic stability concepts presented below, although no more difficult for linear systems, can be applied directly to nonlinear systems.   It is partially for this reason that these more general definitions are chosen, even though our main interest is in classical linear systems.

There are many types of stability that could be defined; Ingwerson (1960), for example, defines 20 different types.   Since most of his definitions apply to nonlinear or time-varying systems and therefore are not of interest here, only stability in the sense of Liapunov and asymptotic stability are defined here.   In addition, the concept of instability of a system is made more precise.   All linear systems fall into one of these three categories.   Since, as is shown later, the type of stability applicable to any *linear* system is always global, the stability of the forced system

$$\dot{\mathbf{x}} = \mathbf{Ax} + \mathbf{Bu} \tag{AB}$$

for any bounded input is completely determined by the unforced system

$$\dot{x} = Ax \tag{A}$$

We shall therefore consider only this system in the following developments. In the unforced system there is only one equilibrium state located at the origin, assuming **A** is nonsingular. The following stability definitions are based on the nature of the system time response that results from initial conditions in a particular region of the state space.

Thus stability definitions are phrased in terms of spherical regions, such as $S(\alpha)$. Let $S(\alpha)$ be the open spherical region of radius $\alpha > 0$ around the origin, that is, $S(\alpha)$ consists of all points **x** such that $\|x\| < \alpha$. The following definitions apply in the neighborhood of the origin.

> **Definition 5.3-1 Stability in the sense of Liapunov** The origin of the state space is said to be *stable in the sense of Liapunov* if corresponding to each $S(R)$ there is an $S(r)$ such that solutions starting in $S(r)$ do not leave $S(R)$ as $t \to \infty$.

Note that in the above definition $S(r)$ may be a function of $S(R)$. The region $S(R)$ is chosen first, and for each $S(R)$ there must be a region of allowable initial conditions $S(r)$ such that trajectories starting in this region do not leave $S(R)$ for all time. According to this definition, a linear oscillator is stable in the sense of Liapunov, as the amplitude of the oscillation remains fixed with time. Regardless of the size of $S(R)$, a region of initial conditions may be chosen so that the oscillating trajectory does not leave $S(R)$.

In the mathematical literature, and even in engineering literature on the second method of Liapunov, a system that is stable in the sense of Liapunov is often said to be stable; i.e., linear oscillators are often referred to as stable. This is contrary to the definitions cited earlier in this section, as the impulse response of an oscillator is not absolutely integrable. Hence, we shall *not* refer to systems that are stable in the sense of Liapunov as being stable. Rather we shall use the word stable to refer to systems which are asymptotically stable.

> **Definition 5.3-2 Asymptotic stability** If the origin of the state space is stable in the sense of Liapunov, and if, in addition, every solution starting in $S(r)$ not only stays within $S(R)$ but approaches the origin as $t \to \infty$, then the system is called *asymptotically stable* or simply *stable*.

This definition corresponds to the usually accepted engineering definition of stability, as stated in Eq. (5.3-1). According to the definition of asymptotic stability, every system that is asymptotically stable is also stable in the sense of Liapunov. The converse is not true.

Control-system engineers go to great lengths to ensure that the systems they design exhibit asymptotically stable behavior, i.e., that the system returns to its equilibrium state after initial disturbances. It is interesting to note that stability is defined here in terms of initial conditions rather than in terms of response to an input, either a bounded input or an impulse. It will be seen later that most modern methods of control-system design are also based upon the design for desired response due to initial conditions rather than upon desired response for a standard input, as a step or sine wave.

A graphical representation of Definitions 5.3-1 and 5.3-2 is shown in Fig. 5.3-1 for a two-dimensional case. In this figure a typical trajectory is plotted for each of the two types of stability. For example, we see that

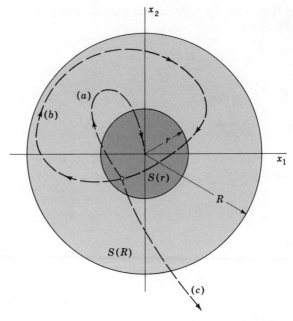

Fig. 5.3-1   Graphical representation of stability definitions. (*a*) Trajectory of an asymptotically stable system; (*b*) trajectory of a system which is stable in the sense of Liapunov; (*c*) an unstable trajectory.

the trajectory of an oscillator, which is stable in the sense of Liapunov, starts in the region $S(r)$ and stays in the region $S(R)$ but does not approach the origin.

The above definitions say nothing about the extent of the region of allowable initial conditions, other than to specify the rather vague region $S(r)$. For nonlinear systems this region may be quite small. If, on the other hand, the region $S(r)$ includes the entire state space, the definitions apply in a global sense. If a linear system is asymptotically stable, or simply stable, it is always globally asymptotically stable.

In order to illustrate this important fact, suppose that the system (**A**) is stable for any initial state $\mathbf{x}(0)$ such that

$$\|\mathbf{x}(0)\| \leq K$$

If we now make the transformation

$$\mathbf{x} = \alpha\mathbf{y}$$

where α is any positive constant greater than unity, then the system (**A**) becomes

$$\alpha\dot{\mathbf{y}} = \mathbf{A}\alpha\mathbf{y}$$

or

$$\dot{\mathbf{y}} = \mathbf{A}\mathbf{y}$$

Since this system is identical to (**A**), it must also be stable for any initial state $\mathbf{y}(0)$ such that

$$\|\mathbf{y}(0)\| \leq K$$

But

$$\|\mathbf{y}(0)\| = \frac{1}{\alpha}\|\mathbf{x}(0)\|$$

and therefore the system (**A**) must also be stable for any initial state such that

$$\|\mathbf{x}(0)\| \leq \alpha K$$

By making α large enough, any given initial state can be included, and the stability is therefore global.

Equivalently, we could argue that the stability must be global, since the stability of the system is determined completely by the eigenvalues of the system, as shown later in Sec. 5.5.

The idea of instability is closely related to that of stability.

Definition 5.3-3 Instability The origin of the state space is said to be unstable if for some positive number R and any r, no matter how small, there is always a point in $S(r)$ such that a trajectory starting at this point leaves $S(R)$.

In the stability definitions cited earlier, a region of initial conditions sufficient to satisfy the definition had to be true for every $S(R)$. On the other hand, it is sufficient to conclude instability if only one region $S(R)$ can be found such that there is no region of initial conditions, no matter how small, such that trajectories starting from a point within $S(r)$ remain in $S(R)$.

If a linear system is unstable, trajectories go to infinity, and regardless of the size of $S(R)$, the boundary of this region is always penetrated. In the nonlinear case, this is not always true, as in a system with a limit cycle. Figure 5.3-1 also includes an unstable trajectory. While it is clear from Fig. 5.3-1 that trajectory c leaves $S(R)$ and is thus unstable, we do not know whether this trajectory ultimately goes to infinity or to a limit cycle.

In the following chapters the concept of asymptotic stability, or more specifically global asymptotic stability, is of primary interest. We are interested in assuring that all systems we design are asymptotically stable. Unfortunately, the concept of asymptotic stability has one disadvantage. The region $S(R)$ is a function of $S(r)$, but the relationship of the size of $S(R)$ with respect to $S(r)$ is not known or specified. Hence it is quite conceivable that a system that is asymptotically stable, or even globally asymptotically stable, may still perform quite badly.

Consider, for example, a linear second-order system with very low damping. Although this system is globally asymptotically stable, its performance is highly oscillatory and hence undesirable. On the other hand, a system which is globally asymptotically stable might be very sluggish in its performance and hence undesirable. One therefore needs more than stability information for adequate design of a control system. This is the topic of the next chapters. It should be pointed out that the classical approach to the stability of linear systems suffers from these same problems.

Some procedure, short of a direct application of the definitions, is needed to determine to which of the three classes of stability a particular system belongs. This is the subject of the next section, where two stability theorems are presented.

5.4   The second method of Liapunov

As was the case with regard to definitions of stability, there are many stability and instability theorems which constitute the second, or direct, method of Liapunov (Antosiewicz, 1958; Hahn, 1963). Only two of the simplest and most useful theorems are presented here. The first is a stability theorem due to LaSalle (1960), and the second is the Cetaev instability theorem (LaSalle and Lefschetz, 1961). These theorems are presented in their general form as applicable to nonlinear systems even though our main interest is linear systems. Although this approach requires a slight amount of additional discussion, it pays a large dividend in the generality of the results.

The original publication of A. M. Liapunov's work appeared in Russian in 1892. In it Liapunov presented two methods for the study of the stability of systems of ordinary differential equations given as

$$\dot{x} = f(x) \qquad\qquad (5.4\text{-}1)$$

The first, or indirect, method requires a knowledge of the solution of the equations and hence contains much more information than simply stability information. The second, or direct, method, on the other hand, requires no knowledge of the solutions and therefore provides a useful engineering approach to the study of stability.

Little engineering use was made of the second method until the early 1940s, when the Russians began to realize the value of the approach in connection with the analysis of nonlinear control systems. Since that time considerable effort has been devoted to the development of this method into a practical engineering tool, both in this country and in Russia, particularly with regard to nonlinear systems. This effort, as yet, has not been totally successful, although many significant advances have been made.

In the case of linear systems, however, the method provides a very simple, straightforward, and highly useful approach to the study of stability. Once again it must be emphasized that no new results are obtained by the use of the second method on linear systems. However, once the method is mastered, which is no more difficult than the classical approach, one can directly extend one's thinking to nonlinear systems. This is not true in the case of the classical approach, where it is necessary to master completely new methods in order to handle nonlinear systems.

Basically, the second method is a generalization of the energy concepts of classical mechanics. For example, a mechanical system is known to be stable if its total energy, $\mathfrak{I} + \mathfrak{V}$, is continuously decreasing. Note that total energy is usually a positive definite function, since both $\mathfrak{I}$ and $\mathfrak{V}$ are generally positive quantities. With this as a starting point, Liapunov formed a generalized energy function, which he also required to be positive definite. This generalized energy function is now commonly known as a *Liapunov function*, or a *V function*, since it is usually denoted by $V(\mathbf{x})$. Any positive definite scalar function $V(\mathbf{x})$ with continuous first partial derivatives is a possible Liapunov function.

The Liapunov function is of prime importance in establishing the stability of Eq. (5.4-1). Since $V(\mathbf{x})$ has continuous first partial derivatives, the chain rule may be used to obtain $dV(\mathbf{x})/dt$, as

$$\frac{dV(\mathbf{x})}{dt} = \dot{V}(\mathbf{x}) = \frac{\partial V(\mathbf{x})}{\partial x_1}\frac{dx_1}{dt} + \frac{\partial V(\mathbf{x})}{\partial x_2}\frac{dx_2}{dt} + \cdots + \frac{\partial V(\mathbf{x})}{\partial x_n}\frac{dx_n}{dt}$$

$$= \sum_{i=1}^{n} \frac{\partial V(\mathbf{x})}{\partial x_i}\dot{x}_i = \sum_{i=1}^{n} \frac{\partial V(\mathbf{x})}{\partial x_i} f_i(\mathbf{x})$$

This may be written compactly as

$$\dot{V}(\mathbf{x}) = \nabla \mathbf{V}^T(\mathbf{x})\dot{x} = \nabla \mathbf{V}^T(\mathbf{x})\mathbf{f}(\mathbf{x}) \tag{5.4-2}$$

where

$$\nabla \mathbf{V}^T(\mathbf{x}) = \left[\frac{\partial V(\mathbf{x})}{\partial x_1} \frac{\partial V(\mathbf{x})}{\partial x_2} \cdots \frac{\partial V(\mathbf{x})}{\partial x_n} \right]$$

If a $V(\mathbf{x})$ can be found such that its derivative taken according to Eq. (5.4-2) is always negative, then as time increases, $V(\mathbf{x})$ takes on smaller and smaller values. We have associated the idea of positive definiteness with the idea of a closed surface in n space, so that as $V(\mathbf{x})$ becomes smaller, $\|\mathbf{x}\|$ is also decreasing. As time goes to infinity, $V(\mathbf{x})$ shrinks to zero, and likewise $\mathbf{x} \to 0$, which indicates stability. A theorem sufficient to establish the stability of Eq. (5.4-1) in an arbitrarily small region about the origin is the following.

Theorem 5.4-1 Asymptotic stability If there exists a real
scalar function $V(\mathbf{x})$, continuous with continuous first partials, such
that

1. $V(0) = 0$
2. $V(\mathbf{x}) > 0$ for $\mathbf{x} \neq 0$
3. $dV(\mathbf{x})/dt < 0$ for $\mathbf{x} \neq 0$

then Eq. (5.4-1) is asymptotically stable in the neighborhood of the
origin.

The proof of this theorem follows directly from the definition of
asymptotic stability by arguments similar to those that preceded the
statement of the theorem. Conditions 1 and 2 ensure that $V(\mathbf{x})$ is positive
definite and hence that $V(\mathbf{x})$ represents a closed surface at least in the
neighborhood of the origin. Condition 3 ensures that $dV(\mathbf{x})/dt$ is always
negative.

While this theorem is basic to the understanding of the second
method, it is somewhat restrictive, because of the fact that $dV(\mathbf{x})/dt$ is
required to be negative definite. It is possible to replace this requirement
of negative definiteness by one of negative semidefiniteness if one additional restriction is imposed on $dV(\mathbf{x})/dt$, namely, that $dV(\mathbf{x})/dt$ not be
identically zero on a solution of the original Eq. (5.4-1) other than at
$\mathbf{x} = 0$. In order to test this requirement, the solution to the equation
$dV(\mathbf{x})/dt = 0$ is substituted into the original Eq. (5.4-1) to be sure that
Eq. (5.4-1) is not satisfied. For the linear systems with which we are
mainly concerned this latter requirement presents no problem, since normally the only equilibrium point of linear systems is the origin.

The following theorem involves this modification on the require-
ments of $dV(\mathbf{x})/dt$ and in addition includes a requirement on $V(\mathbf{x})$ to
ensure that $V(\mathbf{x})$ represents a closed surface in all n space. In this fashion,
global asymptotic stability may be demonstrated with the aid of Theorem
5.4-2.

Theorem 5.4-2 Global asymptotic stability (stability) If
there exists a real scalar function $V(\mathbf{x})$ continuous with continuous
first partials such that

1. $V(0) = 0$
2. $V(\mathbf{x}) > 0$ for $\mathbf{x} \neq 0$
3. $V(\mathbf{x}) \to \infty$ as $\|\mathbf{x}\| \to \infty$
4. $dV(\mathbf{x})/dt \leq 0$

5. $dV(\mathbf{x})/dt$ not identically zero along any trajectory of the system other than the origin

then Eq. (5.4-1) is globally asymptotically stable.

Conceptually this theorem is very similar to the first one. Conditions 1 and 2 ensure positive definiteness, and 3 ensures that $V(\mathbf{x})$ is closed in the whole space. Conditions 4 and 5 ensure that $V(\mathbf{x})$ is always decreasing. As mentioned above, condition 5 is always satisfied for asymptotically stable linear systems. Similarly, if $V(\mathbf{x})$ is a positive definite quadratic form, condition 3 is also automatically satisfied. In the subsequent discussion of linear systems, we restrict ourselves to V functions of this quadratic nature.

The above stability criterion, or theorem, permits a very illustrative geometric interpretation. Assume that the system in question is second-order, so that the system's behavior may be interpreted on a plane rather than in the general n-dimensional state space. The extension to the n-dimensional case follows readily. Since $V(\mathbf{x})$ is positive definite and radially unbounded, $V(\mathbf{x}) = K$, a constant, becomes a family of concentric closed surfaces surrounding the origin such that the surface $V(\mathbf{x}) = K_1$ lies inside $V(\mathbf{x}) = K_2$ whenever $K_1 < K_2$, as in Fig. 5.4-1. Because $V(\mathbf{x})$ is radially unbounded, these closed curves extend over the whole state plane.

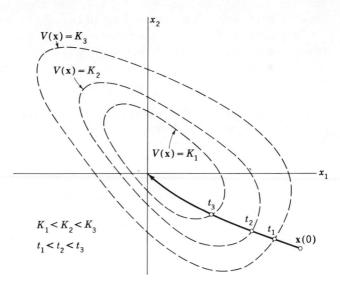

Fig. 5.4-1 Geometric interpretation of the stability theorem.

Since both $V(\mathbf{x})$ and $\dot{V}(\mathbf{x})$ are implicit functions of time and $\dot{V}(\mathbf{x})$ is required to be nonpositive, as time increases, the state of the system must be found on successively "smaller" $V(\mathbf{x}) = K$, a constant, surfaces or must remain stationary. But $\dot{V}(\mathbf{x})$ cannot be zero on any trajectory of the system except $\mathbf{x} = 0$; therefore the state of the system cannot remain stationary. Hence, the system trajectory must move toward the origin, since the smallest value of $V(\mathbf{x})$, zero, occurs only at the origin.

While the physical interpretation of the stability theorem is simple, the problem of determining a Liapunov function for a given system still remains. In the case of linear systems, however, one is able to find an infinite number of such functions in a relatively simple manner, as demonstrated in the next section. For nonlinear systems, this is generally not the case, and one may have great difficulty in finding an adequate Liapunov function.

However, the converse of the stability theorem has been established (Hahn, 1963). If a system is stable, a Liapunov function *must* exist which will prove the stability, and one knows that one is not conducting a futile search for a nonexistent function. The problem of obtaining Liapunov functions for nonlinear systems is discussed briefly in Sec. 5.7.

One of the most powerful features of the second method is the fact that the Liapunov function is *not unique*. No longer is one searching for a single unique solution to the differential equation but rather for one out of many Liapunov functions. However, because the method is only a sufficient condition for stability, some Liapunov functions may provide a better answer than others, particularly in the case of nonlinear systems.

In addition, the failure of a particular V function to prove stability in no way implies that the system is, in fact, unstable. Instability can be established only by direct recourse to one of the instability theorems of the second method, such as the following *Cetaev instability theorem.*

Theorem 5.4-3   Instability   Let N be a spherical region about the origin and let there be given a function $V(\mathbf{x})$ and a region N_1 in N such that:

1. $V(\mathbf{x})$ has continuous first partial derivatives in N_1.
2.   At the boundary points of N_1 inside N, $V(\mathbf{x}) = 0$.
3.   The origin is a boundary point of N_1.
4. $V(\mathbf{x})$ and $\dot{V}(\mathbf{x})$ are positive in N_1.

Under these conditions the origin is unstable.

The situation is illustrated in Fig. 5.4-2 for a second-order system. The boundary of N_1 in N is defined by the curve $V(\mathbf{x}) = 0$, and the curves

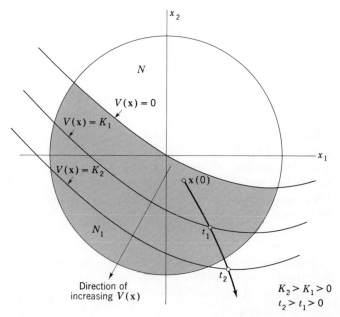

Fig. 5.4-2 Geometric interpretation of the Cetaev instability theorem.

of increasing $V(\mathbf{x})$ are shown. Since $\dot{V}(\mathbf{x})$ is positive in N_1, any trajectory starting from a point in N_1, no matter how close to the origin, must move in the direction of increasing $V(\mathbf{x})$. But the direction of increasing $V(\mathbf{x})$ is away from the origin, and hence the system is unstable. It is obvious that a similar argument follows directly if both $V(\mathbf{x})$ and $\dot{V}(\mathbf{x})$ are negative in N_1.

Joint consideration of this instability theorem and the stability theorems 5.4-1 and 5.4-2 indicates the key role played by $\dot{V}(\mathbf{x})$ in the study of stability.

If $\dot{V}(\mathbf{x})$ can be made at least semidefinite in sign and not identically zero along any trajectory of the system, save the origin, then the stability of the origin can be determined by an investigation of the associated $V(\mathbf{x})$. If $V(\mathbf{x})$ is definite and of the same sign as $\dot{V}(\mathbf{x})$, or if $V(\mathbf{x})$ is indefinite, the origin is unstable. On the other hand, if $V(\mathbf{x})$ is definite and of opposite sign, the origin is stable. Consequently, in order to guarantee results from the stability study, it is only necessary to ensure that $\dot{V}(\mathbf{x})$ is at least semidefinite. This approach, which is taken in the next section, should be contrasted with the technique of selecting positive definite $V(\mathbf{x})$.

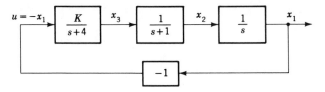

Fig. 5.4-3   Exercise 5.4-1.

The resulting $\dot{V}(\mathbf{x})$ may or may not be definite, in which case no conclusion can be drawn.

The reader has probably noticed that we have not discussed the determination of stability in the sense of Liapunov. This was omitted because systems which are only Liapunov stable have little engineering value and, in the case of linear systems, cannot be realized in practice, since they require the exact placement of poles on the imaginary axis. However, from the above theorem, we can conclude that a system is Liapunov stable if there exists a positive definite $V(\mathbf{x})$ such that $\dot{V}(\mathbf{x})$ is identically zero. If these conditions are satisfied, the system can remain in a fixed oscillatory trajectory. This type of stability is stability in the sense of Liapunov.

Exercises 5.4   *5.4-1.*   Consider the block diagram shown in Fig. 5.4-3. For the state variables indicated the describing equations are

$$\dot{x}_1 = x_2 \qquad \dot{x}_2 = -x_2 + x_3$$
$$\dot{x}_3 = -Kx_1 - 4x_3$$

If $V(\mathbf{x})$ is given by

$$V(\mathbf{x}) = 5Kx_1{}^2 + 2Kx_1x_2 + 20x_2{}^2 + 8x_2x_3 + x_3{}^2$$

show that

$$\frac{dV(\mathbf{x})}{dt} = -(40 - 2K)x_2{}^2$$

Show also that $V(\mathbf{x})$ remains positive definite for the same range of K for which $dV(\mathbf{x})/dt$ is negative semidefinite.

5.4-2.   The second-order nonlinear system of the block diagram shown in Fig. 5.4-4 is described by the two equations

$$\dot{x}_1 = -x_2 \qquad \dot{x}_2 = -2x_2 + K(x_1 - 2x_1{}^3 + x_1{}^5)$$

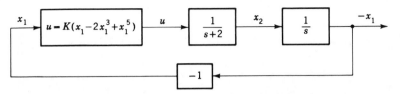

Fig. 5.4-4 Exercise 5.4-2.

If $V(\mathbf{x})$ is

$$V(\mathbf{x}) = K\left(x_1^2 - x_1^4 + \frac{x_1^6}{3}\right) + x_2^2$$

show that $V(\mathbf{x})$ satisfies conditions 1, 2, and 3 of Theorem 5.4-2. Show also that $\dot{V}(\mathbf{x})$ satisfies condition 4 but that condition 5 is violated, so that global asymptotic stability cannot be concluded. (The system has equilibrium points at $x_1 = \pm 1$.)

5.5 Stability of linear systems

In this section the concepts of system stability and the two stability theorems introduced in the preceding sections are used to study the stability of linear autonomous systems. We begin by showing the relationship between system stability and the eigenvalues of the system. Consider, once again, the unforced system

$$\dot{\mathbf{x}} = \mathbf{A}\mathbf{x} \tag{A}$$

For simplicity, assume that the eigenvalues of the system are distinct. Then by the use of a linear transformation $\mathbf{x} = \mathbf{P}\mathbf{z}$, as discussed in Sec. 2.6, it is possible to write Eq. (A) in normal form as

$$\dot{\mathbf{z}} = \mathbf{\Lambda}\mathbf{z} \tag{5.5-1}$$

where $\mathbf{\Lambda}$ is a diagonal matrix of the eigenvalues of $\mathbf{A}$. Therefore Eq. (5.5-1) is equivalent to n first-order differential equations of the form

$$\dot{z}_i = \lambda_i z_i \qquad i = 1, 2, \ldots, n \tag{5.5-2}$$

The reader is reminded that if some of the eigenvalues are complex, the associated canonical variables are likewise complex.

In order to investigate the stability of this system by means of the stability theorems in the previous section, it is necessary to select a V function such that $\dot{V}(\mathbf{x})$ is at least negative semidefinite. Consider the following real scalar function,

$$V(\mathbf{z}) = -\sum_{i=1}^{n} (2 \operatorname{Re} \lambda_i) z_i z_i^* = -\sum_{i=1}^{n} (\lambda_i + \lambda_i^*) z_i z_i^* \tag{5.5-3}$$

where the superscript * is used to indicate the complex conjugate. If the quantity is real, the conjugate operation leaves the quantity unchanged. The time derivative of this scalar function is

$$\dot{V}(\mathbf{z}) = -\sum_{i=1}^{n} (\lambda_i + \lambda_i^*)(\dot{z}_i z_i^* + z_i \dot{z}_i^*)$$

$$= -\sum_{i=1}^{n} (\lambda_i + \lambda_i^*)^2 z_i z_i^* = -\sum_{i=1}^{n} (2 \operatorname{Re} \lambda_i)^2 z_i z_i^* \tag{5.5-4}$$

In the case where the real part of all of the eigenvalues is nonzero, we immediately see that $\dot{V}(\mathbf{z})$ is negative definite. Hence the stability of the system can be determined by an investigation of $V(\mathbf{z})$, Eq. (5.5-3), as discussed at the end of the previous section. We see that $V(\mathbf{z})$ is positive definite, and hence the system is stable if the real part of each eigenvalue is negative. On the other hand, if the real part of *any* of the eigenvalues is positive, then $V(\mathbf{z})$ is indefinite or negative definite, and the system is unstable. Therefore we have the following results for a system with distinct eigenvalues:

1. The system is asymptotically stable if all the eigenvalues or poles have negative real parts.
2. The system is unstable if *any* of the eigenvalues have positive real parts.

These results are identical to those obtained by the classical procedure.

In view of the above statements, one approach to the investigation of the stability of a linear system is to factor the characteristic polynomial to determine the eigenvalues of the system. This procedure becomes difficult or impossible in the case of high-order systems or if some of the coefficients of the characteristic polynomial are nonnumerical, as is often the situation in a design problem. One alternative to this approach is to use some method of determining the sign of the real part of the eigenvalues without actually factoring the characteristic polynomial, such as the familiar Routh-Hurwitz criterion. Although this method is simple and generally quite useful, we shall consider still another approach, which is based more directly on the stability theorems of the previous section and quadratic forms. This approach, like the Routh-Hurwitz approach, is completely algebraic and does not require factoring of the characteristic polynomial. In addition, it can also be used to determine a measure of the performance of the system, as is shown later.

In order to illustrate this approach, consider the general quadratic V function

$$V(\mathbf{x}) = \mathbf{x}^T\mathbf{R}\mathbf{x} \tag{5.5-5}$$

where $\mathbf{R}$ is any positive-definite matrix. The time derivative of $V(\mathbf{x})$ is

$$\dot{V}(\mathbf{x}) = \dot{\mathbf{x}}^T\mathbf{R}\mathbf{x} + \mathbf{x}^T\mathbf{R}\dot{\mathbf{x}} \tag{5.5-6}$$

If the system equation $(\mathbf{A})$ is used to replace $\dot{\mathbf{x}}$, then Eq. (5.5-6) becomes

$$\dot{V}(\mathbf{x}) = \mathbf{x}^T(\mathbf{A}^T\mathbf{R} + \mathbf{R}\mathbf{A})\mathbf{x} = -\mathbf{x}^T\mathbf{Q}\mathbf{x} \tag{5.5-7}$$

where $\mathbf{Q}$ is obviously given by

$$\mathbf{Q} = -(\mathbf{A}^T\mathbf{R} + \mathbf{R}\mathbf{A}) \tag{5.5-8}$$

If we choose an arbitrary positive definite $\mathbf{R}$ matrix for $V(\mathbf{x})$, then the $\mathbf{Q}$ and hence $\dot{V}(\mathbf{x})$ as determined by Eqs. (5.5-7) and (5.5-8) are, in general, indefinite. In this case, no information can be obtained concerning the stability of the system.

If, on the other hand, we select an arbitrary positive definite or semidefinite matrix for $\mathbf{Q}$ and solve the matrix equation (5.5-8) to determine $\mathbf{R}$, then positive definiteness of $\mathbf{R}$ is both necessary and sufficient for the asymptotic stability of the system $(\mathbf{A})$. It can be shown (Bellman, 1959) that the matrix equation (5.5-8) has a unique solution whenever

$$\text{Re } \lambda_i + \text{Re } \lambda_j \neq 0 \qquad \text{for all } i, j$$

It should be noted that since the matrix $\mathbf{R}$ is symmetric, there are only $n(n + 1)/2$ independent equations rather than n^2.

The sufficiency of the result is obvious, since $V(\mathbf{x})$ and $\dot{V}(\mathbf{x})$ then satisfy the stability theorem, and asymptotic stability can be concluded. In order to show that the result is also necessary, suppose that a system is asymptotically stable and $\mathbf{R}$ is not positive definite. This would be a contradiction, since in that case $V(\mathbf{x})$ and $\dot{V}(\mathbf{x})$ would satisfy the Cetaev instability theorem, and instability of the system could be concluded.

Therefore the conditions for the positive definiteness of **R** form necessary and sufficient conditions for the asymptotic stability of the system (**A**). These conditions must obviously be equivalent to the Routh-Hurwitz condition. The procedure to be followed is then:

1. Choose an arbitrary symmetric positive definite or semidefinite matrix for **Q**.
2. Solve the matrix equation (5.5-8) for the $n(n + 1)/2$ elements of the matrix **R**.
3. Use Sylvester's theorem to determine the conditions necessary for **R** to be positive definite. These conditions are equivalent to the Routh-Hurwitz conditions.

The arbitrariness of the **Q** matrix cannot be overemphasized; no matter what positive definite or semidefinite **Q** matrix we choose, the resulting conditions are equivalent to the Routh-Hurwitz criterion. In addition, not only does this procedure yield results equivalent to the Routh-Hurwitz criterion, but it can, in fact, be used to derive this criterion.

Example 5.5.1   As an illustration of this procedure, consider the determination of the conditions for the asymptotic stability of the third-order system

$$\dddot{x}(t) + a\ddot{x}(t) + b\dot{x}(t) + cx(t) = 0 \tag{5.5-9}$$

Since we have no physical information about the system, let us use phase variables to write the system as three first-order equations of the form

$$\dot{x} = Ax$$

where

$$A = \begin{bmatrix} 0 & 1 & 0 \\ 0 & 0 & 1 \\ -c & -b & -a \end{bmatrix}$$

Now if **Q** is chosen as

$$Q = \begin{bmatrix} 0 & 0 & 0 \\ 0 & 2 & 0 \\ 0 & 0 & 0 \end{bmatrix}$$

then Eq. (5.5-8) yields the following six equations for the six unknown elements of **R**.

$$-2cr_{13} = 0$$
$$r_{11} - br_{13} - cr_{23} = 0$$
$$r_{12} - ar_{13} - cr_{33} = 0$$
$$2(r_{12} - br_{23}) = -2$$
$$r_{22} - ar_{23} + r_{13} - br_{33} = 0$$
$$2(r_{23} - ar_{33}) = 0$$

Solving these equations, we find **R** to be

$$\mathbf{R} = \frac{1}{ab - c} \begin{bmatrix} ac & c & 0 \\ c & a^2 + b & a \\ 0 & a & 1 \end{bmatrix}$$

If Sylvester's theorem is applied to this matrix, the three following conditions must be satisfied if **R** is to be positive definite:

1. $\dfrac{ac}{ab - c} > 0$

2. $\dfrac{ac(a^2 + b) - c^2}{(ab - c)^2} = \dfrac{c[a^3 + (ab - c)]}{(ab - c)^2} > 0$

3. $\dfrac{ac(a^2 + b) - c^2 - a^3c}{(ab - c)^3} = \dfrac{c(ab - c)}{(ab - c)^3} > 0$

From condition 3 it is obvious that c must be positive. Using this condition in condition 1, we see that either both $ab - c$ and a are positive or both are negative. However, only the first situation satisfies condition 2, and hence the conditions for asymptotic stability of the system are

$$a, c > 0 \quad \text{and} \quad ab - c > 0$$

which is the well-known result obtained by means of the Routh-Hurwitz criterion.

In order to illustrate the arbitrariness of **Q**, consider

$$\mathbf{Q} = \begin{bmatrix} 0 & 0 & 0 \\ 0 & 0 & 0 \\ 0 & 0 & 2 \end{bmatrix}$$

in which case the **R** matrix is given by

$$\mathbf{R} = \frac{1}{ab - c} \begin{bmatrix} c^2 & bc & 0 \\ bc & ac + b^2 & c \\ 0 & c & b \end{bmatrix}$$

The conditions for **R** to be positive definite are then

1. $\dfrac{c^2}{ab - c} > 0$

2. $\dfrac{c^2(ac + b^2) - b^2c^2}{(ab - c)^2} = \dfrac{ac^3}{(ab - c)^2} > 0$

3. $\dfrac{c^2(ac + b^2)b - c^4 - b^3c^2}{(ab - c)^3} = \dfrac{c^3(ab - c)}{(ab - c)^3} > 0$

which can be easily shown to be equivalent to

$$a, c > 0 \qquad \text{and} \qquad ab - c > 0$$

While it may appear that the Routh-Hurwitz approach is considerably more direct, it must be remembered that the Routh-Hurwitz criterion can be applied only to a single nth-order equation or equivalently to the characteristic polynomial of a system. Therefore in the general case of a system described by n first-order equations, before applying the Routh-Hurwitz criterion it is necessary to find the characteristic polynomial of the system or, equivalently, to put the system into phase variables. Neither one of these tasks is simple if the system is of high order and the **A** matrix has many nonzero elements. The procedure discussed above, on the other hand, does not require either of these manipulations, and stability can therefore be studied directly in terms of physical variables.

Example 5.5-2 Consider, for example, the system shown in Fig. 5.5-1, where the state variables have been chosen as real physical variables, as indicated. The **A** matrix for this system, determined by inspection from Fig. 5.5-1, is

$$\mathbf{A} = \begin{bmatrix} 0 & K & 0 \\ 0 & -2 & 1 \\ -1 & -1 & -1 \end{bmatrix}$$

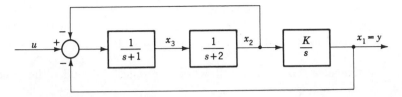

Fig. 5.5-1   Example of a physical system.

Let the **Q** matrix be given by

$$\mathbf{Q} = \begin{bmatrix} 2 & 0 & 0 \\ 0 & 0 & 0 \\ 0 & 0 & 0 \end{bmatrix}$$

Any other positive definite or semidefinite **Q** will also work.   Then by the use of Eq. (5.5-8) we find

$$\mathbf{R} = \frac{1}{9-K} \begin{bmatrix} \dfrac{6K+27}{K} & 9+2K & 9-K \\ 9+2K & K(K+3) & 3K \\ 9-K & 3K & 3K \end{bmatrix}$$

In order for **R** to be positive definite, it is necessary and sufficient that

$$0 < K < 9$$

Hence the system is asymptotically stable for these same conditions.

   While this system is not difficult to study by the use of the Routh-Hurwitz criterion, it does nonetheless illustrate the fact that the second method can be applied directly in terms of real physical variables.

   So far we have not taken advantage of the generality allowed by the arbitrariness of the **Q** matrix.   As we shall see in Chap. 7, the **Q** matrix can be related to the performance of the system, and therefore this generality permits us to use the second method as a design tool in conjunction with the state function of Pontryagin.   Hence, not only does the second method provide information concerning the stability of the system, but in addition it serves as a link between the stability problem and the design problem.

As a brief introduction to the use of the above approach to investigate the performance of systems, the next section discusses how this approach can be used to estimate the transient behavior of a system.

Exercise 5.5   *5.5-1.*   Rework Example 5.5-1 under the assumption that **Q** is

$$\mathbf{Q} = \begin{bmatrix} 2 & 0 & 0 \\ 0 & 0 & 0 \\ 0 & 0 & 0 \end{bmatrix}$$

and show that the resulting **R** is

$$\mathbf{R} = \frac{1}{c(ab - c)} \begin{bmatrix} ab^2 - bc + a^2c & a^2c & ab - c \\ a^2b & a^3 + c & a^2 \\ ab - c & a^2 & a \end{bmatrix}$$

Show that **R** is positive definite for a, c, and $ab - c > 0$ by letting $z_1 = x_3$, $z_2 = x_2$, $z_3 = x_1$ and using Sylvester's theorem.   Often this is a convenient trick.

5.6   Estimation of transient behavior

One of the first uses of the state function of Liapunov, outside the realm of stability, was in the estimation of transient behavior (Kalman and Bertram, 1960; Letov, 1961).   In particular, it was used to obtain an approximation of the settling time.   A method for designing a class of suboptimal control systems has been presented which is based on the concept of making the speed of response as fast as possible by making this approximation of settling time as small as possible (Johnson, 1963).   Our interest at present is directed toward the analysis problem; i.e., given a system, obtain an estimate of its transient behavior.

Let us suppose that for some system

$$\dot{\mathbf{x}} = \mathbf{A}\mathbf{x} \qquad \qquad (\mathrm{A})$$

it is possible to find a positive definite scalar function $V(\mathbf{x})$ whose total time derivative $\dot{V}(\mathbf{x})$ is negative definite.   Then by the use of the second method, it is possible to conclude asymptotic stability of the system.   However, although one knows that the motion of the system tends toward the origin following any perturbation, the rate at which the origin is approached is not known.

In order to obtain an estimate of the rate at which the system approaches the origin, let us define T by the expression

$$T = \max_{\mathbf{x}} \frac{V(\mathbf{x})}{-\dot{V}(\mathbf{x})} \tag{5.6-1}$$

That is, T is the maximum value of the ratio of $V(\mathbf{x})$ to the negative of $\dot{V}(\mathbf{x})$ evaluated at all points in the state space. By the definition (5.6-1) of T we immediately see that

$$\dot{V}(\mathbf{x}) \leq -\frac{1}{T} V(\mathbf{x}) \tag{5.6-2}$$

If we divide both sides of this equation by $V(\mathbf{x})$ and then integrate with respect to time from $t = 0$ to $t = t_s$, we obtain

$$\ln \frac{V[\mathbf{x}(t_s)]}{V[\mathbf{x}(0)]} \leq -\frac{t_s}{T} \tag{5.6-3}$$

or

$$V[\mathbf{x}(t_s)] \leq V[\mathbf{x}(0)]e^{-t_s/T} \tag{5.6-4}$$

Thus, given the value of $V(\mathbf{x})$ at $t = 0$, an upper bound on the value of $V[\mathbf{x}(t_s)]$ at any time $t_s > 0$ can be obtained by the use of Eq. (5.6-4). In other words, from the initial state $\mathbf{x}^0$, the state of the system must be found within or on the surface $V(\mathbf{x}) = V(\mathbf{x}^0)e^{-t_s/T}$ after t_s sec. The time t_s is referred to as the *settling time*.

Consider once again a $\dot{V}(\mathbf{x})$ defined by a quadratic form

$$\dot{V}(\mathbf{x}) = -\mathbf{x}^T\mathbf{Q}\mathbf{x}$$

where $\mathbf{Q}$ is a positive *definite* matrix. Then $V(\mathbf{x})$ is also a quadratic form

$$V(\mathbf{x}) = \mathbf{x}^T\mathbf{R}\mathbf{x}$$

where $\mathbf{R}$ is the positive definite matrix which is the solution of Eq. (5.5-8). For this case, then, T becomes

$$T = \max_{\mathbf{x}} \left[\frac{\mathbf{x}^T\mathbf{R}\mathbf{x}}{\mathbf{x}^T\mathbf{Q}\mathbf{x}} \right] \tag{5.6-5}$$

This division is allowable since $\mathbf{Q}$ is definite, so that the denominator of Eq. (5.6-5) is never zero, except when the numerator is also zero, i.e., at $\mathbf{x} = 0$.   Since the relative shape and size of both $V(\mathbf{x})$ and $\dot{V}(\mathbf{x})$ remain the same through the whole space, it is convenient to consider the ratio in Eq. (5.6-5) along one surface of constant $dV(\mathbf{x})/dt$.   The most convenient surface of $\dot{V}(\mathbf{x})$ is

$$\dot{V}(\mathbf{x}) = \mathbf{x}^T\mathbf{Q}\mathbf{x} = 1$$

This is equivalent to defining T as

$$T = \max_{\mathbf{x}} \, [\mathbf{x}^T\mathbf{R}\mathbf{x}]$$

with the constraint that

$$\mathbf{x}^T\mathbf{Q}\mathbf{x} = 1$$

If we introduce the constraint by the standard Lagrange multiplier approach, then

$$T = \max_{\mathbf{x}} \, [\mathbf{x}^T\mathbf{R}\mathbf{x} - \gamma\mathbf{x}^T\mathbf{Q}\mathbf{x}]$$

where γ is chosen so that

$$\mathbf{x}^T\mathbf{Q}\mathbf{x} = 1$$

Then maximizing $\mathbf{x}^T(\mathbf{R} - \gamma\mathbf{Q})\mathbf{x}$ with respect to $\mathbf{x}$ gives

$$(\mathbf{R} - \gamma\mathbf{Q})\mathbf{x} = 0 \tag{5.6-6}$$

since both $\mathbf{R}$ and $\mathbf{Q}$ are symmetric, or

$$\mathbf{R}\mathbf{x} = \gamma\mathbf{Q}\mathbf{x}$$

Multiplying both sides by $\mathbf{x}^T$, we have

$$\mathbf{x}^T\mathbf{R}\mathbf{x} = \gamma\mathbf{x}^T\mathbf{Q}\mathbf{x} = \gamma$$

Therefore $\mathbf{x}^T\mathbf{R}\mathbf{x}$ is maximum if γ is maximum.   From Eq. (5.6-6), however, we see γ is an eigenvalue of $\mathbf{Q}^{-1}\mathbf{R}$.   Hence

$$T = \text{maximum eigenvalue of } [\mathbf{Q}^{-1}\mathbf{R}] \tag{5.6-7}$$

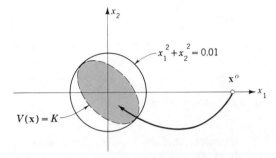

Fig. 5.6-1   Estimation of settling time.

Example 5.6-1   As an illustration of how this procedure can be used to estimate settling time, consider the following system,

$$\dot{\mathbf{x}} = \begin{bmatrix} 0 & 1 \\ -2 & -3 \end{bmatrix} \mathbf{x}$$

It is desired to find an upper bound on the time that it takes the system to get from the initial condition $\mathbf{x}^0 = \text{col}\,(1,0)$ to within the area defined by $x_1^2 + x_2^2 = 0.01$.

In this case it is necessary to find the largest value of K such that the surface $V(\mathbf{x}) = K$ lies entirely within, or at most tangent to, the surface $x_1^2 + x_2^2 = 0.01$, as in Fig. 5.6-1.   Of course $V(\mathbf{x})$ depends on what value is chosen for $\dot{V}(\mathbf{x})$.   Let $\mathbf{Q}$ be chosen to be

$$\mathbf{Q} = \begin{bmatrix} 4 & 0 \\ 0 & 4 \end{bmatrix}$$

It should be noted that the choice of $\mathbf{Q}$ is completely arbitrary as long as it is positive definite.   By the use of Eq. (5.5-8), $\mathbf{R}$ is found to be

$$\mathbf{R} = \begin{bmatrix} 5 & 1 \\ 1 & 1 \end{bmatrix}$$

and therefore $V(\mathbf{x})$ is known.   The value of $V(\mathbf{x}) = K$ that just fits within the area defined by $x_1^2 + x_2^2 = 0.01$ is $K = 7.64 \times 10^{-3}$.

By the use of Eq. (5.6-3) the settling time t_s is

$$t_s \leq -T \left[\ln \frac{K}{V(\mathbf{x}^0)} \right] \tag{5.6-8}$$

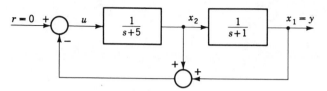

Fig. 5.6-2 Exercise 5.6-1.

However, before this can be computed, it is necessary to find T. Both $\mathbf{Q}$ and $\mathbf{R}$ are known, so T may be calculated from Eq. (5.6-7). T is given by

$$T = \text{maximum eigenvalue of} \begin{bmatrix} \frac{5}{4} & \frac{1}{4} \\ \frac{1}{4} & \frac{1}{4} \end{bmatrix} = 1.31$$

Substitution of the values of T and $V[\mathbf{x}(t_s)] = K$ into Eq. (5.6-8) yields the settling time as

$$t_s \leq -1.31 \ln \frac{7.64 \times 10^{-3}}{5} = 8.48 \text{ sec}$$

In solving Example 5.6-1 for the initial condition $\mathbf{x}^0 = \text{col}\,(1,0)$, we have actually solved many more problems.   For the given $\mathbf{Q}$, $\mathbf{R}$ was found, so that $V(\mathbf{x})$ was actually

$$V(\mathbf{x}) = 5x_1{}^2 + 2\,x_1 x_2 + x_2{}^2$$

For $\mathbf{x}^0 = \text{col}\,(1,0)$,

$$V(\mathbf{x}^0) = 5$$

Any trajectory that starts on or within the $V(\mathbf{x})$ surface $V(\mathbf{x}) = 5$ not only will be within the region defined by $x_1{}^2 + x_2{}^2 = 0.01$ within 8.48 sec but will be within the region bounded by $V(\mathbf{x}) = K = 7.64 \times 10^{-3}$ within that same time.   The significance of the choice of $\mathbf{Q}$ now becomes clear, as the choice of $\mathbf{Q}$ determines $\mathbf{R}$ and thus the shape of $V(\mathbf{x})$.

This procedure provides a simple and effective method for estimating the settling time of a linear system.   If the second method has been used to determine the stability of the system as discussed in the previous section, the labor involved is minimal as long as $\mathbf{Q}$ is chosen to be definite.

It must be emphasized that this approach can also be applied to nonlinear systems.   The computational labor involved, however, is con-

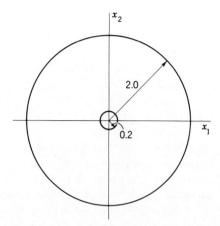

Fig. 5.6-3   Exercise 5.6-1.

siderably greater.   First, forcing $\dot{V}(\mathbf{x})$ to be definite is generally not easy, and, second, T must be computed numerically from the definition (5.6-1). This is but one more demonstration of the generality of the second-method approach.   In the next section we show how the second method may be used to study the stability of nonlinear systems.

Exercise 5.6   *5.6-1.*   Consider the feedback system of Fig. 5.6-2. It is desired to estimate the time required for $\|\mathbf{x}\|$ to decrease from 2 to 0.2, as indicated in Fig. 5.6-3.   This may be accomplished if $V(\mathbf{x})$ is made a measure of the norm, as $V(\mathbf{x}) = x_1{}^2 + x_2{}^2$.   Show that for this $V(\mathbf{x})$, $\mathbf{Q}$ is

$$\mathbf{Q} = \begin{bmatrix} 2 & 0 \\ 0 & 12 \end{bmatrix}$$

and that the settling time is 2.3 sec.

5.7   *Application to nonlinear systems*

In several sections of this chapter the fact that the second-method approach is no more difficult to apply in the case of linear systems than classical procedures has been mentioned.   It can, however, be directly extended to nonlinear and sampled-data systems.   As an illustration of this fact, we discuss the application of the second method to nonlinear systems in this section.   No attempt has been made to make this an exhaustive treatment.   The reader is referred to the references at the end of the chapter, particularly Schultz (1965).

In the case of nonlinear systems, the second method is perhaps the single most effective tool for studying stability. While classical methods may be used to derive results equivalent to the second method for linear systems, they are completely ineffective for nonlinear systems.

Since the stability of nonlinear systems is, in general, not global, one is concerned with finding the largest region surrounding the origin in which stability can be shown. Similarly, the quadratic form may not be the best V function, the one which yields the largest region of stability. One therefore undertakes a search for the best Liapunov function or, alternately, an iterative procedure for improving an initial guess. Although a great deal has been written concerning these problems, the detail and complexity are beyond the simple presentation here.

Our goal here is far less ambitious. We restrict our attention to the determination of a region of stability for the autonomous nonlinear equation $\dot{x} = f(x)$. The procedure is closely related to the approach discussed in Sec. 5.5, and only the use of quadratic V functions is considered. It is assumed that the equilibrium state of interest is located at the origin. This assumption may always be satisfied by a simple linear transformation of coordinates.

The first step in the procedure is to make a Taylor series expansion of the vector function $f(x)$ about the origin,

$$f(x) = f(0) + \sum_{i=1}^{n} \frac{\partial f}{\partial x_i}\bigg|_{x=0} x_i + \sum_{j=1}^{n}\sum_{i=1}^{n} \frac{\partial^2 f}{\partial x_i\,\partial x_j}\bigg|_{x=0} x_i x_j$$

$$+ \text{higher-order terms} \quad (5.7\text{-}1)$$

Since the origin is an equilibrium point, the constant term $f(0)$ is zero. As in Sec. 4.2, let us define

$$a_{ij} = \frac{\partial f_i}{\partial x_j}\bigg|_{x=0}$$

Then Eq. (5.7-1) may be written as

$$\dot{x} = Ax + g(x) \qquad\qquad (5.7\text{-}2)$$

where $g(x)$ contains only terms of second order or greater.

Let us next apply the procedure of Sec. 5.5 to the linear portion of the system (5.7-2),

$$\dot{x} = Ax$$

In particular, let us pick a positive *definite* matrix $\mathbf{Q}$, where

$$\dot{V}(\mathbf{x}) = -\mathbf{x}^T\mathbf{Q}\mathbf{x}$$

and then solve the matrix equation

$$\mathbf{A}^T\mathbf{R} + \mathbf{R}\mathbf{A} = -\mathbf{Q}$$

for the matrix $\mathbf{R}$, where

$$V(\mathbf{x}) = \mathbf{x}^T\mathbf{R}\mathbf{x}$$

This V function may be used to determine the stability of the linearized system. If the linearized system is asymptotically stable, a finite region of stability of the nonlinear system is assured. If the linearized system is only stable in the sense of Liapunov, the nonlinear terms determine the ultimate stability of the overall system. If the linearized system is unstable, there is no need to proceed further. Let us assume that the linearized system is asymptotically stable and we desire to estimate the region of asymptotic stability of the nonlinear system.

Since we have assumed asymptotic stability, $\mathbf{R}$ is definite, and the same V function may be used to determine the region of stability of the original nonlinear equation, so that

$$\dot{V}(\mathbf{x}) = -\mathbf{x}^T\mathbf{Q}\mathbf{x} + 2\mathbf{x}^T\mathbf{R}\mathbf{g}(\mathbf{x})$$

Since the last term, $2\mathbf{x}^T\mathbf{R}\mathbf{g}(\mathbf{x})$, can only contain terms of third order or higher, by making $\mathbf{x}$ small enough the first term, containing only second-order terms, predominates in the neighborhood of the origin. Since $\mathbf{Q}$ was selected to be positive *definite*, $\dot{V}(\mathbf{x})$ is negative for small enough $\mathbf{x}$, and the nonlinear system is therefore asymptotically stable.

In order to determine the region of asymptotic stability, it is only necessary to find the largest value of K such that the surface $V(\mathbf{x}) = K$ lies entirely within the region where $\dot{V}(\mathbf{x})$ is negative. In other words, find the value of K such that the surface $V(\mathbf{x}) = K$ is tangent to the surface $\dot{V}(\mathbf{x}) = 0$. The system has then been shown to be asymptotically stable in the region $V(\mathbf{x}) \leq K$.

The ability to find a specific region of asymptotic stability is to be contrasted to the classical approach of linearization, where one concludes stability in an undefined "sufficiently small" region. This feature emphasizes the fact that linearization is a completely inadequate approach for studying the stability of a nonlinear system, since the stability of a linear system is always global.

Example 5.7-1   In order to illustrate this procedure, let us consider the following nonlinear system,

$$\dot{x}_1 = -x_1 + 2x_2 \qquad \dot{x}_2 = -2x_1 - x_2 + x_2{}^2$$

If this system is put in the form of Eq. (5.7-2), then

$$\mathbf{A} = \begin{bmatrix} -1 & 2 \\ -2 & -1 \end{bmatrix} \quad \text{and} \quad \mathbf{g(x)} = \begin{bmatrix} 0 \\ x_2{}^2 \end{bmatrix}$$

For the linear portion of the system, let the $\mathbf{Q}$ matrix be

$$\mathbf{Q} = \begin{bmatrix} 2 & 0 \\ 0 & 2 \end{bmatrix}$$

Then $\mathbf{R}$ is found to be

$$\mathbf{R} = \begin{bmatrix} 1 & 0 \\ 0 & 1 \end{bmatrix}$$

Using $V(\mathbf{x}) = \mathbf{x}^T\mathbf{R}\mathbf{x}$, we find that $\dot{V}(\mathbf{x})$ for the nonlinear system is

$$\dot{V}(\mathbf{x}) = -2x_2{}^2(1 - x_2) - 2x_1{}^2$$

The surface $-2x_2{}^2(1 - x_2) - 2x_1{}^2 = 0$ is therefore the surface $\dot{V}(\mathbf{x}) = 0$, and we can easily see that $V(\mathbf{x}) = 1$ is the largest $V(\mathbf{x})$-equals-a-constant-surface which lies entirely in the region where $\dot{V}(\mathbf{x})$ is negative (see Fig. 5.7-1). The nonlinear system has been shown to be asymptotically stable in the region $V(\mathbf{x}) = x_1{}^2 + x_2{}^2 \leq 1$.

It must be emphasized that since the stability theorem is only a sufficient condition for stability, the region of stability determined by this procedure may be a conservative estimate of the actual region of stability. The size of the region of stability is dependent on the particular $\mathbf{Q}$ matrix chosen. In general, there is no procedure for determining the "best" $\mathbf{Q}$ matrix.

In some cases, however, this approach yields the exact region of stability. Consider, for example, the system

$$\dot{x}_1 = -x_1 + 2x_2 \qquad \dot{x}_2 = -2x_1 - x_2 - x_2{}^3$$

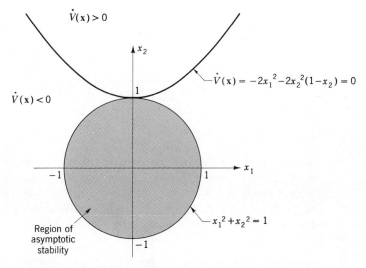

Fig. 5.7-1 Region of stability.

Since the linearized system is the same as above, let us choose **Q** and hence **R** to be the same as before. For the nonlinear system, $\dot{V}(\mathbf{x})$ is then

$$\dot{V}(\mathbf{x}) = -2x_2{}^2(1 + x_2{}^2) - 2x_1{}^2$$

Since $\dot{V}(\mathbf{x})$ is negative in the entire state space, the system is globally asymptotically stable, and hence no better estimate of the region of stability could possibly be obtained.

In this section, we have shown how the second method may be applied to nonlinear systems by a direct extension of the method presented in Sec. 5.5. While the use of a quadratic form for $V(\mathbf{x})$ is generally not the best choice for a nonlinear system, the approach does, however, provide a specific region of stability for nonlinear systems. The reader who is interested in a more complete discussion of the application of the second method to nonlinear systems is directed to the references at the end of this chapter.

Exercises 5.7 *5.7-1.* The second-order control system of Fig. 5.7-2 has a nonlinear gain term, as indicated. It is desired to find a region of initial conditions about the origin for which this control system is stable. In order to do this by the methods of this section, it is necessary to approximate the nonlinear element by a linear gain.

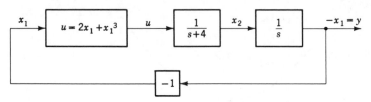

Fig. 5.7-2   Exercise 5.7-1.

One way of doing this is to find du/dx_1 and evaluate it at the origin, or at $x_1 = 0$.   This will give a good approximation at least in the neighborhood of the origin.   If this is done for the system of Fig. 5.7-2, the approximate gain is 2, and the governing equations for this approximate system are

$$\dot{x}_1 = -x_2 \qquad \dot{x}_2 = -4x_2 + 2x_1$$

Show that if $dV(\mathbf{x})/dt$ is constrained to be

$$\frac{dV(\mathbf{x})}{dt} = -4x_1{}^2 - 6x_2{}^2$$

the corresponding $V(\mathbf{x})$ is

$$V(\mathbf{x}) = 6x_1{}^2 - 2x_1x_2 + x_2{}^2$$

Using this $V(\mathbf{x})$ and the actual nonlinear equations, show that $dV(\mathbf{x})/dt$ remains negative for $|x_1| < 3.7$.   To find the region of allowable initial conditions, the curve $dV(\mathbf{x})/dt = 0$ must be plotted and the largest possible $V(\mathbf{x})$ curve must be fitted into the region of $dV(\mathbf{x})/dt$ negative.

5.7-2.   In the previous problem considerable effort is required to find the actual region of allowable initial conditions.   And there is no reason to suspect that this is the maximum region of allowable initial conditions, since the size of the region is indirectly based on the choice of an arbitrary $dV(\mathbf{x})/dt$.   The difficulty arises from the use of a quadratic V function.   If $V(\mathbf{x})$ is allowed to be

$$V(\mathbf{x}) = 4x_1{}^2 + x_1{}^4 + 2x_2{}^2$$

show that this $V(\mathbf{x})$ and the resulting $dV(\mathbf{x})/dt$ satisfy Theorem 5.4-2 and thus global asymptotic stability may be proved.

5.8 Summary and conclusion

In this chapter, the first of the two state functions of modern control, the state function of Liapunov, was introduced. Basically a generalization of total system energy $\mathfrak{I} + \mathfrak{V}$, the Liapunov state function and the second method of Liapunov provide a technique for studying the stability of systems. Although attention was directed mainly to continuous linear systems, the method can be directly applied to nonlinear and sampled-data systems. This should be contrasted with classical procedures, which require completely new concepts and procedures for these cases.

While a powerful tool for studying stability, the state function of Liapunov is even more useful as a design tool when combined with the state function of Pontryagin. As a brief preview of this fact, the Liapunov state function was employed for estimating transient behavior of systems. The use of the Liapunov state function in this design framework is shown in the following chapters. This chapter provides necessary background material for the subsequent work.

5.9 Problems

5.9-1. Use the second method to show that the following linear system is stable for all positive values of K.

$$\dot{\mathbf{x}} = \begin{bmatrix} 0 & 1 & 0 \\ 0 & -1 & 1 \\ -K & -1 - \dfrac{K}{2} & -\dfrac{K}{2} \end{bmatrix} \mathbf{x}$$

5.9-2. Use the second method to show that the following system is stable for all positive α and K.

$$\dot{\mathbf{x}} = \begin{bmatrix} 0 & 1 & 0 \\ 0 & -\alpha & 2 \\ -3K & -\dfrac{75K}{160} & 10 - \dfrac{33K}{80} \end{bmatrix} \mathbf{x}$$

5.9-3. Use the second method to find the Routh-Hurwitz conditions for the fourth-order system

$$\dot{\mathbf{x}} = \begin{bmatrix} 0 & 1 & 0 & 0 \\ 0 & 0 & 1 & 0 \\ 0 & 0 & 0 & 1 \\ -D & -C & -B & -A \end{bmatrix} \mathbf{x}$$

Use $\dot{V} = -(ABC - C^2 - AD)x_2^2$.

5.9-4. Use the method of Sec. 5.6 to estimate the time necessary for the system

$$\dot{\mathbf{x}} = \begin{bmatrix} 0 & 1 \\ -2 & -2 \end{bmatrix} \mathbf{x}$$

to reach the interior of the circle $x_1^2 + x_2^2 = 0.01$ from the initial condition $\mathbf{x}(0) = \text{col}\,(1,1)$. Let $\dot{V}(\mathbf{x}) = -(2x_1^2 + 2x_1x_2 + x_2^2)$.

5.9-5. Use the method of Sec. 5.7 to determine a region of stability for the nonlinear system

$$\dot{\mathbf{x}} = \begin{bmatrix} 0 & 1 \\ -2 & -3 \end{bmatrix} \mathbf{x} + \begin{bmatrix} 0 \\ -x_2^3 \end{bmatrix}$$

Let $\dot{V}(\mathbf{x}) = -(x_1^2 + x_2^2)$.

5.9-6. Show that the second-order nonlinear system

$$\dot{x}_1 = x_2$$
$$\dot{x}_2 = -a(x_1)x_1 - bx_2$$

is stable if

$$a(x_1) > 0 \qquad \text{and} \qquad b > 0$$

Let $V(\mathbf{x}) = 2\displaystyle\int_0^{x_1} a(\zeta)\zeta\,d\zeta + bx_2^2$.

References

Antosiewicz, H.: A Survey of Liapunov's Second Method, in S. Lefschetz (ed.), "Contributions to the Theory of Non-linear Oscillations," vol. 4, pp. 147–166, Princeton University Press, Princeton, N.J., 1958.

Bellman, R. E.: Kronecker Products and the Second Method of Lyapunov, *Math. Nachr.*, 1959.

Bower, J. L., and P. M. Schultheiss: "Introduction to the Design of Servomechanisms," John Wiley & Sons, Inc., New York, 1958.

Hahn, W.: "Theory and Application of Liapunov's Direct Method," Prentice-Hall, Inc., Englewood Cliffs, N.J., 1963.

Ingwerson, D. R.: "A Modified Liapunov Method for Non-linear Stability Problems," doctoral dissertation, Stanford University, Stanford, Calif., 1960.

Johnson, G. W.: "Design of Optimal Control Systems with Stability Constraints via the Direct Method of Liapunov," doctoral dissertation, University of Connecticut, Storrs, Conn., 1963.

Kalman, R. E., and J. E. Bertram: Control System Analysis and Design via the Second Method of Liapunov, Parts I and II, *Trans. ASME*, ser. D, vol. 82, pp. 371–400, 1960.

LaSalle, J. P.: Some Extensions of Liapunov's Second Method, *Res. Inst. Advan. Study Tech. Rept.* 60-5, 1960.

———— and S. Lefschetz: "Stability by Liapunov's Direct Method," Academic Press Inc., New York, 1961.

Letov, A. M.: "Stability in Nonlinear Control Systems," Princeton University Press, Princeton, N.J., 1961.

Schultz, D. G.: The Generation of Liapunov Functions, in C. T. Leondes (ed.), "Advances in Control Systems," vol. 2, Academic Press Inc., New York, 1965.

six   *optimal control and the state function of pontryagin*

6.1   *Introduction and outline of chapter*

As is true of almost all books on control, the material in this book can be divided into three broad categories: (1) problem formulation, (2) system analysis, and (3) system design or synthesis.   In Chaps. 2 and 3 the concepts of problem formulation in terms of state variables were presented by means of classical block diagrams and the more general Lagrange equations and the state function of Lagrange.   The techniques of system analysis were discussed in Chaps. 4 and 5 in terms of the STM and the state function and second method of Liapunov.

This chapter and the next three form the design

portion of the book. They are perhaps the most important chapters, since no control engineer can be content with simply formulating or analyzing a control problem. He must ultimately be concerned with the problem of designing systems.

In the classical approach to system design, one uses such frequency-domain techniques as root locus and Bode diagrams to determine systems with acceptable performance. In contrast, the modern approach is formulated almost exclusively in the time domain. In addition, the modern approach demands not only acceptable performance but optimal performance.

In order to talk of optimal performance it is obviously necessary to specify some method for determining the quality of the performance of a system. In the modern approach, this is most often done by means of an *integral performance index* of the following general form:

$$\text{PI} = \int_{t_i}^{t_f} L(\mathbf{x},\mathbf{u},t) \, dt$$

One then says that a system is optimal over the time interval t_i to t_f if the value of the performance index is minimum (maximum). While this is not the only type of performance index one may consider, it is adequate for our needs, and hence we restrict our attention to the integral performance index.

One of the basic problems of modern control theory is the translation of system specifications, often in such subjective terms as "good rise time with reasonable overshoot," into the form of a performance index. While the answer to this problem is still somewhat unclear, several approaches have been suggested. They are discussed in detail in the next chapters.

Unlike the previous chapters, where the results obtained for linear systems were identical to classical results and differed only in the techniques for obtaining them, this chapter and the three which follow present results which differ markedly from the classical results for linear systems. In particular, it is shown that in the optimal system all the state variables should be fed back, not only the output, as is the case with the classical unity-feedback forward-path compensation system. The importance of this result cannot be overemphasized.

This chapter makes use of the state function of Pontryagin to develop the minimum principle. In the next chapter the state functions of Liapunov and Pontryagin are combined to provide an alternate, and in some ways superior, approach to the optimal-control problem. Chapter 8 discusses the frequency-domain approach to system synthesis, and both exact and approximate techniques are presented for implementing the results of Chap. 7. Here both the root locus and Bode diagram are used, and the criterion for optimality is still the integral performance index. In Chap. 9 the use of the integral performance index is abandoned, and state-variable feedback is used to design control systems to a specified transfer function $y(s)/r(s)$.

Since so much of the modern optimal-control theory is based on the concepts and notation of variational calculus, this chapter begins with a brief discussion of the calculus of variations. No attempt is made to make this a complete treatment; only those features which have a direct bearing on the optimal-control problem are presented.

These classical results are then transformed into the modern optimal-control framework through the introduction of plant-equation constraints. This leads to a formulation of the minimum principle of Pontryagin and the definition of the second of the modern control-theory state functions, the H function of Pontryagin. Both the basic optimal-control problem and the general optimal-control problem are discussed from this point of view.

As an indication of the generality of the modern optimal-control theory, a short discussion of its application to some nonlinear and time-varying problems concludes the chapter.

6.2 *Calculus of variations*

In engineering problems one often encounters the problem of determining the maximum (minimum) values of a given function x. Obtaining the maximum height of a projectile is such a problem. An equally important, although not so well known, problem is that of finding the maxima (minima) of mathematical entities called functionals. By a functional one means a correspondence (or mapping) between the functions of a given class and the real numbers. In a gross sense, one might think of a functional as a "kind of" function whose independent variable is a function rather than a number (or set of numbers).

An example of a functional is the length V of a curve joining two given points on a plane (see Fig. 6.2-1). For any curve [function $x(t)$] the value of the functional V may be obtained in the following manner:

$$V(x) = \int_a^b \sqrt{1 + \dot{x}(t)^2}\, dt$$

Another important example is the integral performance index discussed in the previous section.

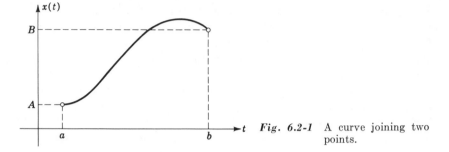

Fig. 6.2-1   A curve joining two points.

The calculus of variations is then concerned with obtaining the maximal (minimal) values of a functional along with the function(s) which maximize or minimize it.   In the above problem, for example, one would seek the equation of a curve joining the two given points for which the length functional V is minimum.

We begin this brief discussion of the elements of variational calculus pertaining to modern optimal-control theory by reviewing some basic mathematical concepts.

6.2-1   Basic concepts

Since the concepts and methods of variational calculus are very similar to those employed in ordinary maxima and minima theory of differential calculus, it is of value to review briefly the theory of ordinary maxima and minima so that the parallels may be easily drawn.   Let us start by defining precisely the concept of a function.

Definition 6.2-1   A numerical-valued function x assigns to each point t in its domain of definition a single real-valued number $x(t)$ called the value of x at t.

We use the variables x and t at this point for notational convenience since they eventually represent the system state and time, respectively. However, such an interpretation is not intended or desired at present. The reader should think of x and t simply as the dependent and independent variables with no further connotation.

One should be careful to distinguish between the function (rule of correspondence) x and the value of the function at a point $x(t)$.   Such a distinction is even more important in the case of functionals.   For simplicity, the following discussion is limited to minimization of a function x; the problem of maximization can be developed in a parallel fashion.

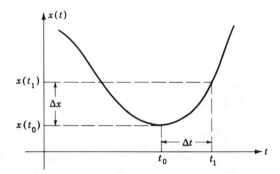

Fig. 6.2-2 Total increments Δx and Δt.

Definition 6.2-2 A function x has a local minimum at a point t_o if there is a neighborhood N of t_o such that $x(t) \geq x(t_o)$ for all $t \in N$.

If the neighborhood N can contain the whole domain of definition, the minimum is called absolute. Since the calculus of variations is normally concerned with relative (local) minimum, and since every absolute minimum is also a local minimum, we restrict our attention to local minimum. For developmental convenience, we assume that x and its derivatives of all orders are continuous at any minimum. This assumption eliminates the so-called "extraordinary minimum," which occur at points of discontinuity of either x or $\dot{x}$. It should be emphasized that all the following results can be derived by requiring only the existence of the first two derivatives of x.

Suppose that a function x achieves a local minimum at a point t_o. Then, by the above definition, a neighborhood N about t_o can be found such that $x(t) \geq x(t_o)$ for all $t \in N$. Now consider another point $t_1 \in N$, and define

$$\Delta t = t_1 - t_o \tag{6.2-1}$$

as the *total increment* in t. The corresponding *total increment* in x is given by (see Fig. 6.2-2)

$$\Delta x = x(t_1) - x(t_o) = x(t_o + \Delta t) - x(t_o)$$

Since t_o minimizes x, $\Delta x \geq 0$. If we expand $x(t_o + \Delta t)$ in a Taylor series about t_o, then Δx becomes

$$\Delta x = \left.\frac{dx}{dt}\right|_{t_o} \Delta t + \frac{1}{2!} \left.\frac{d^2x}{dt^2}\right|_{t_o} \Delta t^2 + \frac{1}{3!} \left.\frac{d^3x}{dt^3}\right|_{t_o} \Delta t^3 + \cdots$$

$$= \dot{x}(t_o)\, \Delta t + \frac{1}{2!}\, \ddot{x}(t_o)\, \Delta t^2 + \frac{1}{3!}\, \dddot{x}(t_o)\, \Delta t^3 + \cdots \tag{6.2-2}$$

where the $x(t_o)$ terms have canceled. $\dot{x}(t_o) \, \Delta t$, $\ddot{x}(t_o) \, \Delta t^2$, . . . are homogeneous polynomials in Δt of the first, second, and higher differentials of x, designated by dx, d^2x, ... (Normally dx is referred to simply as the differential of x.) This development should clarify the difference between the total increment Δx and the differential dx, which is the first-order approximation to Δx. This expansion of Δx also permits a simple proof of the following theorem from elementary calculus.

> **Theorem 6.2-1**   If a differentiable function x takes on a minimum at an internal point t_o, then $dx = 0$ at this point.

The theorem is proved by assuming that $dx \neq 0$ and by showing a contradiction. If $dx \neq 0$, then $\dot{x}(t_o) \neq 0$, and by making Δt small enough, i.e., choosing t_1 close enough to t_o, dx can be made to dominate the remaining terms of Δx, since they are of second order or higher in Δt. But then by making Δt positive or negative, Δx can be made to be both positive and negative, which is a contradiction of the assumption that x had a minimum at t_o. Therefore $dx = 0$ at t_o, and the theorem is proved.

Two points should be made with respect to Theorem 6.2-1. First, the theorem is a *necessary* condition for a *differentiable* function to have a minimum. However, a nondifferentiable function can have a minimum while dx is undefined. This situation also occurs in the case of functionals.

Second, since the theorem is necessary but not sufficient, dx may be zero at a point t_o, but x may not have a minimum there. If d^2x exists, we know from elementary calculus that a sufficient condition for a minimum is that $d^2x > 0$. This condition can be easily proved by means of the series expansion of Δx.

With this brief review of ordinary maxima and minima theory as background, let us proceed to the problem at hand, the minimization of functionals. The following basic concepts of variational calculus are presented in such a manner as to parallel as closely as possible the above presentation of the concepts of differential calculus. It is suggested that the reader make frequent comparison of these two developments in order to lend his understanding of differential calculus to the concepts of variational calculus. In line with this plan, we begin by defining the concept of a functional.

> **Definition 6.2-3**   A numerical-valued functional V assigns to each function x in its domain of definition a real-valued number $V(x)$ called the value of V for x.

Once again, for notational convenience, we use the symbols that are employed in the later optimal-control sections. Whereas, in the case of functions, the domain of definition has an intuitive meaning, e.g., an interval, the concept needs additional clarification in the case of functionals. Basically the domain of definition is a class of functions, e.g., all continuous functions or all continuously differentiable functions. For the present we assume that the domain of definition is the set of all functions possessing a second derivative.

For developmental convenience we assume that V is of the form

$$V(x) = \int_a^b L[x(t),\dot{x}(t),t]\, dt \qquad (6.2\text{-}3)$$

Following the format of the above presentation, we now define the minimum of a functional.

Definition 6.2-4 A functional V has a relative minimum for x_o if there is a neighborhood $\bar{N}$ of x_o such that $V(x) \geq V(x_o)$ for all $x \in \bar{N}$.

Since we are now dealing with function spaces rather than point spaces, it is necessary to generalize the concept of a neighborhood. One possibility is to define the neighborhood of a function x_o as all functions x (in the domain of definition) for which the absolute value of the difference $x - x_o$ is small for all values of t for which the functions are defined. Another possibility is to require not only that the difference $x - x_o$ be small but that the difference $\dot{x} - \dot{x}_o$ also be small. For our purposes, the second possibility is more convenient and meaningful, and hence we shall use it.

Suppose, now, that a functional V achieves a relative minimum for a function x_o. Then, by the above definition, a neighborhood $\bar{N}$ about x_o can be found such that $V(x) \geq V(x_o)$ for all $x \in \bar{N}$. Now consider another function $x_1 \in \bar{N}$ and define

$$\delta x = x_1 - x_o \qquad (6.2\text{-}4)$$

as the *variation* of x. The corresponding *total variation* in V is given by

$$\Delta V = V(x_1) - V(x_o) = V(x_o + \delta x) - V(x_o) \qquad (6.2\text{-}5)$$

Since x_o minimizes V, $\Delta V \geq 0$. If we expand $V(x_o + \delta x)$ in a Taylor series about x_o, then ΔV becomes

$$\Delta V = \frac{\partial V}{\partial x}\Big|_{x_o} \delta x + \frac{1}{2!}\frac{\partial^2 V}{\partial x^2}\Big|_{x_o} \delta x^2 + \frac{1}{3!}\frac{\partial^3 V}{\partial x^3}\Big|_{x_o} \delta x^3 + \cdots$$

where the $V(x_o)$ terms have been canceled. This result may be written in terms of the variations of V as

$$\Delta V = \delta V + \frac{1}{2!}\,\delta^2 V + \frac{1}{3!}\,\delta^3 V + \cdots \tag{6.2-6}$$

where

$$\delta V = \frac{\partial V}{\partial x}\bigg|_{x_o}\,\delta x$$

$$\delta^2 V = \frac{\partial^2 V}{\partial x^2}\bigg|_{x_o}\,\delta x^2$$

$$\cdots\cdots\cdots\cdots$$

Here δV, $\delta^2 V$, ... are integrals of homogeneous polynomials of the first, second, and higher order in δx. Just as $dx/dt\big|_{t_o}\,\Delta t = dx$ was called the differential of the function x, δV is called the *variation* or *first variation* of the function V. Also, $\delta^2 V$ is called the *second variation*, and $\delta^n V$ is the *nth variation* of V.

Once again we observe that δV is the first-order approximation to ΔV. In a manner entirely analogous to that presented above, we can prove the following theorem.

> **Theorem 6.2-2**   If the variation of a functional V exists, and if V takes on a minimum for x_o, then $\delta V = 0$ for x_o.

It must be emphasized that the vanishing of the variation of a functional is a *necessary* condition for a minimum. In other words, δV may be zero for x_o, even though x_o does not minimize V. Once again attention must be directed to the second variation in order to establish sufficient conditions. The condition $\delta V = 0$ is often referred to as the *fundamental necessary condition* of variational calculus. In the next subsection this result is applied to the simplest variational problem.

6.2-2   The fixed end-point problem and the Euler equation

Let us begin our study of concrete variational problems by obtaining the minimum of the functional

$$V(x) = \int_a^b L[x(t),\dot{x}(t),t]\,dt \tag{6.2-3}$$

defined on the set of continuously differential functions that satisfy the boundary conditions

$$x(a) = A \quad \text{and} \quad x(b) = B \tag{6.2-7}$$

The function L is assumed to have continuous first and second partial derivatives with respect to all its arguments.

The first step in the application of the fundamental necessary condition (Theorem 6.2-2) is to form the variation of the functional V. Let us assume that a minimum of V occurs for the function x. Next let x be subjected to an arbitrary variation δx, where, in order for the function

$$x_1 = x + \delta x$$

to satisfy the boundary conditions (6.2-7), it is necessary that

$$\delta x(a) = \delta x(b) = 0 \tag{6.2-8}$$

Then the corresponding total variation in the functional V is given by

$$
\begin{aligned}
\Delta V &= \int_a^b L(x + \delta x,\ \dot{x} + \delta \dot{x},\ t)\ dt - \int_a^b L(x,\dot{x},t)\ dt \\
&= \int_a^b [L(x + \delta x,\ \dot{x} + \delta \dot{x},\ t) - L(x,\dot{x},t)]\ dt
\end{aligned} \tag{6.2-9}
$$

When the integrand is expanded by means of Taylor's theorem about x and $\dot{x}$, ΔV becomes

$$
\begin{aligned}
\Delta V = \int_a^b &\left[\frac{\partial L(x,\dot{x},t)}{\partial x}\ \delta x + \frac{\partial L(x,\dot{x},t)}{\partial \dot{x}}\ \delta \dot{x} + \frac{1}{2!} \frac{\partial^2 L(x,\dot{x},t)}{\partial x^2}\ \delta x^2 \right. \\
&\left. + \frac{\partial^2 L(x,\dot{x},t)}{\partial x\ \partial \dot{x}}\ \delta x\ \delta \dot{x} + \frac{1}{2!} \frac{\partial^2 L(x,\dot{x},t)}{\partial \dot{x}^2}\ \delta \dot{x}^2 + \cdots \right] dt
\end{aligned} \tag{6.2-10}
$$

where the $L(x,\dot{x},t)$ terms have canceled.

The variation of V is found by taking the first-order terms in ΔV,

$$\delta V = \int_a^b \left[\frac{\partial L(x,\dot{x},t)}{\partial x}\ \delta x + \frac{\partial L(x,\dot{x},t)}{\partial \dot{x}}\ \delta \dot{x} \right] dt \tag{6.2-11}$$

Integrating the second term by parts, one obtains

$$\delta V = \int_a^b \left[\frac{\partial L(x,\dot{x},t)}{\partial x} - \frac{d}{dt} \frac{\partial L(x,\dot{x},t)}{\partial \dot{x}} \right] \delta x\ dt + \frac{\partial L(x,\dot{x},t)}{\partial \dot{x}}\ \delta x \,\bigg|_a^b$$

Since $\delta x(a) = \delta x(b) = 0$, δV becomes

$$\delta V = \int_a^b \left[\frac{\partial L(x,\dot{x},t)}{\partial x} - \frac{d}{dt} \frac{\partial L(x,\dot{x},t)}{\partial \dot{x}} \right] \delta x \, dt$$

When Theorem 6.2-2 is applied, a necessary condition for x to minimize V is

$$\delta V = \int_a^b \left[\frac{\partial L(x,\dot{x},t)}{\partial x} - \frac{d}{dt} \frac{\partial L(x,\dot{x},t)}{\partial \dot{x}} \right] \delta x \, dt = 0 \qquad (6.2\text{-}12)$$

This can be true for arbitrary variations in x only if

$$\frac{\partial L(x,\dot{x},t)}{\partial x} - \frac{d}{dt} \frac{\partial L(x,\dot{x},t)}{\partial \dot{x}} = 0 \qquad (6.2\text{-}13)$$

If Eq. (6.2-13) is not satisfied at some point t_o, then because of the continuity properties of L and x, it must be nonzero and definite with respect to sign in some neighborhood of t_o. Now choose δx so that it has a constant sign in the neighborhood and vanishes elsewhere. Then the integral in Eq. (6.2-12) must be nonzero, which is a contradiction of the fundamental necessary condition. Equation (6.2-13) is commonly referred to as the *Euler equation*, after Euler, who first obtained it in 1744. By this development, we have established the following theorem.

Theorem 6.2-3 If a continuously differentiable function x minimizes a functional V of the form

$$V(x) = \int_a^b L(x,\dot{x},t) \, dt \qquad (6.2\text{-}3)$$

where L has continuous first and second partial derivatives with respect to all its arguments, and if x satisfies the boundary conditions

$$x(a) = A \qquad \text{and} \qquad x(b) = B \qquad (6.2\text{-}7)$$

then x satisfies the Euler equation

$$\frac{\partial L(x,\dot{x},t)}{\partial x} - \frac{d}{dt} \frac{\partial L(x,\dot{x},t)}{\partial \dot{x}} = 0 \qquad (6.2\text{-}13)$$

The integral curves of the Euler equation are called *extremals*. It should be pointed out that we have proved Theorem 6.2-3 only for functions which have continuous second derivatives. However, by another method (see Bolza, 1960, pp. 22–26), it is possible to show that every solution of the problem with a continuous first derivative (not only those admitting a continuous second derivative) must satisfy the Euler equation.

Since Euler's equation is second order, its solution, in general, contains two arbitrary constants. These constants are determined by means of the boundary conditions $x(a) = A$ and $x(b) = B$. It must be emphasized that the Euler equation is a *necessary* condition for an extremum but is, in general, not sufficient. However, in many problems, the existence of an extremum is obvious from physical or geometric considerations. In these cases, if there is only one extremal satisfying the boundary conditions, then it must be the correct solution of the variational problem. In a sense one might say that the solutions of the Euler equation are simply candidates for minimizing functions.

Example 6.2-1 As an illustration of the use of the Euler equation to solve a variational problem, let us consider a problem for which the solution is well known, namely, the minimization of the length of a curve joining two points (a,A) and (b,B) on a plane. The functional, as mentioned in the introduction of this section, is

$$V(x) = \int_a^b \sqrt{1 + \dot{x}(t)^2}\, dt$$

with the boundary conditions $x(a) = A$ and $x(b) = B$. Since $L(x,\dot{x},t)$ does not contain x, $\partial L(x,\dot{x},t)/\partial x = 0$, and the Euler equation reduces to

$$\frac{d}{dt} \frac{\partial L(x,\dot{x},t)}{\partial \dot{x}} = 0$$

or

$$\frac{\partial L(x,\dot{x},t)}{\partial \dot{x}} = \text{const}$$

The Euler equation has therefore been reduced to a first-order equation. This reduction is possible in any case where L does not contain x. For the present problem the Euler equation is then

$$\frac{\partial L(x,\dot{x},t)}{\partial \dot{x}} = \frac{\dot{x}}{\sqrt{1 + \dot{x}^2}} = \text{const}$$

from which it can be seen that

$$\dot{x} = K_1 = \text{const}$$

and therefore $x(t) = K_1 t + K_2$. The extremals are straight lines, as we expect. By an application of the boundary conditions it is possible to determine the values of K_1 and K_2.

We consider next the generalization of Theorem 6.2-3 to the case of n unknown functions, $\mathbf{x} = \text{col}(x_1, x_2, \ldots, x_n)$. For this case Theorem 6.2-3 becomes:

Theorem 6.2-4   If a set of continuously differentiable functions $\mathbf{x}$ minimizes a functional V of the form

$$V(\mathbf{x}) = \int_a^b L(\mathbf{x}, \dot{\mathbf{x}}, t)\, dt \tag{6.2-14}$$

where L has continuous first and second partial derivatives with respect to all its arguments, and if $\mathbf{x}$ satisfies the boundary conditions

$$\mathbf{x}(a) = \mathbf{k}_1 \qquad \text{and} \qquad \mathbf{x}(b) = \mathbf{k}_2 \tag{6.2-15}$$

then $\mathbf{x}$ satisfies the Euler equations

$$\frac{\partial L(\mathbf{x}, \dot{\mathbf{x}}, t)}{\partial x_i} - \frac{d}{dt}\frac{\partial L(\mathbf{x}, \dot{\mathbf{x}}, t)}{\partial \dot{x}_i} = 0 \qquad i = 1, 2, \ldots, n \tag{6.2-16}$$

By varying one of the functions while keeping the others constant, this theorem can be proved exactly as Theorem 6.2-3 was, and so the proof is not repeated here.

In order to illustrate the application of this theorem, let us consider the following example.

Example 6.2-2   Find the extremals of the functional

$$V(x) = \int_0^{\pi/2} (\dot{x}_1{}^2 + \dot{x}_2{}^2 + 2x_1 x_2)\, dt$$

subject to the boundary conditions

$$x_1(0) = 0 \qquad x_1\left(\frac{\pi}{2}\right) = 1 \qquad x_2(0) = 0 \qquad x_2\left(\frac{\pi}{2}\right) = -1$$

For this problem, the Euler equations are

$$\ddot{x}_1 - x_2 = 0 \qquad \ddot{x}_2 - x_1 = 0$$

Combining these two equations to eliminate x_2, one obtains

$$x_1^{(iv)} - x_1 = 0$$

This is a linear differential equation with constant coefficients for which the solution is

$$x_1(t) = C_1 c^t + C_2 e^{-t} + C_3 \sin t + C_4 \cos t$$

Then

$$x_2(t) = \ddot{x}_1(t) = C_1 e^t + C_2 e^{-t} - C_3 \sin t - C_4 \cos t$$

From the boundary conditions, we find that

$$C_1 = 0 \qquad C_2 = 0 \qquad C_3 = 1 \qquad \text{and} \qquad C_4 = 0$$

and the solution is therefore

$$x_1(t) = \sin t \qquad x_2(t) = -\sin t$$

Before leaving this section it is well to comment on the relationship between the general Euler equation (6.2-16) and Lagrange's equations from Chap. 3. In Eq. (6.2-16) if the integrand of the performance index $L(\mathbf{x},\dot{\mathbf{x}},t)$ is replaced by the lagrangian $\mathcal{L}(\mathbf{q},\dot{\mathbf{q}},t)$, then Eq. (6.2-16) is indeed Lagrange's equations. In fact, the standard way of proving Lagrange's equations in classical mechanics is to start with Hamilton's principle and use the calculus of variations. Hamilton's principle states that the path of motion of a system from the point $\mathbf{q}(t_1)$ to the point $\mathbf{q}(t_2)$ is such that the following integral involving the lagrangian is minimized:

$$I(\mathbf{q}) = \int_{t_1}^{t_2} \mathcal{L}(\mathbf{q},\dot{\mathbf{q}},t) \, dt$$

Of course this integral is of exactly the same form as that of the performance index, so that the net result of the minimization is that particular set of Euler equations in which $L(\mathbf{x},\dot{\mathbf{x}},t)$ is actually $\mathcal{L}(\mathbf{q},\dot{\mathbf{q}},t)$. For this reason the Euler equations are sometimes referred to as the Euler-Lagrange equations.

6.2-3   Variable-end-point problem

With the fixed-end-point problem as background, we consider next the case where the end points are variable.   Once again, for simplicity, we begin by treating a functional involving only one unknown function

$$V(x) = \int_{t_o}^{t_1} L(x,\dot{x},t)\, dt \tag{6.2-17}$$

If a function x is to minimize V for a problem with variable end points, it must obviously minimize V for the more restricted case of fixed end points.   Hence x must satisfy the necessary condition for an extremum for a problem of fixed end points: the Euler equation.   Consequently, the function x that gives an extremum for the variable-end-point problem must be an extremal.

Since the Euler equation is second order, its solutions involve two arbitrary constants.   In order to determine these constants, two additional conditions are necessary.   In the fixed-end-point problem, the boundary conditions

$$x(t_o) = x_o \qquad \text{and} \qquad x(t_1) = x_1$$

are used.   In the case of variable end points some other conditions are needed to evaluate these arbitrary constants.

Since the solutions of a variable-end-point problem must be extremals, we restrict our attention to such functions.   For simplicity, we assume that the left end point (t_o,x_o) is fixed while the right end point varies from (t_1,x_1) to $(t_1 + \delta t_1,\, x_1 + \delta x_1)$ (see Fig. 6.2-3).   Two admissible functions, x and $x + h$, are considered close if not only the absolute values of h and $\dot{h}$ are small but also the absolute values of δt_1 and δx_1.   Since the functions x and $x + h$ are defined on different intervals I and I', it is necessary to extend x and $x + h$ onto the interval containing both I and I'.   This can be done most easily by drawing a tangent to one of the functions at the right end point, as in Fig. 6.2-3.

The total variation in V is then given by

$$\begin{aligned} \Delta V &= V(x + h) - V(x) \\ &= \int_{t_o}^{t_1 + \delta t_1} L(x + h,\, \dot{x} + \dot{h},\, t)\, dt - \int_{t_o}^{t_1} L(x,\dot{x},t)\, dt \end{aligned}$$

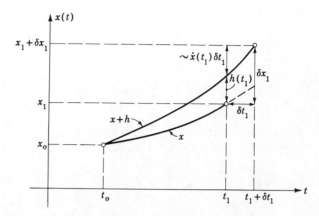

Fig. 6.2-3 Quantities associated with the variable-end-point problem.

which may be rewritten as

$$\Delta V = \int_{t_1}^{t_1 + \delta t_1} L(x + h, \dot{x} + \dot{h}, t) \, dt$$
$$+ \int_{t_0}^{t_1} [L(x + h, \dot{x} + \dot{h}, t) - L(x,\dot{x},t)] \, dt$$

Applying the mean-value theorem for integrals to the first integral, we obtain

$$\int_{t_1}^{t_1 + \delta t_1} L(x + h, \dot{x} + \dot{h}, t) \, dt \sim L(x,\dot{x},t) \Big|_{t_1} \delta t_1 \qquad (6.2\text{-}18)$$

where the symbol $\sim$ indicates equality except for terms of order higher than one in h, $\dot{h}$, δt_1, or δx_1.

Expanding the integrand of the second integral by means of a Taylor series, we obtain

$$\int_{t_0}^{t_1} [L(x + h, \dot{x} + \dot{h}, t) - L(x,\dot{x},t)] \, dt$$
$$\sim \int_{t_0}^{t_1} \left[\frac{\partial L(x,\dot{x},t)}{\partial x} h + \frac{\partial L(x,\dot{x},t)}{\partial \dot{x}} \dot{h} \right] dt$$

Then integrating the term involving $\dot{h}$ by parts gives

$$\int_{t_0}^{t_1} [L(x + h, \dot{x} + \dot{h}, t) - L(x,\dot{x},t)] \, dt$$
$$\sim \int_{t_0}^{t_1} \left[\frac{\partial L(x,\dot{x},t)}{\partial x} - \frac{d}{dt} \frac{\partial L(x,\dot{x},t)}{\partial \dot{x}} \right] h \, dt + \frac{\partial L(x,\dot{x},t)}{\partial \dot{x}} h \Big|_{t_0}^{t_1} \qquad (6.2\text{-}19)$$

Since x is assumed to be an extremal, the integral portion of Eq. (6.2-19) is identically zero.   Thus ΔV is found from the sum of Eqs. (6.2-18) and (6.2-19) to be

$$\Delta V \sim \frac{\partial L(x,\dot{x},t)}{\partial \dot{x}} \, h \Big|_{t_o}^{t_1} + L(x,\dot{x},t) \Big|_{t_1} \delta t_1$$

The left end point is fixed, and therefore $h(t_o) = 0$.   From Fig. 6.2-3 we see that except for terms of higher order than one

$$h(t_1) \sim \delta x_1 - \dot{x}(t_1) \, \delta t_1$$

Therefore the (first) variation of V is found by taking the first-order terms in ΔV, or

$$\delta V = \frac{\partial L(x,\dot{x},t)}{\partial \dot{x}} \Big|_{t_1} [\delta x_1 - \dot{x}(t_1) \, \delta t_1] + L(x,\dot{x},t) \Big|_{t_1} \delta t_1$$

Applying the fundamental necessary condition, $\delta V = 0$, we have

$$\frac{\partial L(x,\dot{x},t)}{\partial \dot{x}} \Big|_{t_1} \delta x_1 + \left[L(x,\dot{x},t) - \dot{x} \, \frac{\partial L(x,\dot{x},t)}{\partial \dot{x}} \right] \Big|_{t_1} \delta t_1 = 0 \qquad (6.2\text{-}20)$$

This result is often referred to as the *generalized boundary condition* at the right end point.   By a similar development, an identical result can be obtained for the left end point.

$$\frac{\partial L(x,\dot{x},t)}{\partial \dot{x}} \Big|_{t_o} \delta x_o + \left[L(x,\dot{x},t) - \dot{x} \, \frac{\partial L(x,\dot{x},t)}{\partial \dot{x}} \right] \Big|_{t_o} \delta t_o = 0 \qquad (6.2\text{-}21)$$

If the variations δt_1 and δx_1 are independent, as is the case with a completely free end point, then it is necessary that the terms multiplying δx_1 and δt_1 be individually zero, that is,

$$\frac{\partial L(x,\dot{x},t)}{\partial \dot{x}} \Big|_{t_1} = 0 \qquad (6.2\text{-}22)$$

and

$$L(x,\dot{x},t) - \dot{x} \, \frac{\partial L(x,\dot{x},t)}{\partial \dot{x}} \Big|_{t_1} = 0 \qquad (6.2\text{-}23)$$

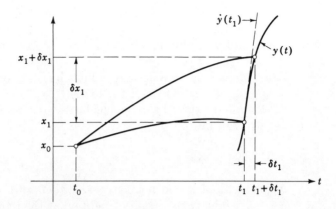

Fig. 6.2-4 The case when the right end point must lie on a curve $y(t)$.

If t_1 is fixed, i.e., the right end point must lie on a vertical line $t = t_1$, then $\delta t_1 = 0$, and Eq. (6.2-20) reduces to

$$\frac{\partial L(x,\dot{x},t)}{\partial \dot{x}}\bigg|_{t_1} = 0 \tag{6.2-24}$$

On the other hand, if the right end point must move along a horizontal line, then $\delta x_1 = 0$, and Eq. (6.2-20) becomes

$$\left[L(x,\dot{x},t) - \dot{x}\,\frac{\partial L(x,\dot{x},t)}{\partial \dot{x}}\right]\bigg|_{t_1} = 0 \tag{6.2-25}$$

In many cases, it is required that the variations of δx_1 and δt_1 be dependent. For example, it may be necessary that the right end point lie on some curve $y(t)$. Then

$$x(t)\,\bigg|_{t_1} = y(t)\,\bigg|_{t_1}$$

and $\delta x_1 \sim \dot{y}(t_1)\,\delta t_1$ (see Fig. 6.2-4). Equation (6.2-20) then reduces to

$$\left[L(x,\dot{x},t) + (\dot{y} - \dot{x})\,\frac{\partial L(x,\dot{x},t)}{\partial \dot{x}}\right]\bigg|_{t_1} = 0 \tag{6.2-26}$$

This condition establishes a relation between the derivatives of x and y which must be satisfied at the right end point. It is called the *transversality condition*. The transversality condition along with the relation

$x(t_1) = y(t_1)$ permits us to evaluate the remaining constant in the general solution of the Euler equation. In order to illustrate the application of this transversality condition, let us consider the following example.

> **Example 6.2-3** It is desired to find the curve of minimum length joining the point $(0,0)$ and the line $y(t) = 2 - t$. From Example 6.2-1 we know that the extremals for the minimum-length problem are straight lines
>
> $$x(t) = K_1 t + K_2$$
>
> Applying the left-end boundary condition, $x(0) = 0$, we find that $K_2 = 0$. The transversality condition at the right end is
>
> $$\left[\sqrt{1 + \dot{x}^2} + (\dot{y} - \dot{x})\,\frac{\dot{x}}{\sqrt{1 + \dot{x}^2}}\right]\Bigg|_{t_1} = 0$$
>
> Since $\dot{x}(t_1) = K_1$ and $\dot{y}(t_1) = -1$, we have
>
> $$\sqrt{1 + K_1^2} + (-1 - K_1)\,\frac{K_1}{\sqrt{1 + K_1^2}} = 0$$
>
> or, solving for K_1,
>
> $$K_1 = 1$$
>
> and the solution is given by
>
> $$x(t) = t$$

As we expect, the answer is a straight line perpendicular to the line $y(t) = 2 - t$. This is a special case of a class of functionals for which transversality is equivalent to orthogonality (see Exercise 6.2-3).

It should be noted that for this simple problem it was not necessary to make use of the relation $x(t_1) = y(t_1)$. This is not the general case; see, for example, Exercise 6.2-6.

The generalization of the above results to functionals which involve n unknown functions, $\mathbf{x} = \text{col}\,(x_1, x_2, \ldots, x_n)$, follows in a relatively direct manner. Once again the functions must first be extremals, i.e., solutions of the related set of Euler equations. In addition, they must satisfy the following generalized boundary conditions:

$$\sum_{i=1}^{n} \frac{\partial L(\mathbf{x},\dot{\mathbf{x}},t)}{\partial \dot{x}_i} \delta x_i \bigg|_{t_1} + \left[L(\mathbf{x},\dot{\mathbf{x}},t) - \sum_{i=1}^{n} \dot{x}_i \frac{\partial L(\mathbf{x},\dot{\mathbf{x}},t)}{\partial \dot{x}_i} \right]\bigg|_{t_1} \delta t_1 = 0$$

$$(6.2\text{-}27)$$

This may be written in matrix form by using the shorthand notation employed in Sec. 3.3,

$$\frac{\partial L}{\partial \dot{\mathbf{x}}} = \begin{bmatrix} \dfrac{\partial L}{\partial \dot{x}_1} \\[2mm] \dfrac{\partial L}{\partial \dot{x}_2} \\ \cdot \\ \cdot \\ \cdot \\ \dfrac{\partial L}{\partial \dot{x}_n} \end{bmatrix}$$

In terms of this notation, Eq. (6.2-27) becomes

$$\delta \mathbf{x}^T \frac{\partial L(\mathbf{x},\dot{\mathbf{x}},t)}{\partial \dot{\mathbf{x}}}\bigg|_{t_1} + \left[L(\mathbf{x},\dot{\mathbf{x}},t) - \dot{\mathbf{x}}^T \frac{\partial L(\mathbf{x},\dot{\mathbf{x}},t)}{\partial \dot{\mathbf{x}}} \right]\bigg|_{t_1} \delta t_1 = 0 \qquad (6.2\text{-}28)$$

Once again if the variations δt_1 and $\delta \mathbf{x}$ are not independent, as, for example, when the end points must lie on given surfaces, then appropriate transversality conditions can be derived.

We shall have considerable use for these generalized boundary conditions and the Euler equation in the following sections, dealing with the optimal-control problem.

Exercises 6.2   *6.2-1.* Repeat the development of the Euler equation for a functional of the form

$$V = \int_a^b L(x_1,\dot{x}_1,x_2,\dot{x}_2,t)\, dt$$

6.2-2.   Find the extremals for the functionals

(a) $\displaystyle\int_a^b \frac{\dot{x}^2}{t^3}\, dt$ (b) $\displaystyle\int_a^b (x^2 + \dot{x}^2 + 2xe^t)\, dt$

(c) $\displaystyle\int_a^b (2x_1x_2 - 2x_1{}^2 + \dot{x}_1{}^2 - \dot{x}_2{}^2)\, dt$

(d) $\displaystyle\int_a^b (\dot{x}_1{}^2 + \dot{x}_2{}^2 + x_1x_2)\, dt$

answers:

(a) $x(t) = c_1 t^4 + c_2$ (b) $x(t) = \frac{1}{2} t e^t + c_1 e^t + c_2 e^{-t}$

(c) $x_1(t) = (c_1 t + c_2) \cos t + (c_3 t + c_4) \sin t$
$x_2(t) = 2 x_1(t) + \ddot{x}_1(t)$

(d) $x_1(t) = c_1 \exp \dfrac{t}{\sqrt{2}} + c_2 \exp \left(-\dfrac{t}{\sqrt{2}} \right)$

$\qquad\qquad + c_3 \exp \dfrac{jt}{\sqrt{2}} + c_4 \exp \left(-\dfrac{jt}{\sqrt{2}} \right)$

6.2-3.   Prove that transversality reduces to orthogonality in the case of functionals of the form

$$V(x) = \int_{t_o}^{t_1} A(x,t) \sqrt{1 + \dot{x}^2}\, dt$$

6.2-4.   Show that if $L(x,\dot{x},t)$ is not an explicit function of t, then the Euler equation has the first integral

$$L(x,\dot{x},t) - \dot{x}\, \frac{\partial L(x,\dot{x},t)}{\partial \dot{x}} = \text{const}$$

6.2-5.   Find the functions for which the functional

$$V(x) = \int_0^{t_1} \frac{\sqrt{1 + \dot{x}^2}}{x}\, dt$$

can have a minimum subject to the boundary conditions

$$x(0) = 0 \qquad \text{and} \qquad x(t_1) = t_1 - 5$$

answer:

$$x(t) = \pm \sqrt{10t - t^2}$$

6.2-6.   Find the function for which the functional

$$V(x) = \int_0^{\pi/4} (x^2 - \dot{x}^2)\, dt$$

can have a minimum if $x(0) = 0$ and the right end point can vary along the line $t = \pi/4$.

answer:

$$x(t) = 0$$

6.3   The state function of Pontryagin

In this section the preceding variational results are used in conjunction with the state function of Pontryagin to solve the *basic optimal-control problem*. In the basic optimal-control problem it is assumed that the plant to be controlled is described by a set of differential equations of the form

$$\dot{\mathbf{x}} = \mathbf{f}(\mathbf{x},\mathbf{u},t) \tag{6.3-1}$$

The performance of this system is judged by means of an integral performance index of the form

$$\text{PI} = \int_{t_i}^{t_f} L(\mathbf{x},\mathbf{u},t)\ dt \tag{6.3-2}$$

Here the time interval of interest is designated as being from t_i to t_f, where t_i is the initial time and t_f the final time of the control period. The integrand of the performance index, $L(\mathbf{x},\mathbf{u},t)$, is assumed to be a positive definite function of $\mathbf{x}$, $\mathbf{u}$, and t. Since this integrand is always greater than zero, the value of the performance index is a monotonically increasing function of t in the interval $t_i \leq t \leq t_f$. The problem is then to find the *optimal control* $\mathbf{u}(t)$ or the *optimal-control law* $\mathbf{u} = \mathbf{k}[\mathbf{x}(t),t]$ which transfers the system (6.3-1) from some given initial condition or state at $\mathbf{x}^i = \mathbf{x}(t_i)$ to some terminal condition or final state $\mathbf{x}^f = \mathbf{x}(t_f)$ while minimizing the integral performance index, Eq. (6.3-2). The trajectory corresponding to the optimal control or the optimal-control law is called the *optimal trajectory*.

The distinction between the optimal control $\mathbf{u}(t)$ and the optimal-control law $\mathbf{u} = \mathbf{k}[\mathbf{x}(t),t]$ is an important one, especially from the practical point of view. If the control $\mathbf{u}$ is known only as a function of time, i.e., as an optimal control, then the utilization of such control implies an open-loop system, as in Fig. 6.3-1a. In practice we are usually interested in finding not only the optimal control but also the optimal-control law $\mathbf{u} = \mathbf{k}[\mathbf{x}(t),t]$, which enables one to generate $\mathbf{u}(t)$ from $\mathbf{x}(t)$ in a true feedback sense. This determination of $\mathbf{u}$ from an operation on the state variables $\mathbf{x}$ is indicated in Fig. 6.3-1b. In addition, the classical unity-feedback system is shown for comparison. Although it may appear that the modern and classical problems have nothing in common, either in the structure of the systems or in the mathematical formulation, they do have many similarities and relations, as is shown in this and the following chapter. They also, however, have many differences.

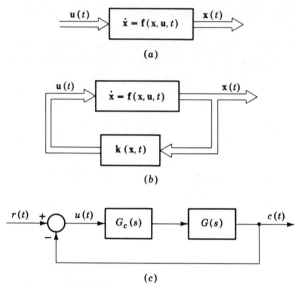

Fig. 6.3-1   (a) The open-loop optimal-control problem;
(b) the closed-loop optimal-control problem;
(c) classical unity-feedback system.

One of the principal differences is evident in the statement of the basic optimal-control problem.   The optimal control is applied in response to initial conditions rather than to an input.   This is quite different from the classical method of design in terms of step function or sinusoidal response, which assumes all initial conditions to be zero, so that the transfer-function concept can be used.

In this section, we apply the calculus-of-variations results obtained in the preceding section to the basic optimal-control problem.   If the statement of the basic optimal-control problem is compared with the statement of the fixed-end-point problem in Theorem 6.2-4, we note some similarities and some differences.   In particular, both problems involve the minimization of a functional, and in both problems the end points on $\mathbf{x}(t)$ are fixed.   There are two immediate differences: (1) the appearance of the control vector $\mathbf{u}(t)$; and (2) the addition of the plant equations (6.3-1).

The inclusion of the control vector could be easily handled by simply considering an $(n + r)$-dimensional vector

$$\mathbf{x}'(t) = \text{col } (x_1, x_2, \ldots, x_n, u_1, u_2, \ldots, u_r)$$

The development in Sec. 6.2-2 could then be applied directly.

However, the addition of the plant equations poses a completely different problem. These plant equations act as restrictions or constraints on the $\mathbf{x}(t)$ and $\mathbf{u}(t)$ vectors. Hence the elements of $\mathbf{x}'(t)$, namely, $\mathbf{x}(t)$ and $\mathbf{u}(t)$, cannot be varied independently, as demanded by the proof of Theorem 6.2-4. For example, if we know $\mathbf{u}(t)$ for $t_i \le t \le t_f$ and $\mathbf{x}(t_i)$, then $\mathbf{x}(t)$ for $t_i \le t \le t_f$ is uniquely determined. On the other hand, if $\mathbf{x}(t)$ and $\dot{\mathbf{x}}(t)$ are known for $t_i \le t \le t_f$, then $\mathbf{u}(t)$ is uniquely determined.

One solution to this problem is to solve Eq. (6.3-1) for $\mathbf{u}$ in terms of $\mathbf{x}$, $\dot{\mathbf{x}}$, and t, that is,

$$\mathbf{u}(t) = \mathbf{g}(\mathbf{x}, \dot{\mathbf{x}}, t) \qquad (6.3\text{-}3)$$

This result may then be substituted into the performance index (6.3-2) to eliminate $\mathbf{u}$ while at the same time obviously satisfying the plant equations. The performance index then becomes

$$\text{PI} = \int_{t_i}^{t_f} L[\mathbf{x}, \mathbf{g}(\mathbf{x}, \dot{\mathbf{x}}, t), t]\, dt = \int_{t_i}^{t_f} L'(\mathbf{x}, \dot{\mathbf{x}}, t)\, dt \qquad (6.3\text{-}4)$$

This problem is then identical to the problem of Sec. 6.2-2, and $\mathbf{x}(t)$ must therefore satisfy the Euler equations (6.2-16). Once $\mathbf{x}(t)$ is known, $\dot{\mathbf{x}}(t)$ may be found and $\mathbf{u}(t)$ computed from Eq. (6.3-3).

Example 6.3-1 In order to illustrate this procedure, let us consider the following simple linear first-order problem. The plant equations are given by

$$\dot{x} = -x + u$$

and the performance index is

$$\text{PI} = \int_0^1 (x^2 + u^2)\, dt$$

Solving the plant equation by inspection, we find that

$$u = \dot{x} + x$$

and the performance index then becomes

$$\text{PI} = \int_0^1 x^2 + (\dot{x} + x)^2\, dt = \int_0^1 (2x^2 + 2x\dot{x} + \dot{x}^2)\, dt$$

The Euler equation

$$\frac{\partial L'(x,\dot{x},t)}{\partial x} - \frac{d}{dt}\frac{\partial L'(x,\dot{x},t)}{\partial \dot{x}} = 0$$

then becomes

$$4x + 2\dot{x} - \frac{d}{dt}(2x + 2\dot{x}) = 0$$

or

$$\ddot{x} - 2x = 0$$

The optimal trajectory is then given by

$$x(t) = K_1 \exp(-\sqrt{2}t) + K_2 \exp\sqrt{2}t$$

and $u(t)$ is

$$u(t) = x(t) + \dot{x}(t) = K_1(1 - \sqrt{2})\exp(-\sqrt{2}t)$$
$$+ K_2(1 + \sqrt{2})\exp\sqrt{2}t$$

The constants K_1 and K_2 may be found by means of the boundary conditions $x(0)$ and $x(1)$.

While the above approach can, in theory, be applied to any problem, the actual application of the technique becomes quite difficult in practice. This is due to the fact that quite often it is difficult actually to solve for **u** in terms of **x**, **ẋ**, and t.   Hence an alternate approach is needed; such an alternate approach is presented below.

First, however, it is worth emphasizing that Eq. (6.3-3) should not be considered to be a control law; i.e., we have not found a closed-loop solution.   The relationship of **u** and **x** and **ẋ** given in Eq. (6.3-3) is nothing more than a statement that **u** equals **u**.   Consider, for example, the obviously meaningless mechanization of the result of the above example shown in Fig. 6.3-2.

In order for a feedback law to have meaning, it must involve only **x** and t.   This must be the case, since **x**(t) provides a complete description of the system state; hence information concerning **ẋ**(t) is unnecessary and redundant.   If **ẋ** as given by the plant equation is substituted into Eq.

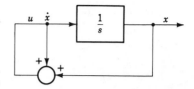

Fig. 6.3-2 Incorrect interpretation of Eq. (6.3-3) as a feedback control law.

(6.3-3), the result is the identity $\mathbf{u} = \mathbf{u}$. Consider once again the above example for a demonstration of this fact.

An alternate approach to the optimal-control problem is based on the use of a technique known as the *undetermined* or *Lagrange multipliers method* to satisfy the plant-equation constraints. In order to understand this technique better, let us begin by considering the constraint problem in ordinary maxima and minima theory.

In this case, we would like to minimize (or maximize) a function $f(x_1, x_2, \ldots, x_n)$ subject to the constraints

$$g_i(x_1, x_2, \ldots, x_n) = 0 \qquad i = 1, 2, \ldots, m \leq n \tag{6.3-5}$$

By the use of the method discussed above, one would solve the m constraint equations (6.3-5) to obtain any m arguments as functions of the remaining $n - m$ arguments. For example, the first m arguments might be obtained as functions of the last $n - m$ arguments,

$$x_i = x_i(x_{m+1}, x_{m+2}, \ldots, x_n) \qquad i = 1, 2, \ldots, m \tag{6.3-6}$$

If this result is then substituted into the original function f, we obtain an ordinary unconstrained minima problem in $m - n$ variables. Although this approach is direct, it is difficult to apply in all but trivial cases.

The Lagrange multiplier method involves the formation of an auxiliary function

$$f' = f + \sum_{i=1}^{m} \lambda_i g_i \tag{6.3-7}$$

where the λ_i's are, as yet, undetermined constant multipliers. With the variables being treated as unconstrained, the function f' is then minimized to obtain the values of x_i which minimize f' in terms of the m Lagrange multipliers λ_i. This result is substituted into the m constraint equations (6.3-5) in order to evaluate the λ_i's. This approach, although seemingly more indirect than the first method, is nevertheless more convenient for the solution of most problems.

Example 6.3-2   As an illustration, consider the problem of maximizing the area of a rectangle of given perimeter.   In this case, the function

$$f(x,y) = xy$$

is to be maximized subject to the constraint

$$P - 2x - 2y = 0$$

where x and y are equal to the length of the sides and P is the given perimeter.

Using the first approach, we should solve the constraint equation to find x as a function of y, as

$$x = \frac{P}{2} - y$$

and then substitute this result into the expression for f,

$$f = y\left(\frac{P}{2} - y\right)$$

The problem is then unconstrained.   By setting $\partial f/\partial y = 0$, y is easily found to be

$$y = \frac{P}{4}$$

In the Lagrange multiplier method, the auxiliary function

$$f' = xy + \lambda(P - 2x - 2y)$$

is formed, and the problem is treated as unconstrained.   Once again the solution is easily found by setting $\partial f/\partial x = 0 = \partial f/\partial y$ so that

$$x = 2\lambda \qquad y = 2\lambda$$

Note that the nature of the solution is given directly, namely $x = y$, even though the exact value of x and y is still unknown since λ has not been evaluated.

Substituting this result into the constraint equation, we have

$$P - 2(2\lambda) - 2(2\lambda) = 0$$

or

$$\lambda = \frac{P}{8}$$

In this case

$$x = y = \frac{P}{4}$$

which is the same solution found above.

In the calculus-of-variations case we are concerned with the minimization of a functional subject to a set of constraint equations

$$g_i(\mathbf{x},\dot{\mathbf{x}},t) = 0 \qquad i = 1, 2, \ldots, m \leq n \tag{6.3-8}$$

The Lagrange multiplier technique presented above can be directly applied in the variational case with the only difference being that the Lagrange multipliers become functions rather than constants. This is not too surprising, since in transforming from the ordinary maxima and minima theory to variational calculus, points are transformed into functions. Hence the constant Lagrange multipliers become functions, as is shown in the following theorem, which is stated without proof (see Elsgolc, 1962).

Theorem 6.3-1   Given a functional of the form

$$V(\mathbf{x}) = \int_{t_i}^{t_f} L(\mathbf{x},\dot{\mathbf{x}},t)\, dt$$

subject to the constraint relations

$$g_i(\mathbf{x},\dot{\mathbf{x}},t) = 0 \qquad i = 1, 2, \ldots, m \leq n \tag{6.3-8}$$

then, if the functions $\mathbf{x}(t)$ minimize $V(\mathbf{x})$, there exists a set of Lagrange multiplier functions $\lambda(t) = \text{col}\ (\lambda_1(t),\lambda_2(t),\ \ldots\ ,\lambda_m(t))$ such that the functions $\mathbf{x}(t)$ minimize the functional

$$V'(\mathbf{x}) = \int_{t_i}^{t_f} [L(\mathbf{x},\dot{\mathbf{x}},t) + \sum_{i=1}^{m} \lambda_i(t)g_i(\mathbf{x},\dot{\mathbf{x}},t)] \, dt$$

$$= \int_{t_i}^{t_f} L'(\mathbf{x},\dot{\mathbf{x}},t) \, dt \tag{6.3-9}$$

That is, they satisfy the Euler equations

$$\frac{\partial L'(\mathbf{x},\dot{\mathbf{x}},t)}{\partial x_i} - \frac{d}{dt} \frac{\partial L'(\mathbf{x},\dot{\mathbf{x}},t)}{\partial \dot{x}_i} = 0 \qquad i = 1, 2, \ldots, n \tag{6.3-10}$$

The method of solution is then to solve simultaneously the n Euler equations (6.3-10) and the m constraint equations (6.3-8) along with the boundary conditions to obtain the n functions $\mathbf{x}(t)$ and the m Lagrange multiplier functions $\lambda(t)$. It should be noted that the constraint equations (6.3-8) are, in general, differential equations.

By the use of this theorem, the optimal-control problem formulated at the beginning of this section can be directly handled by defining an $(n + r)$-dimensional vector

$$\mathbf{x}'(t) = \text{col } (x_1(t),x_2(t), \ldots ,x_n(t),u_1(t), \ldots ,u_r(t))$$

However, for later notational convenience we continue to treat $\mathbf{x}$ and $\mathbf{u}$ separately. This simply yields two sets of Euler equations in terms of $\mathbf{x}$ and $\mathbf{u}$. For the optimal-control problem the constraint equations (6.3-8) are the plant equations and may be written as

$$\mathbf{g}(\mathbf{x},\dot{\mathbf{x}},\mathbf{u},\dot{\mathbf{u}},t) = \mathbf{f}(\mathbf{x},\mathbf{u},t) - \dot{\mathbf{x}} = 0 \tag{6.3-11}$$

In the terminology of Chap. 3, these are nonholonomic constraint equations, since nonintegrable differential equations are involved. The problem is then to minimize the functional

$$V'(\mathbf{x},\mathbf{u}) = \int_{t_i}^{t_f} L'(\mathbf{x},\dot{\mathbf{x}},\mathbf{u},\dot{\mathbf{u}},t) \, dt$$

where

$$L'(\mathbf{x},\dot{\mathbf{x}},\mathbf{u},\dot{\mathbf{u}},t) = L(\mathbf{x},\mathbf{u},t) + \sum_{j=1}^{n} \lambda_j[f_j(\mathbf{x},\mathbf{u},t) - \dot{x}_j] \tag{6.3-12}$$

Let us look first at the Euler equations (6.3-10) in terms of **x**. Substituting Eq. (6.3-12) for L', we have

$$\frac{\partial}{\partial x_i}\left\{L(\mathbf{x},\mathbf{u},t) + \sum_{j=1}^{n} \lambda_j[f_j(\mathbf{x},\mathbf{u},t) - \dot{x}_j]\right\}$$

$$-\frac{d}{dt}\frac{\partial}{\partial \dot{x}_i}\left\{L(\mathbf{x},\mathbf{u},t) + \sum_{j=1}^{n} \lambda_j[f_j(\mathbf{x},\mathbf{u},t) - \dot{x}_j]\right\} = 0$$

$$i = 1, 2, \ldots, n \quad (6.3\text{-}13)$$

Consider each of the partial differentiation operations separately. It is seen that the partial of the $\lambda_j\dot{x}_j$ terms with respect to x_i is zero. In the partial with respect to $\dot{x}_j$, however, only these terms remain. Hence Eq. (6.3-13) reduces to

$$\frac{\partial}{\partial x_i}\left[L(\mathbf{x},\mathbf{u},t) + \sum_{j=1}^{n} \lambda_j f_j(\mathbf{x},\mathbf{u},t)\right] - \frac{d}{dt}\frac{\partial}{\partial \dot{x}_i}\sum_{j=1}^{n}(-\lambda_j\dot{x}_j) = 0$$

But

$$\frac{\partial}{\partial \dot{x}_i}\sum_{j=1}^{n}(-\lambda_j\dot{x}_j) = \sum_{j=1}^{n}\left(-\lambda_j\frac{\partial \dot{x}_j}{\partial \dot{x}_i}\right) = -\lambda_i$$

Therefore the Euler equation becomes

$$\frac{\partial}{\partial x_i}\left[L(\mathbf{x},\mathbf{u},t) + \sum_{j=1}^{n} \lambda_j f_j(\mathbf{x},\mathbf{u},t)\right] - \frac{d}{dt}(-\lambda_i) = 0$$

or

$$\lambda_i = -\frac{\partial}{\partial x_i}\left[L(\mathbf{x},\mathbf{u},t) + \sum_{j=1}^{n} \lambda_j f_j(\mathbf{x},\mathbf{u},t)\right] \quad i = 1, 2, \ldots, n$$

$$(6.3\text{-}14)$$

Looking next at the Euler equations in terms of **u**, we have

$$\frac{\partial}{\partial u_k}\left\{L(\mathbf{x},\mathbf{u},t) + \sum_{j=1}^{n} \lambda_j[f_j(\mathbf{x},\mathbf{u},t) - \dot{x}_j]\right\}$$

$$-\frac{d}{dt}\frac{\partial}{\partial \dot{u}_k}\left\{L(\mathbf{x},\mathbf{u},t) + \sum_{j=1}^{n} \lambda_j[f_j(\mathbf{x},\mathbf{u},t) - \dot{x}_j]\right\} = 0$$

$$k = 1, 2, \ldots, r$$

Once again the $\lambda_j \dot{x}_j$ terms can be eliminated from the differentiation with respect to u_k. However, in this case, the second term is exactly zero since $\dot{u}$ does not appear anywhere. Hence this Euler equation reduces to

$$\frac{\partial}{\partial u_k} \left[L(\mathbf{x},\mathbf{u},t) + \sum_{j=1}^{n} \lambda_j f_j(\mathbf{x},\mathbf{u},t) \right] = 0 \qquad k = 1, 2, \ldots, r$$

$$(6.3\text{-}15)$$

The astute reader immediately recognizes that the quantities involved in the partial differentiation in Eqs. (6.3-14) and (6.3-15) are identical. This realization leads us to the definition of a new state function $H(\mathbf{x},\mathbf{u},\lambda,t)$, and hence to considerable simplification of Eqs. (6.3-14) and (6.3-15). This state function is called the *state function of Pontryagin*, after the Russian mathematician who first brought it to prominence in modern control theory, and is defined by

$$H(\mathbf{x},\mathbf{u},\lambda,t) = \sum_{j=1}^{n} \lambda_j f_j(\mathbf{x},\mathbf{u},t) + L(\mathbf{x},\mathbf{u},t) \qquad (6.3\text{-}16)$$

which may be equivalently written in matrix notation as

$$H(\mathbf{x},\mathbf{u},\lambda,t) = \lambda^T \mathbf{f}(\mathbf{x},\mathbf{u},t) + L(\mathbf{x},\mathbf{u},t) \qquad (6.3\text{-}17)$$

We make use of both forms as convenience dictates.

In terms of the state function of Pontryagin, Eqs. (6.3-14) and (6.3-15) become

$$\dot{\lambda}_i = - \frac{\partial H(\mathbf{x},\mathbf{u},\lambda,t)}{\partial x_i} \qquad i = 1, 2, \ldots, n \qquad (6.3\text{-}18)$$

and

$$0 = \frac{\partial H(\mathbf{x},\mathbf{u},\lambda,t)}{\partial u_k} \qquad k = 1, 2, \ldots, r \qquad (6.3\text{-}19)$$

which may be written compactly as

$$\dot{\lambda} = - \frac{\partial H(\mathbf{x},\mathbf{u},\lambda,t)}{\partial \mathbf{x}} \qquad (6.3\text{-}20)$$

$$0 = \frac{\partial H(\mathbf{x},\mathbf{u},\lambda,t)}{\partial \mathbf{u}} \qquad (6.3\text{-}21)$$

In addition, the plant equations (6.3-1) may be written as

$$\dot{\mathbf{x}} = \frac{\partial H(\mathbf{x},\mathbf{u},\boldsymbol{\lambda},t)}{\partial \boldsymbol{\lambda}} \tag{6.3-22}$$

since

$$\frac{\partial H(\mathbf{x},\mathbf{u},\boldsymbol{\lambda},t)}{\partial \boldsymbol{\lambda}} = \frac{\partial}{\partial \boldsymbol{\lambda}} \left[L(\mathbf{x},\mathbf{u},t) + \boldsymbol{\lambda}^T \mathbf{f}(\mathbf{x},\mathbf{u},t) \right] = \mathbf{f}(\mathbf{x},\mathbf{u},t)$$

In order to solve the optimal-control problem, we must solve Eqs. (6.3-20) to (6.3-22) simultaneously, subject to the boundary conditions $\mathbf{x}^i$ and $\mathbf{x}^f$. This is generally and most conveniently done by first solving the algebraic equation (6.3-21) for the optimal control $\mathbf{u}^o$ in terms of $\mathbf{x}$, $\boldsymbol{\lambda}$, and t,

$$\mathbf{u}^o = \mathbf{u}^o(\mathbf{x},\boldsymbol{\lambda},t) \tag{6.3-23}$$

This result is then substituted into the Pontryagin H function to create the *optimal Pontryagin state function* $H^o(\mathbf{x},\boldsymbol{\lambda},t)$.

$$H^o(\mathbf{x},\boldsymbol{\lambda},t) = H[\mathbf{x},\mathbf{u}^o(\mathbf{x},\boldsymbol{\lambda},t),\boldsymbol{\lambda},t] \tag{6.3-24}$$

The differential equations (6.3-20) and (6.3-22) now become a set of $2n$ coupled first-order differential equations

$$\dot{\mathbf{x}} = \frac{\partial H^o(\mathbf{x},\boldsymbol{\lambda},t)}{\partial \boldsymbol{\lambda}} \tag{6.3-25}$$

$$\dot{\boldsymbol{\lambda}} = - \frac{\partial H^o(\mathbf{x},\boldsymbol{\lambda},t)}{\partial \mathbf{x}} \tag{6.3-26}$$

The optimal trajectory $\mathbf{x}^o(t)$ and $\boldsymbol{\lambda}(t)$ are found by solving these equations with the $2n$ boundary conditions $\mathbf{x}^i$ and $\mathbf{x}^f$. The optimal control $\mathbf{u}^o(t)$ is then obtained by means of Eq. (6.3-23). The complete procedure is summarized in Table 6.3-1.

While theoretically straightforward, the actual solution of Eqs. (6.3-25) and (6.3-26) presents several difficult practical problems.

First, the equations are, in general, nonlinear and time-varying and therefore can usually be numerically solved only by means of a digital computer. Second, for an nth-order system, one must solve a set of $2n$ equations. Hence even a simple second-order system leads to a fourth-order set of equations. These two problems, however, are almost insig-

Table 6.3-1   Summary of the Pontryagin
Procedure for the Basic
Optimal-control Problem

Step 1	Form the Pontryagin H function
	$$H(\mathbf{x},\mathbf{u},\lambda,t) = \lambda^T \mathbf{f}(\mathbf{x},\mathbf{u},t) + L(\mathbf{x},\mathbf{u},t) \qquad (6.3\text{-}17)$$
Step 2	Solve the equation
	$$\frac{\partial H(\mathbf{x},\mathbf{u},\lambda,t)}{\partial \mathbf{u}} = 0 \qquad (6.3\text{-}21)$$
	to obtain
	$$\mathbf{u}^o = \mathbf{u}^o(\mathbf{x},\lambda,t) \qquad (6.3\text{-}23)$$
Step 3	Find the optimal H function
	$$H^o(\mathbf{x},\lambda,t) = H(\mathbf{x},\mathbf{u}^o,\lambda,t) \qquad (6.3\text{-}24)$$
Step 4	Solve the set of $2n$ equations
	$$\dot{\mathbf{x}} = \frac{\partial H^o(\mathbf{x},\lambda,t)}{\partial \lambda} \qquad (6.3\text{-}25)$$
	$$\dot{\lambda} = -\frac{\partial H^o(\mathbf{x},\lambda,t)}{\partial \mathbf{x}} \qquad (6.3\text{-}26)$$
	with the boundary conditions $\mathbf{x}^i$ and $\mathbf{x}^f$
Step 5	Substitute the results of step 4 into the expression for $\mathbf{u}^o$ to obtain the optimal control

nificant compared with the mixed, or two-point, boundary-condition problem that is also involved.

This problem is due to the fact that one half of the $2n$ boundary conditions necessary for a complete specification of the solution of Eqs. (6.3-25) and (6.3-26) is given at the initial time while the other half is given at the terminal time. For example, in the case of the fixed-end-point optimal problem stated at the beginning of this section, the n initial boundary conditions are given by $\mathbf{x}^i$, while the n terminal conditions are given by $\mathbf{x}^f$. As we shall see in Sec. 6.4, this split specification of the boundary conditions is an inherent feature of Pontryagin's method.

The two-point nature of the boundary conditions presents a serious computational problem, since it is not possible to integrate Eqs. (6.3-25) and (6.3-26) forward in time from initial conditions or backward in time from the terminal conditions. Several elegant computational schemes have been developed to solve this problem, although a discussion of these methods is beyond the scope of this book (see, for example, Balakrishnan and Neustadt, 1964). It is possible to avoid this problem, as we show in the next chapter, by an alternate formulation of the solution of the optimal-control problem.

In addition, even if we do solve this two-point boundary-value problem, we still do not have an acceptable solution, since only an open-loop solution for a specific set of initial and terminal states has been found. In other words, u^o is known only as a function of time and not as a feedback control law depending on the system state. If either the initial or terminal states are changed, or if any disturbances act on the system, the control $u^o(t)$ as found above is no longer optimal. This is a serious problem which the approach presented in the next chapter also eliminates. Before entering into a discussion of any alternate approach and before considering a more general control problem, let us consider once again the problem of Example 6.3-1 in order to illustrate the above procedure.

Example 6.3-3 For this example, the plant equation is

$$\dot{x} = -x + u$$

and the performance index is $\text{PI} = \int_0^1 (x^2 + u^2)\, dt$. Following the procedure outlined in Table 6.3-1, we begin by forming the Pontryagin H function

$$H(x,u,\lambda,t) = \lambda(-x + u) + x^2 + u^2$$

From the relation

$$\frac{H(x,u,\lambda,t)}{\partial u} = +\lambda + 2u = 0$$

we find that

$$u^o = -\frac{\lambda}{2}$$

In this case, the optimal value of H becomes

$$H^\circ(x,\lambda,t) = -x\lambda - \frac{\lambda^2}{2} + x^2 + \frac{\lambda^2}{4} = -x\lambda - \frac{\lambda^2}{4} + x^2$$

Equations (6.3-25) and (6.3-26) are then

$$\dot{x} = \frac{\partial H^\circ(x,\lambda,t)}{\partial \lambda} = -x - \frac{\lambda}{2}$$

and

$$\dot{\lambda} = -\frac{\partial H^\circ(x,\lambda,t)}{\partial x} = \lambda - 2x$$

for which one may easily show that the solution is

$$x(t) = K_1 \exp(-\sqrt{2}t) + K_2 \exp\sqrt{2}t$$

and

$$\lambda(t) = -2K_1(1 - \sqrt{2})\exp(-\sqrt{2}t) - 2K_2(1 + \sqrt{2})\exp\sqrt{2}t$$

The optimal control $u^\circ(t)$ is then

$$u^\circ(t) = \frac{\lambda(t)}{2} = K_1(1 - \sqrt{2})\exp(-\sqrt{2}t) + K_2(1 + \sqrt{2})\exp\sqrt{2}t$$

which is exactly the same as the solution found in Example 6.3-1. Once again the constants K_1 and K_2 are determined by the boundary conditions on $x(0)$ and $x(1)$. Let us suppose, for example, that $x(0) = 1$ and $x(1) = 0$; then using the equation for $x(t)$, we find

$$1 = K_1 + K_2 \qquad 0 = K_1 \exp(-\sqrt{2}) + K_2 \exp\sqrt{2}$$

Therefore we find that

$$K_1 = \frac{1}{1 - \exp(-2\sqrt{2})} \qquad K_2 = \frac{1}{1 - \exp 2\sqrt{2}}$$

It should be pointed out that we have considered only the very special case of optimal-control problems in which the state is fixed at both the initial and terminal time and **u** is unconstrained.   In Sec. 6.4 we discuss several generalizations of the problems.

One additional point should be made before we leave this section. This is in regard to the similarity of the state function H of Pontryagin [Eq. (6.3-17)] to the hamiltonian $\mathcal{3C}$ of classical mechanics [Eq. (3.3-19)] and the similarity of Eqs. (6.3-25) and (6.3-26) to Hamilton's canonical equations [Eq. (3.3-20)].   If one realizes that $\mathbf{f}(\mathbf{x},\mathbf{u},t)$ is nothing more than $\dot{\mathbf{x}}$, the only apparent difference in form is in the change of the sign preceding $L(\mathbf{x},\mathbf{u},t)$.   In fact, by choosing a slightly different avenue of development, we could have defined H such that the sign before L would have been negative.

This extreme similarity in form has led many people to refer to H as the *control hamiltonian* or even just the *hamiltonian*.   We shall avoid this terminology because while H and $\mathcal{3C}$ do have similar forms, they have far different physical meanings.   For example, although **p** and λ appear to occupy equivalent positions in the two schemes, they have no other relation.   The **p** is the generalized momentum vector, and the p_i are state variables, while λ has meaning only in a mathematical sense as a Lagrange multiplier.

To be specific, for an nth-order system, there are $n/2$ q_i's and $n/2$ p_i's, but in the control case there are n x_i's and n λ_i's.   The **x** vector contains both the **q** and **p** or **q** and $\dot{\mathbf{q}}$ vectors, since it completely describes the behavior of the system; the n-dimensional λ vector is adjoined to this basic nth-order system as a mathematical convenience.

One might note that if λ has only this mathematical connotation, then H is not a legitimate state function, since it does not depend only on the state and time.   At the present point in the development, such a conclusion would be correct.   However, in the next chapter, we find an alternate and more physical interpretation of λ and show that it is a function of **x** and t, and hence H does depend only on **x** and t.   Hence H is a state function.

Exercises 6.3   *6.3-1.*   For the system

$$\dot{x} = -2x + u$$

with the performance index

$$\mathrm{PI} = \frac{1}{2}\int_0^1 u^2 \, dt$$

find the optimal control $u(t)$ which drives the system from the initial state $x(0) = 1$ to the terminal state $x(1) = 0$.

answer:

$$u(t) = \frac{-4}{1 - e^{-4}} e^{2(t-2)}$$

6.3-2. For the system

$$\dot{x} = \begin{bmatrix} 0 & 1 \\ 0 & 0 \end{bmatrix} x + \begin{bmatrix} 0 \\ 10 \end{bmatrix} u$$

find the optimal control $u(t)$ such that the performance index

$$PI = \frac{1}{2} \int_0^1 u^2 \, dt$$

is minimized. The initial and terminal conditions are $x(0) =$ col $(1,1)$ and $x(1) =$ col $(0,0)$.

answer:

$$u(t) = 1.8t - 1.0$$

6.3-3. Find Eqs. (6.3-25) and (6.3-26) for the system

$$\dot{x} = \begin{bmatrix} 0 & 1 \\ -2 & -3 \end{bmatrix} x + \begin{bmatrix} 0 \\ 1 \end{bmatrix} u$$

(*a*)   with the performance index

$$PI = \frac{1}{2} \int_0^1 (x_1^2 + u^2) \, dt$$

(*b*)   with the performance index

$$PI = \frac{1}{2} \int_0^1 (x_1^2 + x_2^2 + u^2) \, dt$$

answers:

(a)
$$\dot{x} = \begin{bmatrix} 0 & 1 \\ -2 & -3 \end{bmatrix} x + \begin{bmatrix} 0 & 0 \\ 0 & -1 \end{bmatrix} \lambda$$

$$\lambda = \begin{bmatrix} -1 & 0 \\ 0 & 0 \end{bmatrix} x + \begin{bmatrix} 0 & 2 \\ -1 & 3 \end{bmatrix} \lambda$$

(b)
$$\dot{x} = \begin{bmatrix} 0 & 1 \\ -2 & -3 \end{bmatrix} x + \begin{bmatrix} 0 & 0 \\ 0 & -1 \end{bmatrix} \lambda$$

$$\lambda = \begin{bmatrix} -1 & 0 \\ 0 & -1 \end{bmatrix} x + \begin{bmatrix} 0 & 2 \\ -1 & 3 \end{bmatrix} \lambda$$

6.3-4. Find the optimal control for the system

$$\dot{x} = \begin{bmatrix} 0 & 1 \\ -10 & 0 \end{bmatrix} x + \begin{bmatrix} 0 \\ 10 \end{bmatrix} u$$

with the performance index

$$PI = \frac{1}{2} \int_0^1 u^2 \, dt$$

and the boundary conditions $x(0) = \text{col } (1,1)$ and $x(1) = \text{col } (0,0)$.

answer:

$$u(t) = \frac{2}{\sqrt{10}} (\sin \sqrt{10} \, t - 0.316 \cos \sqrt{10} \, t)$$

6.4   The general optimal-control problem

In this section the Pontryagin approach of Sec. 6.3 is extended to the solution of what we shall call the *general optimal-control problem*. The statement of this problem is summarized in Table 6.4-1. While this problem is not the most general problem which can be treated by the Pontryagin approach, it is the most general problem of practical significance. Even in this form it is very difficult to obtain a numerical solution for any but trivial problems, although the formulation of the solution may be very easy.

Let us examine each of the four items of Table 6.4-1 in the specifications of the general optimal-control problem in order to determine how

Table 6.4-1 The General Optimal-control Problem

Plant equation	$\dot{\mathbf{x}} = \mathbf{f}(\mathbf{x},\mathbf{u},t)$ (6.4-1)
Boundary conditions	(a) Initial state and time fixed; that is, $\mathbf{x}^i$ and t_i are given (b) The terminal time t_f may be fixed or free (c) The terminal state $\mathbf{x}^j$ may be fixed, completely free, or specified by a set of relations of the form $h_i(\mathbf{x}^j,t_f) = 0$ $i = 1, 2, \ldots, m \leq n$
Performance index	$\mathrm{PI} = \displaystyle\int_{t_i}^{t_f} L(\mathbf{x},\mathbf{u},t)\, dt + S[\mathbf{x}(t_f),t_f]$ (6.4-2)
Control region	The control vector $\mathbf{u}$ is required to be a member of a set U called the control region. U may be either open or closed and bounded or unbounded

and why they differ from the specifications of the basic optimal-control problem. First of all, notice that the description of the plant is unchanged. This is due to the fact that the nonlinear time-varying form of Eq. (6.3-1) is adequate for almost all practical control problems.

On the other hand, the boundary conditions have been generalized considerably from the fixed end-point conditions of the basic optimal-control problem. This generalization is very important for the proper and direct treatment of many practical problems, as is shown by specific examples at the end of this section.

The performance index has also been generalized by the addition of the *terminal-condition cost function* S to the previous integral performance index of Sec. 6.3. As an illustration of the usefulness of this additional term, consider the problem of maximizing the altitude of a missile at a given terminal time. In this case we might set $S = -x_1(t_f)$, where x_1 is the state variable related to the altitude, so that minimizing S would maximize $x_1(t_f)$. At the same time we could weigh the performance during the climb by means of the integral performance index.

It should be mentioned that it is not necessary that both L and S be contained in every problem, although, of course, one or the other must be. In some problems, it may be desirable to have either L or S identically equal to zero.

As we shall see below, it is possible to transform this performance index into an equivalent performance index of the integral type. While such a transformation is possible, it is often desirable to maintain the identity of the two separate terms to assist in the physical interpretation of the problem.

The requirement that **u** must belong to a control region U is simply a concession to the practical fact that no system has unbounded control available. The control is always limited by such things as saturation, limited power source, or finite radius of turning.

Unfortunately, a closed and bounded control region cannot be easily handled by the direct calculus-of-variations approach, since it violates the assumption that arbitrary and independent variations can be made in the control vector. For this reason we initially assume that the control region is unbounded, so that our development can proceed from the calculus-of-variations results of Sec. 6.2. After this development is complete, the modification that must be made to allow U to be closed and bounded is indicated.

The approach of this section follows closely the Lagrange multiplier development in Sec. 6.3. In order to use this approach, it is convenient to transform the performance index (6.4-2) into a purely integral type of performance index. In order to see how this may be done, let us consider the following performance index:

$$\text{PI} = \int_{t_i}^{t_f} \left[L(\mathbf{x},\mathbf{u},t) + \frac{dS(\mathbf{x},t)}{dt} \right] dt$$

$$= \int_{t_i}^{t_f} L(\mathbf{x},\mathbf{u},t)\, dt + \int_{t_i}^{t_f} dS(\mathbf{x},t) \tag{6.4-3}$$

Integrating the second term, we have

$$\text{PI} = \int_{t_i}^{t_f} L(\mathbf{x},\mathbf{u},t)\, dt + S[\mathbf{x}(t_f),t_f] - S[\mathbf{x}(t_i),t_i] \tag{6.4-4}$$

Since $\mathbf{x}(t_i)$ and t_i are assumed to be fixed, the minimization of the performance index (6.4-4) or equivalently (6.4-3) is equal to the minimization of the performance index (6.4-2). Therefore, the performance index (6.4-2) has been transformed into the integral performance index (6.4-3), which is used in the following development.

It is, however, convenient to rewrite Eq. (6.4-3) slightly by making use of the chain rule for differentiation to express dS/dt as

$$\frac{dS(\mathbf{x},t)}{dt} = \left[\frac{\partial S(\mathbf{x},t)}{\partial \mathbf{x}} \right]^T \dot{\mathbf{x}} + \frac{\partial S(\mathbf{x},t)}{\partial t}$$

The performance index then becomes

$$\text{PI} = \int_{t_i}^{t_f} \left\{ L(\mathbf{x},\mathbf{u},t) + \left[\frac{\partial S(\mathbf{x},t)}{\partial \mathbf{x}} \right]^T \dot{\mathbf{x}} + \frac{\partial S(\mathbf{x},t)}{\partial t} \right\} dt \qquad (6.4\text{-}5)$$

Although the entire integrand could be written as a new function of $\mathbf{x}$, $\mathbf{u}$, and t, the above form is retained since, as we shall see, the functions L and S play different roles in the eventual solution of the problem.

If the constraint relations (6.4-1), i.e., the plant equations, are added to the performance index by means of Lagrange multipliers, as in Sec. 6.3, the problem is to minimize the functional

$$V'(\mathbf{x},\mathbf{u}) = \int_{t_i}^{t_f} L'(\mathbf{x},\dot{\mathbf{x}},\mathbf{u},\dot{\mathbf{u}},t)\, dt$$

where

$$L'(\mathbf{x},\dot{\mathbf{x}},\mathbf{u},\dot{\mathbf{u}},t) = L(\mathbf{x},\mathbf{u},t) + \left[\frac{\partial S(\mathbf{x},t)}{\partial \mathbf{x}} \right]^T \dot{\mathbf{x}}$$
$$+ \frac{\partial S(\mathbf{x},t)}{\partial t} + \lambda^T \mathbf{f}(\mathbf{x},\mathbf{u},t) - \lambda^T \dot{\mathbf{x}} \quad (6.4\text{-}6)$$

The general optimal-control problem is now in such a form that the calculus of variations may be directly applied. The reader is reminded that we are assuming, for the present, that the control region U is unbounded.

Once again two sets of Euler equations are obtained, one in terms of $\mathbf{x}$ and one in terms of $\mathbf{u}$. Considering first the Euler equation in terms of $\mathbf{x}$, we have

$$\frac{\partial}{\partial \mathbf{x}} L'(\mathbf{x},\dot{\mathbf{x}},\mathbf{u},\dot{\mathbf{u}},t) - \frac{d}{dt}\left[\frac{\partial}{\partial \dot{\mathbf{x}}} L'(\mathbf{x},\dot{\mathbf{x}},\mathbf{u},\dot{\mathbf{u}},t) \right] = 0 \qquad (6.4\text{-}7)$$

If Eq. (6.4-6) is substituted for $L'(\mathbf{x},\dot{\mathbf{x}},\mathbf{u},\dot{\mathbf{u}},t)$ and the terms which are zero are removed, Eq. (6.4-7) becomes

$$\frac{\partial}{\partial \mathbf{x}} \left\{ L(\mathbf{x},\mathbf{u},t) + \left[\frac{\partial S(\mathbf{x},t)}{\partial \mathbf{x}} \right]^T \dot{\mathbf{x}} + \frac{\partial S(\mathbf{x},t)}{\partial t} + \lambda^T \mathbf{f}(\mathbf{x},\mathbf{u},t) \right\}$$
$$- \frac{d}{dt}\left[\frac{\partial S(\mathbf{x},t)}{\partial \mathbf{x}} - \lambda \right] = 0$$

Next let us carry out the indicated differentiations only on the three terms involving $S(\mathbf{x},t)$ to obtain

$$\frac{\partial}{\partial \mathbf{x}} [L(\mathbf{x},\mathbf{u},t) + \lambda^T \mathbf{f}(\mathbf{x},\mathbf{u},t)] + \frac{\partial^2 S(\mathbf{x},t)}{\partial \mathbf{x}^2} \dot{\mathbf{x}} + \frac{\partial^2 S(\mathbf{x},t)}{\partial \mathbf{x}\,\partial t}$$
$$- \frac{\partial^2 S(\mathbf{x},t)}{\partial \mathbf{x}^2} \dot{\mathbf{x}} - \frac{\partial^2 S(\mathbf{x},t)}{\partial t\,\partial \mathbf{x}} + \lambda = 0 \quad (6.4\text{-}8)$$

If we assume that $S(\mathbf{x},t)$ has continuous second partial derivatives with respect to $\mathbf{x}$ and t, the four terms involving S cancel, and Eq. (6.4-8) becomes

$$\lambda = - \frac{\partial}{\partial \mathbf{x}} [L(\mathbf{x},\mathbf{u},t) + \lambda^T \mathbf{f}(\mathbf{x},\mathbf{u},t)] \qquad (6.4\text{-}9)$$

It is obvious that this result is identical to the result obtained in Sec. 6.3. In a similar fashion, one may show that the Euler equations in terms of $\mathbf{u}$ also reduce to the previous result

$$\frac{\partial}{\partial \mathbf{u}} [L(\mathbf{x},\mathbf{u},t) + \lambda^T \mathbf{f}(\mathbf{x},\mathbf{u},t)] = 0 \qquad (6.4\text{-}10)$$

Then, in terms of the Pontryagin state function, these results may be written as

$$\lambda = - \frac{\partial}{\partial \mathbf{x}} H(\mathbf{x},\mathbf{u},\lambda,t) \qquad (6.4\text{-}11)$$

and

$$0 = \frac{\partial}{\partial \mathbf{u}} H(\mathbf{x},\mathbf{u},\lambda,t) \qquad (6.4\text{-}12)$$

As before, the original plant or constraint equations may be written, using H, as

$$\dot{\mathbf{x}} = \frac{\partial}{\partial \lambda} H(\mathbf{x},\mathbf{u},\lambda,t) \qquad (6.4\text{-}13)$$

From here on, the solution for the general optimal-control problem may be found by the procedure presented in Sec. 6.3. This begins with solving the algebraic equation (6.4-12) for the optimal control $\mathbf{u}^o$ in terms of $\mathbf{x}$, λ, t,

$$\mathbf{u}^o = \mathbf{u}^o(\mathbf{x},\lambda,t) \qquad (6.4\text{-}14)$$

This result is then substituted into the Pontryagin state function H to create the *optimal Pontryagin state function $H^o(\mathbf{x},\lambda,t)$*.

$$H^o(\mathbf{x},\lambda,t) = H[\mathbf{x},\mathbf{u}^o(\mathbf{x},\lambda,t),\lambda,t] \qquad (6.4\text{-}15)$$

In terms of $H^o(\mathbf{x},\lambda,t)$, Eqs. (6.4-11) and (6.4-12) once again become a set of $2n$ coupled first-order equations

$$\dot{\mathbf{x}} = \frac{\partial H^o(\mathbf{x},\lambda,t)}{\partial \lambda} \qquad (6.4\text{-}16)$$

$$\dot{\lambda} = -\frac{\partial H^o(\mathbf{x},\lambda,t)}{\partial \mathbf{x}} \qquad (6.4\text{-}17)$$

While in the basic optimal-control problem the solution of these equations is uniquely specified by the initial and terminal conditions on $\mathbf{x}$, this is no longer true in the general optimal-control problem. In the latter case, not only may some or all of the states at the terminal time be unspecified, but the terminal time itself may be unknown.

To specify a solution completely some additional boundary conditions are needed. These additional boundary conditions are provided by the generalized boundary conditions (6.2-28), rewritten here in terms of the optimal-control problem for reference,

$$\left[\frac{\partial L'(\mathbf{x},\dot{\mathbf{x}},\mathbf{u},\dot{\mathbf{u}},t)}{\partial \dot{\mathbf{x}}}\right]^T dx \bigg|_{t_f} + \left\{ L'(\mathbf{x},\dot{\mathbf{x}},\mathbf{u},\dot{\mathbf{u}},t) \right.$$
$$\left. - \left[\frac{\partial L'(\mathbf{x},\dot{\mathbf{x}},\mathbf{u},\dot{\mathbf{u}},t)}{\partial \dot{\mathbf{x}}}\right]^T \dot{\mathbf{x}} \right\} dt \bigg|_{t_f} = 0 \qquad (6.4\text{-}18)$$

For the general optimal-control problem $\partial L'/\partial \dot{\mathbf{x}}$ is given by

$$\frac{\partial L'(\mathbf{x},\dot{\mathbf{x}},\mathbf{u},\dot{\mathbf{u}},t)}{\partial \dot{\mathbf{x}}} = \frac{\partial S(\mathbf{x},t)}{\partial \mathbf{x}} - \lambda$$

Equation (6.4-18) then becomes

$$\left[\frac{\partial S(\mathbf{x},t)}{\partial \mathbf{x}} - \lambda\right]^T dx \bigg|_{t_f} + \left\{ L(\mathbf{x},\mathbf{u},t) + \left[\frac{\partial S(\mathbf{x},t)}{\partial \mathbf{x}}\right]^T \dot{\mathbf{x}} + \frac{\partial S(\mathbf{x},t)}{\partial t} \right.$$
$$\left. + \lambda^T \mathbf{f}(\mathbf{x},\mathbf{u},t) - \lambda^T \dot{\mathbf{x}} - \left[\frac{\partial S(\mathbf{x},t)}{\partial \mathbf{x}} - \lambda\right]^T \dot{\mathbf{x}} \right\} dt \bigg|_{t_f} = 0$$

which may be reduced to

$$\left[\frac{\partial S(\mathbf{x},t)}{\partial \mathbf{x}} - \lambda\right]^T d\mathbf{x}\bigg|_{t_f} + \left[L(\mathbf{x},\mathbf{u},t) + \lambda^T \mathbf{f}(\mathbf{x},\mathbf{u},t) + \frac{\partial S(\mathbf{x},t)}{\partial t}\right] dt\bigg|_{t_f} = 0$$

(6.4-19)

This expression may be further simplified by recognizing the first two terms in the second quantity as $H(\mathbf{x},\mathbf{u},\lambda,t)$. In actuality, they are not just H but are $H^o(\mathbf{x},\lambda,t)$, since we derived the generalized boundary condition (6.2-28) under the assumption that the path is an extremal. In the optimal-control case this means that the control must be $\mathbf{u}^o$. Making this substitution, then, we can rewrite Eq. (6.4-19) as

$$\left[\frac{\partial S(\mathbf{x},t)}{\partial \mathbf{x}} - \lambda\right]^T d\mathbf{x}\bigg|_{t_f} + \left[H^o(\mathbf{x},\lambda,t) + \frac{\partial S(\mathbf{x},t)}{\partial t}\right] dt\bigg|_{t_f} = 0 \qquad (6.4\text{-}20)$$

In case the reader has forgotten, let us consider the exact significance of the $d\mathbf{x}$ and dt terms in the above expression. They are respectively the deviations in position and time *between* the end points of the optimal trajectory and some arbitrary variational trajectory. This is to be contrasted with a differential taken *along* the optimal trajectory or any other trajectory.

Through the use of the generalized boundary condition (6.4-20) it is now possible to obtain a unique solution to Eqs. (6.4-16) and (6.4-17). This is due to the fact that the generalized boundary condition supplies just enough additional conditions on the terminal values of $\mathbf{x}$, λ, and H^o to compensate for any lack of specification of $\mathbf{x}(t_f)$ or t_f. As a simple illustration of this fact consider the two extreme cases, first with $\mathbf{x}(t_f)$ and t_f completely specified and second with $\mathbf{x}(t_f)$ and t_f completely unspecified.

In the first case $d\mathbf{x}$ and dt are both zero, since all trajectory must terminate at the same position and time. Therefore, the generalized boundary condition is trivially satisfied with no further restrictions on the terminal values of $\mathbf{x}$, λ, or H^o. This is as it should be, since the solution is already uniquely determined.

On the other hand, in the second case, where $\mathbf{x}(t_f)$ and t_f are free, $d\mathbf{x}$ and dt are arbitrary. Therefore, in order to satisfy the generalized boundary condition, it is necessary that

$$\left[\frac{\partial S(\mathbf{x},t)}{\partial \mathbf{x}} - \lambda\right]\bigg|_{t_f} = 0$$

and

$$\left[H^o(\mathbf{x},\lambda,t) + \frac{\partial S(\mathbf{x},t)}{\partial t}\right]\bigg|_{t_f} = 0$$

These relations place $n + 1$ additional restrictions on the terminal conditions of the problem, and hence once more the solution is uniquely determined. We consider various specific cases of the use of the generalized boundary conditions later in this section.

So far in the formulation of the solution of the general optimal-control problem we have assumed that the control region U was unbounded. This was done in order that the calculus-of-variations approach could be directly applied to the solution. That is, in order to write the Euler equations, Eqs. (6.3-20) and (6.3-21), it was necessary to take the partial derivative of $H(\mathbf{x},\mathbf{u},\lambda,t)$ with respect to $\mathbf{u}$. The second Euler equation (6.3-21) may also be viewed as a minimization of $H(\mathbf{x},\mathbf{u},\lambda,t)$ with respect to $\mathbf{u}$. This operation of partial differentiation is only possible for arbitrary $\mathbf{x}$, λ, and t if $\mathbf{u}$ is completely unconstrained. In the situation presently under discussion, this is not the case. Here $\mathbf{u}$ is bounded or $\mathbf{u}$ is a member of U. Hence we can no longer proceed in a manner completely analogous to that of the calculus of variations. Pontryagin (1962) has shown that regardless of any constraints that exist on $\mathbf{u}$, $\mathbf{u}$ must still be chosen to minimize H.

A rigorous proof of the fact that $\mathbf{u}^o$ must be chosen to minimize H is perhaps Pontryagin's most significant contribution to optimal-control theory. For this reason the approach presented here is often referred to as *Pontryagin's minimum principle*. In Pontryagin's initial work H was defined slightly differently, and therefore it was necessary to maximize H rather than minimize it, as we have done here. Hence the approach is also referred to as the *maximum principle*.

Unfortunately, the rigorous proof of the minimum principle is beyond the scope of this book. The interested reader is therefore directed to Pontryagin's book for a complete development.

In the case of a closed and bounded control region, the optimal control $\mathbf{u}^o(\mathbf{x},\lambda,t)$ is found by minimizing $H(\mathbf{x},\mathbf{u},\lambda,t)$ with respect to controls $\mathbf{u}$ in the given control region U while treating the other variables as constants. In other words, $\mathbf{u}^o(\mathbf{x},\lambda,t)$ is the admissible control vector for which $H(\mathbf{x},\mathbf{u},\lambda,t)$ has its minimum value. The optimal Pontryagin state function then becomes

$$H^o(\mathbf{x},\lambda,t) = H[\mathbf{x},\mathbf{u}^o(\mathbf{x},\lambda,t),\lambda,t] = \min_{\mathbf{u}\varepsilon U} H(\mathbf{x},\mathbf{u},\lambda,t) \qquad (6.4\text{-}21)$$

If U is unbounded, it is obvious that Eq. (6.4-12) is a special case of the above procedure, since the minimum of H can then be obtained by setting the partial derivative of H with respect to $\mathbf{u}$ equal to zero.

Example 6.4-1   In order to illustrate the application of this procedure, consider the following system,

$$\dot{x}_1 = x_2 \qquad \dot{x}_2 = u$$

with the performance index

$$PI = \int_0^T |u| \, dt$$

where U is the set of all values of u such that $|u| \leq 1$.   For this problem H is

$$H(\mathbf{x}, u, \lambda, t) = |u| + \lambda_1 x_2 + \lambda_2 u$$

In order to minimize H it is necessary that u be given by

$$u^\circ = \begin{cases} 1 & \text{if } \lambda_2 \leq -1 \\ 0 & \text{if } -1 < \lambda_2 < 1 \\ -1 & \text{if } \lambda_2 \geq 1 \end{cases}$$

Therefore

$$H^\circ(\mathbf{x}, \lambda, t) = \begin{cases} 1 + \lambda_1 x_2 + \lambda_2 & \text{if } \lambda_2 \leq -1 \\ \lambda_1 x_2 & \text{if } -1 < \lambda_2 < 1 \\ 1 + \lambda_1 x_2 - \lambda_2 & \text{if } \lambda_2 \geq 1 \end{cases}$$

This example points out a very valuable feature of the Pontryagin approach to the case of a closed and bounded control region.   Although we still have no idea of the exact time behavior of the optimal control, a great deal of information has been obtained concerning the *form* of the optimal control.   In particular for this problem, we see that the optimal control can consist only of sequences of three possible values, 1, 0, and -1. In other words, the system must be subjected to maximum control in either the positive or negative direction or must be allowed to coast uncontrolled.   The fact that we are able to find the form of the optimal control easily is a general feature of the approach and is often a significant key in finding an optimal closed-loop system.

With the addition of the minimum principle for handling the case of a closed and bounded control region, the formulation of the solution of the general optimal-control problem is complete.   The entire procedure is summarized in Table 6.4-2 for quick reference.

Table 6.4-2   Summary of the Pontryagin Procedure for Solving the General Optimal-control Problem

---

Step 1	Form the Pontryagin H function

$$H(\mathbf{x},\mathbf{u},\lambda,t) = L(\mathbf{x},\mathbf{u},t) + \lambda^T \mathbf{f}(\mathbf{x},\mathbf{u},t) \qquad (6.3\text{-}17)$$

Step 2	Minimize $H(\mathbf{x},\mathbf{u},\lambda,t)$ with respect to all admissible control vectors to find

$$\mathbf{u}^o = \mathbf{u}^o(\mathbf{x},\lambda,t)$$

Step 3	Find the optimal H function

$$H^o(\mathbf{x},\lambda,t) = H(\mathbf{x},\mathbf{u}^o,\lambda,t) = \min_{\mathbf{u}\varepsilon U} H(\mathbf{x},\mathbf{u},\lambda,t) \qquad (6.4\text{-}21)$$

Step 4	Solve the set of $2n$ equations

$$\dot{\mathbf{x}} = \frac{\partial H^o(\mathbf{x},\lambda,t)}{\partial \lambda} \qquad (6.4\text{-}16)$$

$$\dot{\lambda} = -\frac{\partial H^o(\mathbf{x},\lambda,t)}{\partial \mathbf{x}} \qquad (6.4\text{-}17)$$

with the given initial and terminal boundary conditions and the generalized boundary condition

$$\left[\frac{\partial S(\mathbf{x},t)}{\partial \mathbf{x}} - \lambda\right]^T dx \bigg|_{t_f} + \left[H^o(\mathbf{x},\lambda,t) + \frac{\partial S(\mathbf{x},t)}{\partial t}\right] dt \bigg|_{t_f} = 0 \quad (6.4\text{-}20)$$

Step 5	Substitute the results of step 4 into the expression for $\mathbf{u}^o$ to obtain the optimal control

---

Once again, although the formulation of the solution is quite easy, the actual computation problem of obtaining it is far more difficult. The problem is even more difficult than before because of the more complicated nature of the terminal boundary conditions. In general, a solution may be obtained only by machine methods, and then only if elaborate computational procedures are used. This is an unfortunate feature of the modern optimal-control approach. It is the price one must pay for demanding the best performance from a system.

The rest of this section consists solely of examples illustrating various special cases of the general optimal-control problem. By means of these examples, it is hoped to point out various features of the solution procedure while at the same time demonstrating the wide range of application of this general problem. In particular, emphasis is placed on the use of the generalized boundary condition, since it is the only feature which is significantly different from the basic optimal-control-problem procedure.

Example 6.4-2 As a first example, let us consider a problem in which the terminal time is fixed but the terminal state is free. The plant equation is

$$\dot{x} = -2\sqrt{2}x + u$$

and the performance index is

$$PI = \int_0^1 (x^2 + u^2) \, dt$$

The control region is assumed to be unbounded, and $x(0) = 2$.

Following the procedure outlined in Table 6.4-2, we find that Eqs. (6.4-16) and (6.4-17) become

$$\dot{x} = -2\sqrt{2}x - \frac{\lambda}{2} \qquad \dot{\lambda} = -2x + 2\sqrt{2}\lambda$$

with

$$u^o = -\frac{\lambda}{2}$$

In order to find a unique solution to these equations, it is necessary to have two boundary conditions. Only one is given by the initial value of x. The other boundary condition is obtained from the generalized boundary condition (6.4-20). For this problem $S(\mathbf{x},t)$ is zero, and dt is also zero, since the terminal time is fixed. Therefore Eq. (6.4-20) becomes

$$\lambda(1) \, dx = 0$$

Since the terminal state is free, dx is arbitrary, and the equation can be satisfied for arbitrary dx only by $\lambda(1) = 0$. If this boundary condition is combined with the given initial state, we find that

$$\lambda(t) = 0.687(e^{-3t} - e^{-6}e^{3t})$$

The optimal control is then

$$u^o(t) = -\frac{\lambda(t)}{2} = -0.343(e^{-3t} - e^{-6}e^{3t})$$

It should be obvious that the results of the above example can be generalized to cover any problem in which the terminal state is free and $S(\mathbf{x},t) = 0$. For such a problem it is necessary that $\lambda(t_f) = 0$. In addition, if the terminal time is also free, one may easily show that H^o must be zero at the termination of the problem.

Example 6.4-3 As a second example, consider the so-called "rendezvous problem." The plant equation is

$$\dot{\mathbf{x}} = \mathbf{f}(\mathbf{x},\mathbf{u},t)$$

with the performance index

$$\text{PI} = \int_{t_i}^{t_f} L(\mathbf{x},\mathbf{u},t)\ dt$$

The problem is to force the plant, which might be a satellite, to rendezvous with another object, perhaps another satellite or the moon, whose trajectory is given as $\mathbf{y}(t)$. The problem is represented graphically in Fig. 6.4-1.

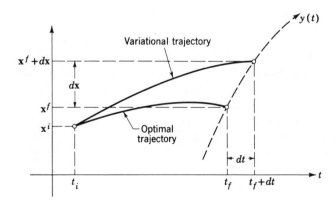

Fig. 6.4-1 The rendezvous problem.

The generalized boundary condition for this problem becomes

$$\lambda^T(t_f)\, d\mathbf{x} + H^\circ[\mathbf{x}(t_f),\lambda(t_f),t_f]\, dt = 0$$

However, from Fig. 6.4-1 we can easily see that $d\mathbf{x} = \dot{\mathbf{y}}(t_f)\, dt$, and therefore, since dt is arbitrary, it is necessary that

$$\lambda^T(t_f)\dot{\mathbf{y}}(t_f) + H^\circ[\mathbf{x}(t_f),\lambda(t_f),t_f] = 0$$

With this condition and the fact that $\mathbf{x}(t_f) = \mathbf{y}(t_f)$, the solution is completely specified.

In some problems, it might be desirable to combine the results of Examples 6.4-2 and 6.4-3. Suppose, for example, that it is only necessary that $x_1(t_f)$ and $y_1(t_f)$ be equal. Then $x_2, x_3, \ldots, x_n$ are unspecified, and therefore it is necessary that $\lambda_2(t_f) = \lambda_3(t_f) = \cdots = \lambda_n(t_f) = 0$.

Example 6.4-4 Let us suppose that the plant and performance index are as given in the previous example but that now it is desired that at the terminal time $x_1(t_f) = x_2(t_f)$, while the other state variables and the terminal time are fixed. The generalized boundary condition for this problem is

$$\lambda_1(t_f)\, dx_1 + \lambda_2(t_f)\, dx_2 = 0$$

From Fig. 6.4-2, we see that $dx_1 = dx_2$, and therefore it is necessary that

$$[\lambda_1(t_f) + \lambda_2(t_f)]\, dx_1 = 0$$

This can only be true for arbitrary dx_1 if

$$\lambda_1(t_f) = -\lambda_2(t_f)$$

Once again, this result combined with the fact $x_1(t_f) = x_2(t_f)$ completely specifies a solution.

The above example is a special case of the terminal manifold problem in which it is required that the terminal state be a member of a given set. In general, it can be shown that it is necessary for λ to be perpendicular to

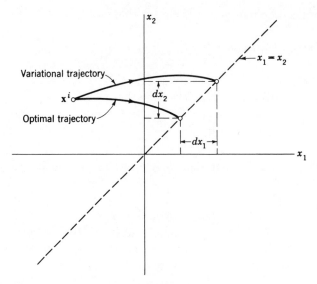

Fig. 6.4-2 Terminal state on the line $x_1 = x_2$.

this terminal manifold.   This condition is obviously satisfied by the above example.

In all the above examples we have assumed that $S(\mathbf{x},t) = 0$.   The next example illustrates the use of this term.

> **Example 6.4-5**   Let us suppose that the plant equations of an airplane are given with the state variables defined as
>
> $x_1 = $ horizontal position
> $x_2 = $ horizontal velocity
> $x_3 = $ vertical position
> $x_4 = $ vertical velocity
>
> The problem is to find the flight plan for the airplane to follow to achieve maximum altitude under various conditions.   The performance index is
>
> $$PI = -x_3(t_f)$$
>
> where we have set $S(\mathbf{x},t) = -x_3$, since we wish to maximize $x_3(t_f)$. If we assume that the terminal time is fixed, the generalized boundary

condition for this problem is

$$\left[\left(\frac{\partial S}{\partial x_1} - \lambda_1\right) dx_1 + \left(\frac{\partial S}{\partial x_2} - \lambda_2\right) dx_2 + \left(\frac{\partial S}{\partial x_3} - \lambda_3\right) dx_3 \right.$$
$$\left.+ \left(\frac{\partial S}{\partial x_4} - \lambda_4\right) dx_4\right]\Big|_{t_f} = 0$$

which becomes

$$[-\lambda_1\, dx_1 - \lambda_2\, dx_2 - (1 + \lambda_3)\, dx_3 - \lambda_4\, dx_4]\Big|_{t_f} = 0$$

If no requirements are made on the other state variables, we see that

$$\lambda_1(t_f) = \lambda_2(t_f) = \lambda_4(t_f) = 0 \quad \text{and} \quad \lambda_3(t_f) = -1$$

On the other hand, if we specify the range at the end of the flight, $x_1(t_f)$ is fixed, and we have

$$\lambda_2(t_f) = \lambda_4(t_f) = 0 \quad \text{and} \quad \lambda_3(t_f) = -1$$

If, in addition, we assume that the plane must end in level flight, that is, $x_4(t_f) = 0$, then we may require only that

$$\lambda_2(t_f) = 0 \quad \text{and} \quad \lambda_3(t_f) = -1$$

The four examples presented above are in no sense an exhaustive list of the variety of problems that find their way into the framework of the general optimal-control problem. The number of combinations and permutations is almost infinite. What was intended was a brief illustration of the generality of the Pontryagin approach and some additional illustration of its application.

Exercises 6.4 *6.4-1.* Find the missing terminal boundary conditions for the system

$$\dot{\mathbf{x}} = \begin{bmatrix} 0 & 1 & 0 \\ 0 & 0 & 1 \\ 0 & 0 & 0 \end{bmatrix} \mathbf{x} + \begin{bmatrix} 0 \\ 0 \\ 1 \end{bmatrix} u$$

with the performance index

$$PI = \int_0^T (x_1{}^2 + u^2)\, dt + x_2(T)$$

if

(a) $x_1(T)^2 + x_2(T)^2 = 1$, $x_3(T) = 0$, and T is fixed
(b) $x_1(T) = T$, $x_2(T) = x_3(T)$, and T is unspecified
(c) $x_1(T)^2 + x_2(T)^2 = T^2$, and $x_3(T) = 0$

answers:

(a) $\lambda_1(T)x_2(T) = \lambda_2(T)x_1(T)$
(b) $\lambda_1(T) = H(T)$, $\lambda_2(T) + \lambda_3(T) = 1$
(c) $H(T)x_1(T) = T\lambda_1(T)$, $H(T)x_2(T) = T\lambda_2(T)$

6.4-2.   Find the optimal control for the first-order system

$$\dot{x} = -x + u$$

with an initial state $x(0) = 0$ in order to maximize the terminal value of x while minimizing the cost functional $\left(\int_0^1 u^2\, dt\right)/2$. Assume that the weighting between these two objectives is Γ, so that the performance index becomes

$$PI = \frac{1}{2}\int_0^1 u^2\, dt - \Gamma x_1(1)$$

answer:

$$u(t) = \Gamma e^{t-1}$$

6.4-3.   For the second-order system

$$\dot{\mathbf{x}} = \begin{bmatrix} 0 & 1 \\ -2 & -3 \end{bmatrix} \mathbf{x} + \begin{bmatrix} 0 \\ 1 \end{bmatrix} u$$

with the initial condition $\mathbf{x}(0) = \operatorname{col}(1,1)$, find $u(t)$ and $\mathbf{x}(t)$ in order to minimize the performance index

$$PI = \int_0^\infty (x_1{}^2 + u^2)\, dt$$

answer:

$$u(t) = 0.28e^{-1.9t} - 0.59e^{-1.18t}$$

6.4-4. Find the remaining terminal boundary conditions for a fifth-order system whose performance index is

$$PI = \int_0^T (x_1{}^2 + x_3{}^2 + 10u^2)\, dt + x_4(T) - 2x_5(T)$$

The following terminal conditions are known:

$$x_1(T) = 2x_2(T) \qquad x_3(T) = 0$$

and $x_4(T)$, $x_5(T)$, and T are unspecified.

answer:

$$\lambda_1(T) = -\frac{\lambda_2(T)}{2} \qquad \lambda_4(T) = +1 \qquad \lambda_5(T) = -2$$

$$H^o\Big|_T = 0$$

6.5 Summary and conclusion

The examples that concluded the last section illustrated the details of the solution procedure associated with the application of the minimum principle. In particular, the examples illustrated the use of the generalized boundary condition but stopped short of the actual determination of $\mathbf{u}(t)$. There are two important reasons for this. The first is that it is difficult to solve the two-point boundary problem, even though the boundary conditions have been correctly evaluated. Usually numerical methods are necessary, and they are often highly sophisticated procedures that are apt to tax the largest computers. In this book if our primary interest were in the general control problem, as specified in the previous section, we should have no recourse but to go into these numerical methods. Since our interest is not in the general control problem but in the linear control problem, we feel free to bypass the actual determination of $\mathbf{u}(t)$.

The second reason for not concentrating on methods of arriving at the optimal control $\mathbf{u}(t)$ is that we are not really interested in $\mathbf{u}(t)$. We want $\mathbf{u} = \mathbf{k}[\mathbf{x}(t),t]$; that is, we want our control to be a function of the system state, so that feedback can be used to control the system. Even if we were able to find $\mathbf{u}(t)$ exactly and in closed form, that would not represent the type of answer in which we are interested. For this reason we seek an alternate approach that ensures that $\mathbf{u}$ is given as a function of the state variables. This alternate approach is through the Hamilton-Jacobi equation, and the method makes a joint use of both the state function of Liapunov and that of Pontryagin. This is the subject of the next chapter.

6.6 Problems

6.6-1. For the linear system

$$\dot{\mathbf{x}} = \begin{bmatrix} -1 & -1 \\ 1 & 0 \end{bmatrix} \mathbf{x} + \begin{bmatrix} 1 & 0 \\ 0 & 0 \end{bmatrix} \mathbf{u}$$

find the optimal-control vector $\mathbf{u}$ which transfers the system from the state $\mathbf{x}(0) = \text{col}\ (2,1)$ to the final state $\mathbf{x}(1) = \text{col}\ (0,0)$ with a minimum value of the performance index

$$PI = \int_0^1 (u_1{}^2 + u_2{}^2)\ dt$$

6.6-2. For the system

$$\dot{\mathbf{x}} = \begin{bmatrix} 0 & 1 \\ -2 & -3 \end{bmatrix} \mathbf{x} + \begin{bmatrix} 0 \\ 1 \end{bmatrix} u$$

with the initial condition $\mathbf{x}(0) = \text{col}\ (1,1)$, find the optimal control $u(t)$ such that the performance index

$$PI = \int_0^1 (x_1{}^2 + u^2)\ dt$$

is minimized.

6.6-3. Repeat Prob. 6.6-2 with the added condition that at the terminal time $x_1(1) = -x_2(1)$.

6.6-4. One method of including an *isoperimetric* constraint of the form

$$\int_{t_i}^{t_f} g(\mathbf{x},\mathbf{u},t)\ dt = A$$

is by defining a new state variable as

$$x_{n+1}(t) = \int_{t_i}^{t} g(\mathbf{x},\mathbf{u},t')\, dt'$$

Therefore

$$\dot{x}_{n+1}(t) = g(\mathbf{x},\mathbf{u},t)$$

and the boundary conditions are

$$x_{n+1}(t_i) = 0 \quad \text{and} \quad x_{n+1}(t_f) = A$$

Use this technique to find the optimal control for the system

$$\dot{x} = -x + u$$

in order to minimize the performance index

$$\text{PI} = \frac{1}{2} \int_0^1 x^2\, dt$$

subject to the constraint that

$$\frac{1}{2} \int_0^1 u^2\, dt = 10$$

with the initial condition $x(0) = 1$ and unspecified terminal state.

6.6-5. Use the technique of the previous problem to find the optimal control for the system

$$\dot{\mathbf{x}} = \begin{bmatrix} 0 & 1 \\ -1 & -1 \end{bmatrix} \mathbf{x} + \begin{bmatrix} 0 \\ 1 \end{bmatrix} u$$

subject to the constraint that

$$\int_0^T u^2\, dt = 10$$

The system is to be transferred from $x(0) = \text{col}\,(1,2)$ to the origin in minimum time so that the performance index is

$$\text{PI} = \int_0^T dt$$

6.6-6. For the linear system

$$\dot{x} = Ax + bu$$

with $A^T + A = 0$, $x(0) = \text{col } (2, 2)$, $x(T) = 0$, and $|u| \le 1$, show that the control which minimizes the performance index

$$PI = \int_0^T |u|\, dt$$

is not unique.   In addition show that the control which minimizes the above performance index and has the smallest value for T minimizes the performance index

$$PI = \int_0^T dt$$

6.6-7. For the system

$$\dot{x} = -x^3 + u$$

find the control which minimizes the performance index

$$PI = \int_0^1 (x^2 + u^2)\, dt$$

with $x(0) = 1$.

6.6-8. For the second-order system

$$\dot{x} = \begin{bmatrix} 0 & 1 \\ -10 & 0 \end{bmatrix} x + \begin{bmatrix} 0 \\ 10 \end{bmatrix} u$$

with the initial condition $x(0) = \text{col } (1,1)$, find the optimal input $u(t)$ to minimize

(a) $PI = \dfrac{1}{2} \int_0^1 (x_1^2 + u^2)\, dt$

(b) $PI = \int_0^{t_f} dt$ $x(t_f) = 0$ and $|u| \le 1$

6.6-9. Set up the equations and boundary conditions necessary to obtain the optimal control for the system

$$\dot{x}_1 = x_2 \qquad \dot{x}_2 = -\alpha x_1 - x_2 + u$$

for the performance index

$$\text{PI} = \int_0^T (x_1{}^2 + u^2)\, dt$$

The initial state is given, and $\mathbf{x}(T)$ and T are unspecified. Here α is a constant parameter which must be selected along with $u(t)$ by the designer for optimum performance.

6.6-10. Set up the equations and boundary conditions necessary to obtain the optimal control for the system

$$\dot{x}_1 = x_2 + x_2 u_1 \qquad \dot{x}_2 = -x_1 - x_1 u_2$$

for the performance index

$$\text{PI} = \int_0^1 \|\mathbf{u}\|^2\, dt$$

subject to the constraints that

(a) $\|\mathbf{u}\| \leq 1$
(b) $x_1(t)^2 + x_2(t)^2 = 1$ for all t
(c) $\mathbf{x}(0) = \text{col}\,(1,0)$ and $\mathbf{x}(1) = \text{col}\,(0,1)$

References

Athans, M., and P. L. Falb: "Optimal Control," McGraw-Hill Book Company, New York, 1966.

Balakrishnan, A. V., and L. W. Neustadt (eds.): "Computing Methods in Optimization Problems," Academic Press Inc., New York, 1964.

Bliss, G. A.: "Lectures on the Calculus of Variations," Phoenix Science Series, The University of Chicago Press, Chicago, 1946.

Bolza, O.: "Calculus of Variations," Chelsea Publishing Company, New York, 1960.

Elsgolc, L. E.: "Calculus of Variations," Addison-Wesley Publishing Company, Inc., Reading, Mass., 1962.

Gelfand, I. M., and S. V. Fomin: "Calculus of Variations," Prentice-Hall, Inc., Englewood Cliffs, N.J., 1963.

Leitmann, G.: "Optimization Techniques with Applications to Aerospace Systems," Academic Press Inc., New York, 1962.

Merriam, C. W.: "Optimization Theory and the Design of Feedback Control Systems," McGraw-Hill Book Company, New York, 1964.

Pontryagin, L. S., et al.: "The Mathematical Theory of Optimal Processes," John Wiley & Sons, Inc., New York, 1962.

Tou, J. T.: "Modern Control Theory," McGraw-Hill Book Company, New York, 1964.

seven   *state-function approach to linear system synthesis*

7.1   *Introduction and outline of chapter*

In the previous chapter the Pontryagin approach to the optimal-control problem was introduced, along with a definition of the second state function of modern control, the state function of Pontryagin. An alternate approach is developed in this chapter by combining the Pontryagin method with concepts from the second method of Liapunov. This alternate approach eliminates the two major problems of the Pontryagin method. First, it removes the necessity for solving a two-point boundary-value problem, and, second, the approach yields a closed-loop solution in the form of an optimal-control law $\mathbf{u}^o(\mathbf{x},t)$.

However, as one might almost expect, this closed-loop approach also has its problems. Chief among these is the necessity of solving a nonlinear partial differential equation known as the Hamilton-Jacobi equation. In fact, the solution of this equation is so difficult that it has been accomplished only for a few special cases. Hence one must often return to the Pontryagin approach with its undesirable open-loop answer in order to be able to achieve a solution.

This added difficulty of the Hamilton-Jacobi approach is not without explanation. In the Pontryagin approach we sought the solution for only one specific set of initial conditions. Now, by stipulating a closed-loop solution we seek the solution for a whole family of initial conditions.

There is, however, one class of problems of significant practical importance for which it is possible to solve the Hamilton-Jacobi equation in a reasonably simple manner. This fact would, by itself, justify the development of the Hamilton-Jacobi approach. It is with the formulation and solution of this problem that this chapter is mainly concerned.

The problem of interest is the optimal control of the linear system

$$\dot{\mathbf{x}} = \mathbf{A}\mathbf{x} + \mathbf{B}\mathbf{u} \tag{AB}$$

with a quadratic performance index

$$\text{PI} = \int_0^\infty (\mathbf{x}^T\mathbf{Q}\mathbf{x} + \mathbf{u}^T\mathbf{P}\mathbf{u})\,dt \tag{7.1-1}$$

The matrices $\mathbf{Q}$ and $\mathbf{P}$ are symmetric with $\mathbf{Q}$ at least *positive semidefinite* while $\mathbf{P}$ must be *positive definite*. This problem is often described as the linear control problem with quadratic cost or simply as the *linear control problem*.

This development of the optimal linear control problem with quadratic cost is in keeping with the basic concern of this book, linear control systems. By developing techniques for linear systems not only are valuable answers obtained, but, in addition, a basic understanding of the modern optimal-control theory may be obtained in a simple framework. These techniques are then available for use on more general systems.

The actual solution of the linear control problem is approached from three different viewpoints. First, the Hamilton-Jacobi approach is directly applied to the above problem to develop a matrix form of solution in the time domain known as the matrix Riccati equation. Some concepts from the second method of Liapunov are employed, in two alternate approaches, to derive this same matrix result. In addition, this section contains a discussion of the stability of the optimal system. The third approach concerns the translation of the above matrix result into a frequency-domain expression commonly referred to as the Kalman equation. This frequency-domain result is employed in the next chapter for the practical design of single input–single output systems.

In each of the above sections it is assumed that all the state variables are available for measurement. In practical systems this assumption is often not justified, and one must seek some method for generating unmeasurable states. Section 7.6 presents one approach to this problem, known as the Kalman filter. An alternate and much less mathematical approach is presented in Chap. 9.

This chapter represents somewhat of a departure from the framework of the past chapters in that the most general problem, multiple input and output, is treated from the very beginning, rather than at the end. This is due to the fact that the techniques for solving the optimal linear problem require, in general, the use of a digital computer for all but trivial problems. Hence one may as well consider a general problem if it is necessary to use a digital computer in any case.

Although digital computers are readily enough available so that the requirement for their use is no real restriction, it is desirable at times to be able to treat problems by hand. The next chapters cater to this need by treating the classical single input–single output system by techniques related to classical control theory and without the use of digital computers.

Since it is not the aim of this book to turn every reader into a digital-computer programmer, the examples presented throughout the chapter are purposely kept simple so that they may be followed by reasonable hand computations. On the other hand, the reader will find it a very satisfying experience to write or obtain a program which solves these problems.

7.2   *The Hamilton-Jacobi approach*

The preceding chapter used the Lagrange multiplier–Pontryagin method for solving the basic optimal-control problem, in which the system is described by

$$\dot{\mathbf{x}} = \mathbf{f}(\mathbf{x}, \mathbf{u}, t) \tag{7.2-1}$$

with the performance index

$$\mathrm{PI} = \int_{t_i}^{t_f} L(\mathbf{x}, \mathbf{u}, t) \, dt \tag{7.2-2}$$

The computational problem involved the solution of a two-point boundary problem, and, in addition, only open-loop control was obtained. This section considers an alternate approach through the use of the Hamilton-Jacobi equation. This approach is not without computational difficulties, but fortunately, for the class of problems in which we are primarily interested, it is possible to solve the Hamilton-Jacobi equation in a straight-forward and, in some cases, even simple manner. Of equal importance, the resulting control law is a function of the state variables, which implies closed-loop control. This is important from a practical, implementation point of view.

Since a closed-loop solution is desired, we begin the development by assuming that $\mathbf{u}$ is given by an optimal-control law $\mathbf{u}^o(\mathbf{x},t)$. The explicit dependence of $\mathbf{u}^o$ on t should be explained, lest it be confused with the open-loop solution found in Chap. 6. The time variation of the control law is due to inherent time-varying features of the problem, such as a time-varying plant or performance index, and is not dependent on the initial state, as is the open-loop solution.

Next, we define a scalar function $V(\mathbf{x},t)$ as the minimum value of the performance index for an initial state $\mathbf{x}$ at time t, that is,

$$V(\mathbf{x},t) = \int_t^{t_f} L[\mathbf{x}(\tau),\mathbf{u}^o(\mathbf{x},\tau),\tau]\,d\tau$$

In other words, $V(\mathbf{x},t)$ is the value of the performance index when evaluated along an optimal trajectory which begins at $\mathbf{x}(t)$. Later we shall show that $V(\mathbf{x},t)$ may be treated as a Liapunov function. As noted above, we are now searching for the optimal control, not for a specific initial state, but rather for general unspecified initial conditions. This must be the case if the resulting control law is to have any meaning.

The total time derivative of $V(\mathbf{x},t)$ is given by

$$\dot{V}(\mathbf{x},t) = -L[\mathbf{x},\mathbf{u}^o(\mathbf{x},t),t] \tag{7.2-3}$$

where the negative sign appears because the differentiation is with respect to the lower limit of the integral. On the other hand, a straightforward application of the chain rule for differentiation yields the following expression for $\dot{V}(\mathbf{x},t)$:

$$\dot{V}(\mathbf{x},t) = \sum_{i=1}^{n} \frac{\partial V(\mathbf{x},t)}{\partial x_i} f_i[\mathbf{x},\mathbf{u}^o(\mathbf{x},t),t] + \frac{\partial V(\mathbf{x},t)}{\partial t}$$

$$= \nabla \mathbf{V}^T(\mathbf{x},t)\mathbf{f}[\mathbf{x},\mathbf{u}^o(\mathbf{x},t),t] + \frac{\partial V(\mathbf{x},t)}{\partial t} \tag{7.2-4}$$

where once again the optimal control has been substituted for **u**.   Equating these two expressions for $\dot{V}(\mathbf{x},t)$, we obtain

$$\nabla\mathbf{V}^T(\mathbf{x},t)\mathbf{f}[\mathbf{x},\mathbf{u}^o(\mathbf{x},t),t] + \frac{\partial V(\mathbf{x},t)}{\partial t} = -L[\mathbf{x},\mathbf{u}^o(\mathbf{x},t),t] \qquad (7.2\text{-}5)$$

or

$$\nabla\mathbf{V}^T(\mathbf{x},t)\mathbf{f}[\mathbf{x},\mathbf{u}^o(\mathbf{x},t),t] + \frac{\partial V(\mathbf{x},t)}{\partial t} + L[\mathbf{x},\mathbf{u}^o(\mathbf{x},t),t] = 0 \qquad (7.2\text{-}6)$$

If $\mathbf{u}^o(\mathbf{x},t)$ were known, this expression would represent a partial differential equation for $V(\mathbf{x},t)$, although it would not be clear why one would want to solve it.   On the other hand, if $V(\mathbf{x},t)$ were known, it would be possible to solve the equation for $\mathbf{u}^o(\mathbf{x},t)$.   The actual manner in which we shall use Eq. (7.2-6) is a combination of these two possibilities.   The control law $\mathbf{u}^o(\mathbf{x},t)$ will be found as a function of $\nabla\mathbf{V}$, $\mathbf{x}$, and t, and this relation is substituted for $\mathbf{u}^o$ in Eq. (7.2-6).   This results in a partial differential equation which may be solved for $V(\mathbf{x},t)$.   With $V(\mathbf{x},t)$ known, $\mathbf{u}^o(\mathbf{x},t)$ may be found.

In order to derive the expression for $\mathbf{u}^o$ in terms of $\nabla\mathbf{V}$, $\mathbf{x}$, and t, $\nabla\mathbf{V}$ and $\boldsymbol{\lambda}$ are shown to play similar roles in the formulation of the optimal-control problem.   This is done first by taking the partial derivative of both sides of Eq. (7.2-6) with respect to x_j to obtain

$$\frac{\partial}{\partial x_j}\left(\sum_{i=1}^{n} \frac{\partial V}{\partial x_i} f_i\right) + \frac{\partial^2 V}{\partial x_j\,\partial t} + \frac{\partial L}{\partial x_j} = 0$$

or

$$\sum_{i=1}^{n} \frac{\partial^2 V}{\partial x_j\,\partial x_i} f_i + \sum_{i=1}^{n} \frac{\partial V}{\partial x_i} \frac{\partial f_i}{\partial x_j} + \frac{\partial^2 V}{\partial x_j\,\partial t} + \frac{\partial L}{\partial x_j} = 0 \qquad (7.2\text{-}7)$$

Next, we take the total time derivative of $\nabla V_j = \partial V/\partial x_j$, which may be written, using the chain rule, as

$$\frac{d}{dt} \frac{\partial V}{\partial x_j} = \sum_{i=1}^{n} \frac{\partial^2 V}{\partial x_i\,\partial x_j} f_i + \frac{\partial^2 V}{\partial t\,\partial x_j} \qquad (7.2\text{-}8)$$

If the second partial derivatives of $V(\mathbf{x},t)$ with respect to $\mathbf{x}$ and t are assumed to be continuous, Eq. (7.2-8) may also be written as

$$\frac{d}{dt}\frac{\partial V}{\partial x_j} = \sum_{i=1}^{n} \frac{\partial^2 V}{\partial x_j \, \partial x_i} f_i + \frac{\partial^2 V}{\partial x_j \, \partial t} \tag{7.2-9}$$

by interchanging the partial-derivative operations. While there are some important problems for which this assumption is not satisfied, for almost all practical situations it is satisfied. In particular, the assumption is justified for the linear problems in which we are primarily interested.

By comparing Eqs. (7.2-7) and (7.2-9) one notes that the first and third terms of Eq. (7.2-7) are identical to the right-hand side of Eq. (7.2-9). Therefore by combining these two expressions Eq. (7.2-9) may be written as

$$\frac{d}{dt}\frac{\partial V}{\partial x_j} = -\left(\sum_{i=1}^{n} \frac{\partial V}{\partial x_i}\frac{\partial f_i}{\partial x_j} + \frac{\partial L}{\partial x_j} \right)$$

or, if all the arguments are included, this becomes

$$\frac{d}{dt}\frac{\partial V(\mathbf{x},t)}{\partial x_j} = -\left[\sum_{i=1}^{n} \frac{\partial V(\mathbf{x},t)}{\partial x_i}\frac{\partial f_i(\mathbf{x},\mathbf{u}^o,t)}{\partial x_j} + \frac{\partial L(\mathbf{x},\mathbf{u}^o,t)}{\partial x_j} \right] \tag{7.2-10}$$

To assist in making the following identification, let us return to the defining equation for the adjoint variables, namely,

$$\boldsymbol{\lambda} = -\frac{\partial H^o(\mathbf{x},\boldsymbol{\lambda},t)}{\partial \mathbf{x}} \tag{7.2-11}$$

where $H^o(\mathbf{x},\boldsymbol{\lambda},t)$ was defined in Chap. 6 (see Table 6.3-1) as

$$H^o(\mathbf{x},\boldsymbol{\lambda},t) = H(\mathbf{x},\mathbf{u}^o,\boldsymbol{\lambda},t) = \boldsymbol{\lambda}^T\mathbf{f}(\mathbf{x},\mathbf{u}^o,t) + L(\mathbf{x},\mathbf{u}^o,t) \tag{7.2-12}$$

under the assumption that

$$\mathbf{u}^o = \mathbf{u}^o(\mathbf{x},\boldsymbol{\lambda},t) \tag{7.2-13}$$

The jth component of Eq. (7.2-11) is

$$\lambda_j = -\left[\sum_{i=1}^{n} \lambda_i \frac{\partial f_i(\mathbf{x},\mathbf{u}^o,t)}{\partial x_j} + \frac{\partial L(\mathbf{x},\mathbf{u}^o,t)}{\partial x_j} \right] \tag{7.2-14}$$

From an examination of Eqs. (7.2-10) and (7.2-14) it is seen that ∇V_j satisfies the differential equation for λ_j, and since j is arbitrary, this must be true for all j. In other words, ∇V satisfies the differential equation for λ; that is, the time behavior of the ∇V is identical to λ, not only for one specific set of initial conditions, but for all initial conditions. Therefore ∇V may be substituted for λ in Eq. (7.2-13) for u^o since the resulting time behavior of u^o is unchanged. That is, u^o is found by solving the algebraic equation

$$0 = \frac{\partial H(\mathbf{x},\mathbf{u},\nabla \mathbf{V},t)}{\partial \mathbf{u}} \tag{7.2-15}$$

when the control is unconstrained, or minimizing $H(\mathbf{x},\mathbf{u},\nabla \mathbf{V},t)$ with respect to $\mathbf{u} \ \varepsilon \ U$ in general, for the optimal control u^o in terms of $\mathbf{x}$, $\nabla \mathbf{V}$, and t. In terms of $\nabla \mathbf{V}$, u^o is

$$\mathbf{u}^o = \mathbf{u}^o(\mathbf{x},\nabla \mathbf{V},t) \tag{7.2-16}$$

and $H(\mathbf{x},\mathbf{u},\nabla \mathbf{V},t)$ is given by

$$H(\mathbf{x},\mathbf{u},\nabla \mathbf{V},t) = \nabla \mathbf{V}^T \, \mathbf{f}(\mathbf{x},\mathbf{u},t) + L(\mathbf{x},\mathbf{u},t) \tag{7.2-17}$$

There is, however, one very important difference in the expression for u^o. Since ∇V is a function of $\mathbf{x}$ and t, u^o is now a feedback-control law and provides the optimal control for any initial conditions. Thus the assumption made at the outset of this discussion, namely, that $\mathbf{u}^o = \mathbf{u}^o(\mathbf{x},t)$, has been shown to be valid. However, before this expression for u^o can be used, it is necessary to know the function $V(\mathbf{x},t)$. As indicated above, $V(\mathbf{x},t)$ may be found by solving the partial differential equation which arises when Eq. (7.2-16) is substituted into Eq. (7.2-6), or

$$\nabla \mathbf{V}^T \, \mathbf{f}[\mathbf{x},\mathbf{u}^o(\mathbf{x},\nabla \mathbf{V},t),t] + \frac{\partial V}{\partial t} + L[\mathbf{x},\mathbf{u}^o(\mathbf{x},\nabla \mathbf{V},t),t] = 0 \tag{7.2-18}$$

In order to present this result in a more compact form let us consider the optimal Pontryagin state function, in which once again $\nabla \mathbf{V}$ is substituted for λ.

$$\begin{aligned}
H^o(\mathbf{x},\nabla \mathbf{V},t) &= H[\mathbf{x},\mathbf{u}^o(\mathbf{x},\nabla \mathbf{V},t),\nabla \mathbf{V},t] \\
&= \nabla \mathbf{V}^T \, \mathbf{f}[\mathbf{x},\mathbf{u}^o(\mathbf{x},\nabla \mathbf{V},t),t] + L[\mathbf{x},\mathbf{u}^o(\mathbf{x},\nabla \mathbf{V},t),t]
\end{aligned} \tag{7.2-19}$$

Comparing Eqs. (7.2-18) and (7.2-19), we immediately see that Eq. (7.2-18) may be written as

$$H^o[\mathbf{x}, \nabla V(\mathbf{x},t), t] + \frac{\partial V(\mathbf{x},t)}{\partial t} = 0 \qquad (7.2\text{-}20)$$

which is referred to as the *Hamilton-Jacobi equation.*

The function $V(\mathbf{x},t)$ is found by solving this first-order nonlinear partial differential equation. In order to determine $V(\mathbf{x},t)$ completely and uniquely it is necessary to specify appropriate boundary conditions on $V(\mathbf{x},t)$. For example, in the case of the fixed terminal state of the basic optimal-control problem, it is necessary, in general, that $V(\mathbf{x},t)$ be zero for $\mathbf{x} = \mathbf{x}^f$ and $t = t_f$ and nonzero otherwise. This is necessary since

Table 7.2-1   *Summary of the Hamilton-Jacobi Procedure for the Computation of the Optimal-control law* $\mathbf{u}^o(\mathbf{x},t)$

Step 1	Form the Pontryagin state function with λ replaced by ∇V $$H(\mathbf{x},\mathbf{u},\nabla V,t) = \nabla V^T \mathbf{f}(\mathbf{x},\mathbf{u},t) + L(\mathbf{x},\mathbf{u},t) \quad (7.2\text{-}17)$$
Step 2	Minimize $H(\mathbf{x},\mathbf{u},\nabla V,t)$ with respect to $\mathbf{u} \; \varepsilon \; U$ to obtain $$\mathbf{u}^o = \mathbf{u}^o(\mathbf{x},\nabla V,t) \qquad (7.2\text{-}16)$$
Step 3	Find the optimal H $$H^o(\mathbf{x},\nabla V,t) = H[\mathbf{x},\mathbf{u}^o(\mathbf{x},\nabla V,t),\nabla V,t] \qquad (7.2\text{-}19)$$
Step 4	Solve the partial differential equation (Hamilton-Jacobi equation) $$H^o(\mathbf{x},\nabla V,t) + \frac{\partial V}{\partial t} = 0 \qquad (7.2\text{-}20)$$ with the appropriate boundary conditions to obtain $V(\mathbf{x},t)$
Step 5	Substitute the results of step 4 into the expression for $\mathbf{u}^o(\mathbf{x},t)$ to obtain the optimal-control law

the only situation for which the performance index is zero is when the system starts from $\mathbf{x}^f$ at t^f. If, on the other hand, the terminal state is free, $V(\mathbf{x}, t_f)$ is zero for any $\mathbf{x}$.

Once $V(\mathbf{x}, t)$ is obtained, its gradient $\nabla V(\mathbf{x}, t)$ can be determined and substituted into Eq. (7.2-16) to create the optimal-control law $\mathbf{u}^o(\mathbf{x}, t)$. The complete procedure for the use of the Hamilton-Jacobi approach is summarized in Table 7.2-1.

Unfortunately, this approach has two very serious difficulties, which severely limit its usefulness. First, it is almost impossible to solve the Hamilton-Jacobi equation even for trivial problems. In addition, no general technique of solution is known. Second, even if the Hamilton-Jacobi equation can be solved, often the control law is impractical to implement. For these reasons, the Hamilton-Jacobi approach is generally not acceptable, and one is forced to resort to the Pontryagin approach of Sec. 6.4 in order to obtain an answer, even if it is only open-loop.

On the other hand, in favor of the Hamilton-Jacobi approach is the fact that the one problem for which it is possible to obtain a solution in a relatively straightforward manner is of significant practical importance. It is to this one problem that the whole of Chaps. 8 and 9 is devoted. In the next sections, this problem is formulated, and several alternate methods for solving it are presented. Chapters 8 and 9 are then concerned with various aspects of the practical implementation of the solution.

Before leaving this section, the reader may note that the optimal Pontryagin state function as given in Eq. (7.2-19) is a function only of $\mathbf{x}$ and t, since ∇V is a function of $\mathbf{x}$ and t. Hence $H^o(\mathbf{x}, \nabla V, t)$ is indeed a state function.

Exercises 7.2   *7.2-1.* Find the optimal closed-loop control law for the system

$$\dot{x} = -2x + u$$

with the performance index

$$\text{PI} = \int_0^\infty (x^2 + u^2)\, dt$$

Hint: Assume that $V(\mathbf{x}, t)$ is of the form αx^2.

answer:

$$u^o(x, t) = -(\sqrt{5} - 2)x$$

7.2-2. Find the Hamilton-Jacobi equation for the system

$$\dot{x}_1 = x_2 \qquad \dot{x}_2 = -x_2 - x_1^2 + u$$

if the performance index is

$$\mathrm{PI} = \int_0^T (x_1^2 + u^2)\, dt$$

answer:

$$\frac{\partial V}{\partial t} + \nabla V_1\, x_2 - \nabla V_2\, x_2 - \nabla V_2\, x_1^2 - \tfrac{1}{4}(\nabla V_2)^2 + x_1^2 = 0$$

7.2-3. Show that the solution of the Hamilton-Jacobi equation for the system

$$\dot{\mathbf{x}} = \mathbf{A}\mathbf{x} + \mathbf{u}$$

where $\mathbf{A}$ is skew-symmetric, that is, $\mathbf{A} + \mathbf{A}^T = 0$, with the performance index

$$\mathrm{PI} = \int_0^T dt$$

and the constraint that $\|\mathbf{u}\| \le 1$ is

$$V(\mathbf{x}) = \|\mathbf{x}\|$$

What is the optimal-control law for this problem?

answer:

$$\mathbf{u}(\mathbf{x}) = \frac{-\mathbf{x}}{\|\mathbf{x}\|}$$

7.3 The matrix Riccati equation

The previous section developed the Hamilton-Jacobi approach to the basic optimal-control problem, in which the system is described by Eq. (7.2-1) and the performance index by Eq. (7.2-2). The linear control problem is a subset of the general optimal-control problem in which the system is described by Eq. (**AB**) and the performance index by

$$PI = \int_0^\infty (\mathbf{x}^T\mathbf{Q}\mathbf{x} + \mathbf{u}^T\mathbf{P}\mathbf{u}) \, dt$$

and **u** is unconstrained.

In this section, we begin our solution of the linear control problem with a direct application of the Hamilton-Jacobi approach. In the following sections, the problem is approached by means of the second method of Liapunov and the frequency domain.

Before applying the Hamilton-Jacobi approach, let us generalize the problem slightly by assuming that the upper limit on the performance index is a finite time T rather than infinity. The performance index is then

$$PI = \int_0^T (\mathbf{x}^T\mathbf{Q}\mathbf{x} + \mathbf{u}^T\mathbf{P}\mathbf{u}) \, dt \tag{7.3-1}$$

The first step in the application of the Hamilton-Jacobi procedure, as outlined in Table 7.2-1, is the formation of the Pontryagin H function. For the above problem this becomes

$$H(\mathbf{x},\mathbf{u},\nabla V,t) = \nabla V^T(\mathbf{A}\mathbf{x} + \mathbf{B}\mathbf{u}) + \mathbf{x}^T\mathbf{Q}\mathbf{x} + \mathbf{u}^T\mathbf{P}\mathbf{u} \tag{7.3-2}$$

Upon setting $\partial H/\partial \mathbf{u} = 0$, we obtain

$$\mathbf{B}^T \nabla V + 2\mathbf{P}\mathbf{u} = 0$$

Therefore $\mathbf{u}^o(\mathbf{x},t)$ is given by

$$\mathbf{u}^o = -\tfrac{1}{2}\mathbf{P}^{-1}\mathbf{B}^T \nabla V(\mathbf{x},t) \tag{7.3-3}$$

We see that **P** must be required to be positive definite so that $\mathbf{P}^{-1}$ will always exist. In more physical terms, if **P** were only semidefinite, some elements or linear combinations of the elements of the control vector could become infinite without affecting the value of the performance index. If this result is substituted into H in Eq. (7.3-2), the optimal Pontryagin state function is

$$\begin{aligned} H^o(\mathbf{x},\nabla V,t) &= \nabla V^T \mathbf{A}\mathbf{x} - \tfrac{1}{2}\nabla V^T \mathbf{B}\mathbf{P}^{-1}\mathbf{B}^T \nabla V + \mathbf{x}^T\mathbf{Q}\mathbf{x} \\ &\qquad + \tfrac{1}{4}\nabla V^T \mathbf{B}\mathbf{P}^{-1}\mathbf{P}\mathbf{P}^{-1}\mathbf{B}^T \nabla V \\ &= \nabla V^T \mathbf{A}\mathbf{x} - \tfrac{1}{4}\nabla V^T \mathbf{B}\mathbf{P}^{-1}\mathbf{B}^T \nabla V + \mathbf{x}^T\mathbf{Q}\mathbf{x} \end{aligned}$$

The Hamilton-Jacobi equation then becomes

$$\nabla \mathbf{V}^T \mathbf{A}\mathbf{x} - \tfrac{1}{4}\nabla \mathbf{V}^T \mathbf{B}\mathbf{P}^{-1}\mathbf{B}^T \nabla \mathbf{V} + \mathbf{x}^T\mathbf{Q}\mathbf{x} + \frac{\partial V}{\partial t} = 0 \qquad (7.3\text{-}4)$$

Therefore, in order to find the optimal-control law $\mathbf{u}^o(\mathbf{x},t)$, it is necessary to solve this partial differential equation.   We shall solve the equation by assuming that the solution is a time-varying quadratic form and by then showing that such a solution satisfies the Hamilton-Jacobi equation.
We assume that $V(\mathbf{x},t)$ is given by

$$V(\mathbf{x},t) = \mathbf{x}^T\mathbf{R}(t)\mathbf{x} = \int_t^T (\mathbf{x}^T\mathbf{Q}\mathbf{x} + \mathbf{u}^T\mathbf{P}\mathbf{u})\, d\tau \qquad (7.3\text{-}5)$$

where $\mathbf{R}(t)$ is a positive definite symmetric matrix for all $t < T$ and $\mathbf{R}(T) = 0$.   This latter condition is due to the boundary condition on $V(\mathbf{x},t)$, since with $\mathbf{x}(T)$ free it is obvious that

$$V(\mathbf{x},T) = \int_T^T (\mathbf{x}^T\mathbf{Q}\mathbf{x} + \mathbf{u}^T\mathbf{P}\mathbf{u})\, dt = 0$$

independent of $\mathbf{x}$.   The requirement that $\mathbf{R}(t)$ be positive definite is necessary since the value of the integrand of the performance index is a positive definite function.
For this $V(\mathbf{x},t)$, $\nabla \mathbf{V}$ and $\partial V/\partial t$ are given by

$$\nabla \mathbf{V} = 2\mathbf{R}(t)\mathbf{x} \qquad (7.3\text{-}6)$$

and

$$\frac{\partial V}{\partial t} = \mathbf{x}^T\dot{\mathbf{R}}(t)\mathbf{x} \qquad (7.3\text{-}7)$$

Substituting these results into the Hamilton-Jacobi equation, we obtain

$$2\mathbf{x}^T\mathbf{R}(t)\mathbf{A}\mathbf{x} - \mathbf{x}^T\mathbf{R}(t)\mathbf{B}\mathbf{P}^{-1}\mathbf{B}^T\mathbf{R}(t)\mathbf{x} + \mathbf{x}^T\mathbf{Q}\mathbf{x} + \mathbf{x}^T\dot{\mathbf{R}}(t)\mathbf{x} = 0$$

or

$$\mathbf{x}^T[2\mathbf{R}(t)\mathbf{A} - \mathbf{R}(t)\mathbf{B}\mathbf{P}^{-1}\mathbf{B}^T\mathbf{R}(t) + \mathbf{Q} + \dot{\mathbf{R}}(t)]\mathbf{x} = 0 \qquad (7.3\text{-}8)$$

It would appear that the only way that this equation can be satisfied for arbitrary $\mathbf{x}$ is that the quantity inside the brackets be equal to zero.

This statement is not exactly correct, however. Because of the quadratic nature of Eq. (7.3-8), it is necessary only that the symmetric part of the bracketed expression be zero. The reader will remember from Chap. 5 that only the symmetric part of the matrix in a quadratic form is of importance.

An examination of Eq. (7.3-8) reveals that all the terms within the brackets are already symmetric except for the first term. Therefore in order to set the symmetric part of the bracketed quantity to zero it is necessary only to make the first term symmetric. This is done by the technique discussed in Sec. 2.3,

$$\text{Sym } [2\mathbf{R}(t)\mathbf{A}] = 2 \frac{\mathbf{R}(t)\mathbf{A} + \mathbf{A}^T\mathbf{R}(t)}{2} = \mathbf{R}(t)\mathbf{A} + \mathbf{A}^T\mathbf{R}(t)$$

where the transpose has been omitted on $\mathbf{R}(t)$ since it is symmetric. Therefore in order for Eq. (7.3-8) to be satisfied, it is necessary that $\mathbf{R}(t)$ satisfy the following differential equation:

$$\dot{\mathbf{R}}(t) + \mathbf{Q} - \mathbf{R}(t)\mathbf{B}\mathbf{P}^{-1}\mathbf{B}^T\mathbf{R}(t) + \mathbf{R}(t)\mathbf{A} + \mathbf{A}^T\mathbf{R}(t) = 0 \qquad (7.3\text{-}9)$$

subject to the boundary condition $\mathbf{R}(T) = 0$. This equation is known as the *matrix Riccati equation.*

Although general methods are available for obtaining an analytic solution for $\mathbf{R}(t)$, they are unwieldy for any systems of higher than second order (Kalman and Bucy, 1961). On the other hand, it is very easy to obtain a numerical solution for $\mathbf{R}(t)$ on a digital computer. This is done by integrating the Riccati equation backward in time from the known terminal condition over the time interval of interest.

Once $\mathbf{R}(t)$ is known for $0 \leq t \leq T$, the optimal-control law may be obtained from Eqs. (7.3-3) and (7.3-6) as

$$\mathbf{u}^o(\mathbf{x},t) = -\mathbf{P}^{-1}\mathbf{B}^T\mathbf{R}(t)\mathbf{x} \qquad (7.3\text{-}10)$$

This is often written in the form

$$\mathbf{u}^o(\mathbf{x},t) = -\mathbf{K}^T(t)\mathbf{x} \qquad (7.3\text{-}11)$$

where

$$\mathbf{K}(t) = \mathbf{R}(t)\mathbf{B}\mathbf{P}^{-1} \qquad (7.3\text{-}12)$$

The elements of the matrix $\mathbf{K}(t)$ are referred to as the *feedback coefficients,* since the optimal control consists of a time-weighted linear combination

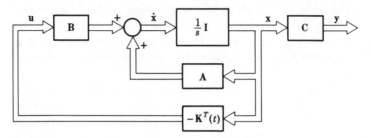

Fig. 7.3-1   Optimal-feedback-control structure.

of the state variables.   This result is important since it indicates that in an optimal system all the state variables are to be fed back, not only the output, as is customary in classical control theory.   A graphical representation of this optimal system is presented in Fig. 7.3-1.

> **Example 7.3-1**   In order to illustrate this procedure, let us consider the following example.   The system is given by
>
> $$\dot{x} = -x + u$$
>
> and the performance index is
>
> $$\text{PI} = \int_0^T (x^2 + u^2)\, dt$$
>
> For this problem, the matrices **A**, **B**, **Q**, and **P** reduce to scalars and are given by
>
> $$A = a = -1 \qquad B = b = 1$$
> $$Q = q = 1 \qquad\ \ P = p = 1$$
>
> In addition, the matrix $\mathbf{R}(t)$ also reduces to a scalar function of time $r(t)$.   The matrix Riccati equation then becomes the scalar differential equation
>
> $$\dot{r}(t) + 1 - r^2(t) - 2r(t) = 0$$

with the boundary condition $r(T) = 0$. The analytic solution to the above equation, which may be verified by direct substitution, is

$$r(t) = \frac{\exp[-\sqrt{2}\,(t-T)] - \exp[\sqrt{2}\,(t-T)]}{(\sqrt{2}+1)\exp[-\sqrt{2}\,(t-T)] + (\sqrt{2}-1)\exp[-\sqrt{2}\,(t-T)]}$$

If one uses Eq. (7.3-10), the optimal-control law is

$$u^o(x,t) = -\frac{\{\exp[-\sqrt{2}\,(t-T)] - \exp[\sqrt{2}\,(t-T)]\}x}{(\sqrt{2}+1)\exp[-\sqrt{2}\,(t-T)] + (\sqrt{2}-1)\exp[-\sqrt{2}\,(t-T)]}$$

The reader is reminded that the explicit time variations in u_o are independent of the state of the system.

If we return now to our original problem, where $T = \infty$, the **R** matrix becomes constant, thereby simplifying its determination. The fact that **R** is constant may be easily established by the simple argument that $V(\mathbf{x},t_1)$ must be equal to $V(\mathbf{x},t_2)$ for any finite t_1 and t_2. This must be true, since the plant and performance criteria are time-invariant, and therefore a finite translation of the time scale does not affect the problem.

This constant **R** matrix, often designated by $\mathbf{R}_o$, may be found in several ways. One way is to perform a limit operation on the solution for the time-varying problem. In order to use this approach, think of the time-varying solution of the Riccati equation $\mathbf{R}(t)$ not only as a function of time but also as dependent on the initial and final value of the time interval of interest, that is, 0 and T. Therefore, we can write $\mathbf{R}(t)$ as $\mathbf{R}(t,0,T)$ to indicate this dependence.

The solution of the stationary infinite-control-interval problem $\mathbf{R}_o$ is then given by

$$\mathbf{R}_o = \lim_{T \to \infty} \mathbf{R}(0,0,T) \tag{7.3-13}$$

In other words, $\mathbf{R}_o$ is the initial value of the **R** matrix for the control interval 0 to T as T increases without bound.

For this case, the optimal-feedback-control law becomes

$$\mathbf{u}^o(\mathbf{x}) = -\mathbf{P}^{-1}\mathbf{B}^T\mathbf{R}_o\mathbf{x} \qquad (7.3\text{-}14)$$

which is often written as

$$\mathbf{u}^o(\mathbf{x}) = -\mathbf{K}^T\mathbf{x} \qquad (7.3\text{-}15)$$

where $\mathbf{K}$ is given by

$$\mathbf{K} = \mathbf{R}_o\mathbf{B}\mathbf{P}^{-1} \qquad (7.3\text{-}16)$$

The elements of the matrix $\mathbf{K}$ are once again referred to as feedback coefficients, since the optimal-control law consists of linear combinations of the state variables fed back to form the optimal control.

There is a major difference in the nature of the optimal control represented by Eq. (7.3-14) or (7.3-15) as compared with Eq. (7.3-10). In the present case, the feedback coefficients are constants, and hence the implementation of the optimal-control law is considerably easier.

Example 7.3-2   In order to demonstrate this technique, consider once again the problem presented in Example 7.3-1. Let us suppose that the control interval is infinite, that is,

$$\text{PI} = \int_0^\infty (x^2 + u^2)\, dt$$

Using Eq. (7.3-13), we find that r_o is

$$r_o = \lim_{T \to \infty} r(0,0,T)$$
$$= \lim_{T \to \infty} \frac{\exp(\sqrt{2}\, T) - \exp(-\sqrt{2}\, T)}{(\sqrt{2}+1)\exp(\sqrt{2}\, T) + (\sqrt{2}-1)\exp(-\sqrt{2}\, T)}$$
$$= \sqrt{2} - 1$$

The optimal-control law as given by Eq. (7.3-14) is then

$$u^o(x) = -(\sqrt{2} - 1)x$$

The optimal system is illustrated in Fig. 7.3-2.

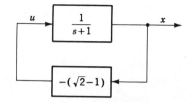

Fig. 7.3-2 Optimal-feedback system for Example 7.3-2.

In practice, the above technique is not utilized because the analytic expression for $\mathbf{R}(t)$ is usually not known. What is done is to integrate the Riccati equation (7.3-9) backward in time from the known terminal condition $\mathbf{R}(\infty) = 0$ until the desired degree of accuracy is reached. This can be done very easily on a digital computer, since only the steady-state solution is needed, and therefore the numerical-integration technique can be very simple.

The $\mathbf{R}_o$ matrix may also be found by utilizing the fact that $\mathbf{R}_o$ is constant, and therefore its time derivative $\dot{\mathbf{R}}_o$ is zero. Substituting this result into the Riccati equation (7.3-9), we obtain

$$\mathbf{A}^T\mathbf{R}_o + \mathbf{R}_o\mathbf{A} - \mathbf{R}_o\mathbf{B}\mathbf{P}^{-1}\mathbf{B}^T\mathbf{R}_o + \mathbf{Q} = 0 \qquad (7.3\text{-}17)$$

which is often referred to as the *reduced* or *degenerate Riccati equation*. In this case we have $n(n + 1)/2$ nonlinear algebraic equations to solve for the elements of $\mathbf{R}_o$.

Unfortunately the solution of Eq. (7.3-17) is not unique as a result of the fact that the equation is quadratic in $\mathbf{R}_o$. Of the several possible solutions, the desired answer is obtained by enforcing the requirement that $\mathbf{R}_o$ be positive definite. If this is done, a unique solution is obtained, which is identical to the answer found by the limiting procedure discussed previously.

Because of the nonlinear character of Eq. (7.3-17) and the necessity of enforcing the positive definiteness of $\mathbf{R}_o$ in order to obtain the correct answer, the solution of Eq. (7.3-17) is difficult to program on a digital computer. On the other hand, the solution can be achieved by hand with relative ease for second- and even third-order systems.

Example 7.3-3 As an illustration of this procedure, let us consider once again the problem of Example 7.3-2. For this problem the reduced Riccati equation becomes

$$-2r_o - r_o{}^2 + 1 = 0$$

The solution of the equation can be obtained by using the quadratic formula

$$r_o = -1 \pm \sqrt{2}$$

Even in this simple problem we observe the feature that the solution of the reduced Riccati equation is not unique. If r_o is required to be positive, we see that

$$r_o = \sqrt{2} - 1$$

is the only possible solution. This solution agrees with the answer found in Example 7.3-2.

Example 7.3-4 As another example, let us consider the system

$$\dot{x} = \begin{bmatrix} 0 & 1 \\ 0 & 0 \end{bmatrix} x + \begin{bmatrix} 0 \\ 1 \end{bmatrix} u$$

with the performance index

$$PI = \int_0^\infty (4x_1^2 + u^2) \, dt$$

In this case Eq. (7.3-17) becomes

$$\begin{bmatrix} 0 & 0 \\ 1 & 0 \end{bmatrix} \begin{bmatrix} r_{11} & r_{12} \\ r_{12} & r_{22} \end{bmatrix} + \begin{bmatrix} r_{11} & r_{12} \\ r_{12} & r_{22} \end{bmatrix} \begin{bmatrix} 0 & 1 \\ 0 & 0 \end{bmatrix}$$
$$- \begin{bmatrix} r_{11} & r_{12} \\ r_{12} & r_{22} \end{bmatrix} \begin{bmatrix} 0 \\ 1 \end{bmatrix} \begin{bmatrix} 0 & 1 \end{bmatrix} \begin{bmatrix} r_{11} & r_{12} \\ r_{12} & r_{22} \end{bmatrix} + \begin{bmatrix} 4 & 0 \\ 0 & 0 \end{bmatrix} = 0$$

which reduces to the three algebraic equations

$$-r_{12}^2 + 4 = 0 \qquad r_{11} - r_{12}r_{22} = 0 \qquad \text{and} \qquad -r_{22}^2 + 2r_{12} = 0$$

The only solution of these equations for which $\mathbf{R}_o$ is positive definite is

$$r_{11} = 4 \qquad r_{12} = 2 \qquad r_{22} = 2$$

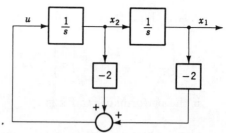

Fig. 7.3-3 Optimal-feedback system
for Example 7.3-4.

The optimal-control law is then given by Eq. (7.3-14),

$$u^o(\mathbf{x}) = -\mathbf{P}^{-1}\mathbf{b}^T\mathbf{R}_o\mathbf{x} = -2(x_1 + x_2)$$

The resulting optimal-feedback system is shown in Fig. 7.3-3.

Before discussing the derivation of the Kalman equation in which the reduced Riccati equation is transformed into a frequency-domain relation, let us consider first two alternate developments of the reduced Riccati equation.   We do so in order to demonstrate the generality of the Riccati equation and the close relationship between the second method of Liapunov and optimal control.

Exercises 7.3   *7.3-1.* Find the optimal-feedback coefficients for the system

$$\dot{x} = -3x + u$$

if the performance index is

$$PI = \int_0^\infty (x^2 + pu^2)\, dt$$

where

(a) $p = 0.1$ (b) $p = 1.0$ (c) $p = 10.0$

Compare the response of the three systems for an initial condition of $x(0) = 1$.

answers:

(a) $k = 1.36$ (b) 0.162 (c) 0.0166

7.3-2.   Find the optimal-feedback coefficients for the system

$$\dot{x} = \begin{bmatrix} 0 & 1 \\ -2 & -1 \end{bmatrix} x + \begin{bmatrix} 0 \\ 2 \end{bmatrix} u$$

if the performance index is

$$PI = \int_0^\infty (x_1{}^2 + u^2)\, dt$$

answer:

k = col (0.414,0.315)

7.3-3.   Find the optimal-feedback coefficients for the system

$$\dot{x} = \begin{bmatrix} 0 & 1 \\ -2 & -3 \end{bmatrix} x + \begin{bmatrix} 0 \\ 1 \end{bmatrix} u$$

if the performance index is

$$PI = \int_0^\infty (\alpha x_1{}^2 + u^2)\, dt$$

where

(*a*) $\alpha = 1.0$ (*b*) $\alpha = 10.0$

answers:

(*a*)   **k** = col (0.236,0.0777)   (*b*)   **k** = col (1.74,0.533)

7.3-4.   Repeat Exercise 7.3-3 using the performance index

$$PI = \int_0^\infty (x_1{}^2 + x_2{}^2 + u^2)\, dt$$

answer:

k = col (0.236,0.236)

7.3-5.   Find the optimal-feedback-coefficient matrix for the system

$$\dot{\mathbf{x}} = \begin{bmatrix} 0 & 1 \\ 1 & 1 \end{bmatrix} \mathbf{x} + \begin{bmatrix} 1 & 1 \\ 0 & 1 \end{bmatrix} \mathbf{u}$$

if the performance index is

$$\mathrm{PI} = \int_0^\infty (x_1{}^2 + u_1{}^2 + u_2{}^2)\, dt$$

answer:

$$\mathbf{K}^T = \begin{bmatrix} 0.720 & 0.479 \\ 1.200 & 1.878 \end{bmatrix}$$

7.3-6.   Repeat Exercise 7.3-5 for the system

$$\dot{\mathbf{x}} = \begin{bmatrix} 0 & 1 & 0 \\ 0 & 0 & 1 \\ 0 & -2 & -3 \end{bmatrix} \mathbf{x} + \begin{bmatrix} 1 & 0 \\ 0 & 0 \\ 0 & 1 \end{bmatrix} \mathbf{u}$$

and the performance index

$$\mathrm{PI} = \int_0^\infty (x_1{}^2 + x_2{}^2 + 4u_1{}^2 + u_2{}^2)\, dt$$

answer:

$$\mathbf{K}^T = \begin{bmatrix} 0.455 & 0.380 & 0.103 \\ 0.413 & 0.732 & 0.228 \end{bmatrix}$$

7.4   *The second method of Liapunov and the linear control problem*

We have already mentioned that the value function $V(\mathbf{x},t)$ could be considered a Liapunov function. In this section the tie-in between the second method of Liapunov and optimal control is illustrated for the special case of the linear control problem. The reader will recall that in the linear control problem the system is described by Eq. (**AB**) and the performance index is given by

$$\mathrm{PI} = \int_0^\infty (\mathbf{x}^T\mathbf{Q}\mathbf{x} + \mathbf{u}^T\mathbf{P}\mathbf{u})\, dt \tag{7.1-1}$$

and $\mathbf{u}$ is unconstrained. Because of the infinite upper limit in Eq. (7.1-1), we have seen in the previous section that $V(\mathbf{x},t)$ is independent of t and is actually $V(\mathbf{x})$.

In order to demonstrate the relation between the second method and optimal control in the linear control problem it is necessary to begin by assuming, as we did in the last section, that $\mathbf{u}^o$ is $\mathbf{u}^o = \mathbf{u}^o(\mathbf{x})$. Here we must go a little farther, however, and assume that the optimal-control law is actually the linear combination of state variables, which we know is the correct answer. The initial assumption, then, is that

$$\mathbf{u}^o = \mathbf{u}^o(\mathbf{x}) = -\mathbf{K}^T\mathbf{x} \tag{7.4-1}$$

On the basis of this assumption the plant equation (**AB**) becomes

$$\dot{\mathbf{x}} = \mathbf{A}\mathbf{x} + \mathbf{B}(-\mathbf{K}^T\mathbf{x}) = (\mathbf{A} - \mathbf{B}\mathbf{K}^T)\mathbf{x} \tag{7.4-2}$$

We consider first the *parameter-optimization approach* to the problem. Therefore we assume that the form of the optimal-control law is given by Eq. (7.4-1) but that the elements of $\mathbf{K}$ are unknown. The problem is then to pick the elements of $\mathbf{K}$ such that the performance index of Eq. (7.1-1) is minimized. This result is accomplished by finding the value of the performance index as a function of $\mathbf{K}$ and then setting its partial derivative with respect to $\mathbf{K}$ equal to zero in order to generate an equation for the optimal value of $\mathbf{K}$.

Let us suppose that we define a Liapunov function by the relation

$$V[\mathbf{x}(t)] = \int_t^\infty (\mathbf{x}^T\mathbf{Q}\mathbf{x} + \mathbf{u}^T\mathbf{P}\mathbf{u})\, dt$$

which may be written, using Eq. (7.4-1), as

$$V[\mathbf{x}(t)] = \int_t^\infty \mathbf{x}^T(\mathbf{Q} + \mathbf{K}\mathbf{P}\mathbf{K}^T)\mathbf{x}\, dt \tag{7.4-3}$$

Then the value of the performance for a trajectory starting at $\mathbf{x}(0)$ is given by $V[\mathbf{x}(0)]$. The total time derivative of $V(\mathbf{x})$ as given by Eq. (7.4-3) is

$$\dot{V}(\mathbf{x}) = -\mathbf{x}^T(\mathbf{Q} + \mathbf{K}\mathbf{P}\mathbf{K}^T)\mathbf{x} \tag{7.4-4}$$

Notice that $\dot{V}(\mathbf{x})$ is the negative of the integrand of the performance index.

Since $\dot{V}(\mathbf{x})$ is quadratic in $\mathbf{x}$, and since the plant equation is linear, let us suppose that $V(\mathbf{x})$ is also given by a quadratic form,

$$V(\mathbf{x}) = \mathbf{x}^T \mathbf{R}_o \mathbf{x} \tag{7.4-5}$$

where we have used $\mathbf{R}_o$ because of our knowledge of the end result rather than as an implied relation to the previous results. The time derivative of $V(\mathbf{x})$ as given by Eq. (7.4-5) is

$$\dot{V}(\mathbf{x}) = \dot{\mathbf{x}}^T \mathbf{R}_o \mathbf{x} + \mathbf{x}^T \mathbf{R}_o \dot{\mathbf{x}}$$

Substituting for $\dot{\mathbf{x}}$ from the plant equation (7.4-2), we have

$$\dot{V}(\mathbf{x}) = \mathbf{x}^T[(\mathbf{A} - \mathbf{B}\mathbf{K}^T)^T\mathbf{R}_o + \mathbf{R}_o(\mathbf{A} - \mathbf{B}\mathbf{K}^T)]\mathbf{x} \tag{7.4-6}$$

Comparing this result with Eq. (7.4-4), we see that it is necessary that $\mathbf{R}_o$ satisfy the following equation:

$$(\mathbf{A} - \mathbf{B}\mathbf{K}^T)^T\mathbf{R}_o + \mathbf{R}_o(\mathbf{A} - \mathbf{B}\mathbf{K}^T) = -\mathbf{Q} - \mathbf{K}\mathbf{P}\mathbf{K}^T \tag{7.4-7}$$

In order to apply the parameter-optimization approach directly to this problem, it would now be necessary to solve Eq. (7.4-7) for the elements of $\mathbf{R}_o$ in terms of $\mathbf{K}$. Then one would set $\partial \mathbf{R}_o / \partial \mathbf{K}$ equal to zero in order to solve for the optimal value of $\mathbf{K}$, since the only part of $V[\mathbf{x}(0)]$ which depends on $\mathbf{K}$ is $\mathbf{R}_o$. Unfortunately the expressions for the elements of $\mathbf{R}_o$ in terms of $\mathbf{K}$ are very complicated and difficult to obtain, with the partial-derivative operation making them even worse. Therefore, we shall choose a different and somewhat indirect route.

We begin by taking the partial derivative of both sides of Eq. (7.4-7) with respect to $\mathbf{K}$ requiring that $\partial \mathbf{R}_o / \partial \mathbf{K} = 0$ in order to obtain the optimal value for $\mathbf{K}$. In addition we know that $\partial \mathbf{K} / \partial \mathbf{K} = \mathbf{I}$. The result is that

$$-2\mathbf{R}_o\mathbf{B} = -2\mathbf{K}\mathbf{P}$$

Therefore

$$\mathbf{K} = \mathbf{R}_o\mathbf{B}\mathbf{P}^{-1} \tag{7.4-8}$$

Substituting this into Eq. (7.4-7), we obtain

$$(\mathbf{A} - \mathbf{B}\mathbf{P}^{-1}\mathbf{B}^T\mathbf{R}_o)^T\mathbf{R}_o + \mathbf{R}_o(\mathbf{A} - \mathbf{B}\mathbf{P}^{-1}\mathbf{B}^T\mathbf{R}_o)$$
$$= -\mathbf{Q} - \mathbf{R}_o\mathbf{B}\mathbf{P}^{-1}\mathbf{P}\mathbf{P}^{-1}\mathbf{B}^T\mathbf{R}_o$$

If this equation is simplified by canceling the two $R_oBP^{-1}B^TR_o$ terms, it becomes

$$A^TR_o + R_oA - R_oBP^{-1}B^TR_o + Q = 0$$

which is nothing more than the reduced Riccati equation. We also note that the feedback coefficients as given by Eq. (7.4-8) are identical to those given by Eq. (7.3-16). Hence this development has led us back to exactly the same problem we had before.

As another approach, let us suppose that $\dot{V}(x)$ is still given by the negative of the integrand of the performance index. However, rather than minimizing $V(x)$, we simply pick $V(x)$ and find the corresponding $u(x)$. Therefore we select $V(x)$ as

$$V(x) = x^TR_ox$$

where R_o is assumed to be any known positive definite matrix. The time derivative of $V(x)$ is once again given by Eq. (7.4-6),

$$\dot{V}(x) = x^T(A^TR_o + R_oA)x - x^T(KB^TR_o + R_oBK^T)x$$

But $\dot{V}(x)$ is also equal to the negative of the integrand of the performance index (7.4-4); therefore

$$x^T(A^TR_o + R_oA)x - x^T(KB^TR_o + R_oBK^T)x = -x^TQx - x^TKPK^Tx$$

or, in other words,

$$(A^TR_o + R_oA + Q) - (KB^TR_o + R_oBK^T) + KPK^T = 0 \qquad (7.4\text{-}9)$$

While this result is the same as Eq. (7.4-7), the problem is quite different. In this case, R_o is assumed to be known, and we wish to find K such that the equation is satisfied. In order to solve this equation for K it is necessary to use the following result from matrix algebra.

There exists a real matrix solution Z to the matrix quadratic equation

$$M + NZ^T + ZN^T + ZPZ^T = 0 \qquad (7.4\text{-}10)$$

where P is symmetric and positive definite and M and N are real matrices if the matrix $NP^{-1}N^T - M$ is at least positive semidefinite. This solution is given by

$$Z = \sqrt{NP^{-1}N^T - M}\; L \sqrt{P^{-1}} - NP^{-1}$$

where $\mathbf{L}$ is an arbitrary orthogonal matrix, that is, $\mathbf{LL}^T = \mathbf{I}$. By the square root of a positive definite or semidefinite matrix $\mathbf{H}$ we mean the matrix $\mathbf{G}$ such that $\mathbf{GG}^T = \mathbf{H}$, that is, $\sqrt{\mathbf{H}} = \mathbf{G}$. This result may be easily proved by direct substitution. In addition, it is simple to demonstrate that in the scalar case the well-known result is obtained.

Comparing Eq. (7.4-9) with Eq. (7.4-10), we see that

$$\mathbf{M} = \mathbf{A}^T\mathbf{R}_o + \mathbf{R}_o\mathbf{A} + \mathbf{Q}$$

$\mathbf{N} = -\mathbf{R}_o\mathbf{B}$, and $\mathbf{P} = \mathbf{P}$. The matrix of feedback coefficients $\mathbf{K}$ is therefore

$$\mathbf{K} = \sqrt{\mathbf{R}_o\mathbf{BP}^{-1}\mathbf{B}^T\mathbf{R}_o - \mathbf{A}^T\mathbf{R}_o - \mathbf{R}_o\mathbf{A} - \mathbf{Q}} \ \mathbf{L} \ \sqrt{\mathbf{P}^{-1}} + \mathbf{R}_o\mathbf{BP}^{-1}$$
$$(7.4\text{-}11)$$

with the requirement that

$$\mathbf{R}_o\mathbf{BP}^{-1}\mathbf{B}^T\mathbf{R}_o - \mathbf{A}^T\mathbf{R}_o - \mathbf{R}_o\mathbf{A} - \mathbf{Q} \geq 0 \qquad (7.4\text{-}12)$$

Since the only positive term in this constraint relation is quadratic in $\mathbf{R}_o$, it is obvious that the smaller $\mathbf{R}_o$ is, the less likely it is that the requirement will be satisfied. This makes sense, since if we make $\mathbf{R}_o$ too small, we may have requested a value of the performance index that is smaller than the minimum. Hence the best value of $\mathbf{R}_o$ that we could select would be the value which made Eq. (7.4-12) become an equality, that is,

$$\mathbf{R}_o\mathbf{BP}^{-1}\mathbf{B}^T\mathbf{R}_o - \mathbf{A}^T\mathbf{R}_o - \mathbf{R}_o\mathbf{A} - \mathbf{Q} = 0$$

But, except for the unimportant change of signs, this is nothing more or less than the reduced Riccati equation. Once again we have returned to our starting point.

In addition, we see that if $\mathbf{R}_o$ does satisfy the reduced Riccati equation, $\mathbf{K}$ is given by

$$\mathbf{K} = \mathbf{R}_o\mathbf{BP}^{-1}$$

which is also identical to the previous results.

Throughout this development it has been tacitly assumed that the controlled linear system is stable, so that $\mathbf{x}(\infty) = 0$ and $V[\mathbf{x}(\infty)] = 0$. Kalman (1964) has shown that in order to ensure stability, the pair $[\mathbf{A}, \mathbf{\Gamma}^T]$

must be completely observable, where $\boldsymbol{\Gamma}$ is defined by

$$\mathbf{Q} = \boldsymbol{\Gamma}\boldsymbol{\Gamma}^T$$

This is equivalent to the statement that

$$\text{rank } [\boldsymbol{\Gamma}, \mathbf{A}^T\boldsymbol{\Gamma}, \ldots, (\mathbf{A}^T)^{n-1}\boldsymbol{\Gamma}] = n \tag{7.4-13}$$

If Eq. (7.4-13) is compared with Eq. (2.4-4) in Theorem 2.4-1, it is seen that $\mathbf{C}$ corresponds to $\boldsymbol{\Gamma}^T$. If one then defines a *synthetic output* as

$$\bar{\mathbf{y}} = \boldsymbol{\Gamma}^T\mathbf{x}$$

Eq. (7.4-13) corresponds to the requirement that the *synthetic output* $\bar{\mathbf{y}}$ be observable. A discussion of the synthetic output and its relation to the performance index is presented in the next chapter.

In the next section, the reduced Riccati equation is used to develop a frequency-domain criterion for the optimal-control law.

Exercise 7.4   *7.4-1.* Show that the optimal closed-loop system for the plant

$$\dot{\mathbf{x}} = \begin{bmatrix} 0 & 0 \\ 0 & 1 \end{bmatrix} \mathbf{x} + \begin{bmatrix} 1 \\ 1 \end{bmatrix} u$$

$$y = [1 \quad 1]\mathbf{x}$$

and the performance index

$$\text{PI} = \int_0^\infty (x_1{}^2 + u^2)\, dt$$

is unstable by finding the optimal-feedback coefficients and determining the closed-loop poles. Note that this system and performance index violate the controllability of the synthetic-output condition of Eq. (7.4-13), although the system is controllable and observable.

7.5   *Frequency-domain criterion for optimality*

The techniques discussed in the previous two sections for determining the feedback-coefficient matrix $\mathbf{K}$ are characterized by the necessity of finding first the solution of the Riccati equation $\mathbf{R}_o$. The feedback coefficients are then computed by means of Eq. (7.3-16). Since our interest is basically in the feedback coefficients, it would be desirable to develop an approach which would eliminate the requirement of finding R_o. This is particularly helpful if the number of control variables r is less than $(n + 1)/2$, since then one would have to solve for only n times r feedback coefficients rather than n times $(n + 1)/2$ elements of R_o. In many problems the control is scalar, and such a saving of computational effort can be considerable.

Two interesting features occur in this development: (1) the resulting expression is considerably simpler than might be expected, and (2) the expression is stated in the frequency domain. The second feature, which may seem very strange considering the almost complete dependence of the modern approach on the time domain, is helpful in comparing the modern approach with classical synthesis procedures, which are entirely dependent on the frequency domain.

The development, which follows closely the original development of Kalman (1964), begins with the algebraic Riccati equation, repeated here for convenience,

$$A^T R_o + R_o A - R_o B P^{-1} B^T R_o + Q = 0 \qquad (7.5\text{-}1)$$

The first step is to rewrite the matrices Q and P as

$$Q = \Gamma \Gamma^T \qquad P = DD^T$$

which may always be done, since Q and P are either positive definite or semidefinite. In addition, since P is always positive definite, D can always be chosen to be symmetric and positive definite. Therefore P may also be written as

$$P = DD$$

and P^{-1} is given by

$$P^{-1} = D^{-1}D^{-1}$$

where D^{-1} must exist, since D is positive definite.

Substituting these results into Eq. (7.5-1) and rewriting slightly, we have

$$-R_o A - A^T R_o + R_o B D^{-1} D^{-1} B^T R_o = \Gamma \Gamma^T \qquad (7.5\text{-}2)$$

From Eq. (7.3-16) we see that

$$\mathbf{K} = \mathbf{R}_o \mathbf{B} \mathbf{P}^{-1} = \mathbf{R}_o \mathbf{B} \mathbf{D}^{-1} \mathbf{D}^{-1}$$

and therefore

$$\mathbf{KD} = \mathbf{R}_o \mathbf{B} \mathbf{D}^{-1}$$

Equation (7.5-2) may then be written as

$$-\mathbf{R}_o \mathbf{A} - \mathbf{A}^T \mathbf{R}_o + \mathbf{KDDK}^T = \boldsymbol{\Gamma}\boldsymbol{\Gamma}^T \tag{7.5-3}$$

Now, adding and subtracting $s\mathbf{R}_o$ on the left side of Eq. (7.5-3), we obtain

$$\mathbf{R}_o(s\mathbf{I} - \mathbf{A}) + (-s\mathbf{I} - \mathbf{A}^T)\mathbf{R}_o + \mathbf{KDDK}^T = \boldsymbol{\Gamma}\boldsymbol{\Gamma}^T \tag{7.5-4}$$

The next step is to multiply both sides of this equation from the left by $\mathbf{D}^{-1}\mathbf{B}^T\boldsymbol{\Phi}^T(-s)$ and from the right by $\boldsymbol{\Phi}(s)\mathbf{B}\mathbf{D}^{-1}$, where $\boldsymbol{\Phi}(s)$ is the resolvent matrix $(s\mathbf{I} - \mathbf{A})^{-1}$. The matrix $\boldsymbol{\Phi}^T(-s)$ is therefore

$$\boldsymbol{\Phi}^T(-s) = (-s\mathbf{I} - \mathbf{A}^T)^{-1}$$

Equation (7.5-4) then becomes

$$\begin{aligned}
\mathbf{D}^{-1}\mathbf{B}^T\boldsymbol{\Phi}^T(-s)\mathbf{R}_o\mathbf{B}\mathbf{D}^{-1} &+ \mathbf{D}^{-1}\mathbf{B}^T\mathbf{R}_o\boldsymbol{\Phi}(s)\mathbf{B}\mathbf{D}^{-1} \\
&+ \mathbf{D}^{-1}\mathbf{B}^T\boldsymbol{\Phi}^T(-s)\mathbf{KDDK}^T\boldsymbol{\Phi}(s)\mathbf{B}\mathbf{D}^{-1} \\
&= \mathbf{D}^{-1}\mathbf{B}^T\boldsymbol{\Phi}^T(-s)\boldsymbol{\Gamma}\boldsymbol{\Gamma}^T\boldsymbol{\Phi}(s)\mathbf{B}\mathbf{D}^{-1} \quad (7.5\text{-}5)
\end{aligned}$$

Once again, using the fact that $\mathbf{R}_o\mathbf{B}\mathbf{D}^{-1} = \mathbf{KD}$, we can reduce this equation to

$$\begin{aligned}
\mathbf{D}^{-1}\mathbf{B}^T\boldsymbol{\Phi}^T(-s)\mathbf{KD} &+ \mathbf{DK}^T\boldsymbol{\Phi}(s)\mathbf{B}\mathbf{D}^{-1} \\
+ \mathbf{D}^{-1}\mathbf{B}^T\boldsymbol{\Phi}^T(-s)\mathbf{KDDK}^T\boldsymbol{\Phi}(s)\mathbf{B}\mathbf{D}^{-1} &= \mathbf{D}^{-1}\mathbf{B}^T\boldsymbol{\Phi}^T(-s)\boldsymbol{\Gamma}\boldsymbol{\Gamma}^T\boldsymbol{\Phi}(s)\mathbf{B}\mathbf{D}^{-1}
\end{aligned}$$

With this equation we have achieved our desired result, since $\mathbf{R}_o$ has been completely eliminated from the equation, and we are left with only n times r (nonlinear) algebraic equations for the elements of $\mathbf{K}$. However, by adding the $r \times r$ identity matrix to both sides of the equation, it is possible to obtain a simpler expression of the result, which may be written as

$$[I + D^{-1}B^T\Phi^T(-s)KD][I + DK^T\Phi(s)BD^{-1}]$$
$$= I + [D^{-1}B^T\Phi^T(-s)\Gamma][\Gamma^T\Phi(s)BD^{-1}] \quad (7.5\text{-}6)$$

This may be further simplified by using the notation $\{M(s)\}^2$ to indicate the matrix multiplication

$$\{M(s)\}^2 = M^T(-s)M(s)$$

In terms of this notation Eq. (7.5-6) may be written

$$\{I + DK^T\Phi(s)BD^{-1}\}^2 = I + \{\Gamma^T\Phi(s)BD^{-1}\}^2 \quad (7.5\text{-}7)$$

This result and the various simplifications that we shall discuss below are commonly referred to as the *Kalman equation*.

Quite often the **P** matrix is assumed to be equal to the $r \times r$ identity matrix. This assumption can always be justified by appropriate modification of the **Q** or **B** matrices. For this case the **D** matrix is also equal to **I**, and Eq. (7.5-7) then becomes

$$\{I + K^T\Phi(s)B\}^2 = I + \{\Gamma^T\Phi(s)B\}^2 \quad (7.5\text{-}8)$$

In many practical control systems the control is scalar, and the **B** matrix reduces to a column matrix **b**. The $r \times r$ identity matrix then becomes a unity scalar, and the scalar control u is simply $u = -k^Tx$, with **k** a vector rather than a matrix. Then Eq. (7.5-8) may be rewritten as

$$|1 + k^T\Phi(s)b|^2 = 1 + \|\Gamma^T\Phi(s)b\|^2 \quad (7.5\text{-}9)$$

In Eq. (7.5-9) the term $k^T\Phi(s)b$ is a scalar, and hence the left side of this equation involves a scalar magnitude. Here the notation

$$|m(s)|^2 = m(-s)m(s)$$

is used for simplicity even though this is true only for $s = j\omega$. The term $\Gamma^T\Phi(s)b$, however, is a vector, whose magnitude is indicated by the norm-squared notation.

As we shall show in Sec. 8.2, there is no loss of generality for the scalar input and output case in assuming that Γ is a column matrix γ.

Using this assumption, we can further reduce Eq. (7.5-9) to the form

$$|1 + \mathbf{k}^T \boldsymbol{\Phi}(s)\mathbf{b}|^2 = 1 + |\boldsymbol{\gamma}^T \boldsymbol{\Phi}(s)\mathbf{b}|^2 \tag{7.5-10}$$

Considerable use is made of this last form of Kalman's equation in the next chapter. First, however, let us consider a simple example to illustrate the application of the Kalman equation and to point out some of the difficulties inherent in its use.

> **Example 7.5-1**   The system equations for this multiple-input case are given by
>
> $$\dot{\mathbf{x}} = \begin{bmatrix} 0 & 1 \\ 0 & 0 \end{bmatrix} \mathbf{x} + \begin{bmatrix} 1 & 0 \\ 0 & 1 \end{bmatrix} \mathbf{u}$$
>
> with the performance index
>
> $$\text{PI} = \int_0^\infty \left\{ \mathbf{x}^T \begin{bmatrix} 1 & 0 \\ 0 & 1 \end{bmatrix} \mathbf{x} + \mathbf{u}^T \begin{bmatrix} 1 & 0 \\ 0 & 1 \end{bmatrix} \mathbf{u} \right\} dt$$
>
> Since **P** and **Q** are both equal to identity matrices, $\boldsymbol{\Gamma}$ and **D** are also identity matrices, and Eq. (7.5-7) becomes
>
> $$\{\mathbf{I} + \mathbf{K}^T \boldsymbol{\Phi}(s)\mathbf{B}\}^2 = \mathbf{I} + \{\boldsymbol{\Phi}(s)\mathbf{B}\}^2$$
>
> In addition, $\mathbf{B} = \mathbf{I}$, and therefore we have
>
> $$\{\mathbf{I} + \mathbf{K}^T \boldsymbol{\Phi}(s)\}^2 = \mathbf{I} + \{\boldsymbol{\Phi}(s)\}^2 \tag{7.5-11}$$
>
> For this problem, the resolvent matrix $\boldsymbol{\Phi}(s)$ is
>
> $$\boldsymbol{\Phi}(s) = (s\mathbf{I} - \mathbf{A})^{-1} = \begin{bmatrix} s & -1 \\ 0 & s \end{bmatrix}^{-1} = \begin{bmatrix} \dfrac{1}{s} & \dfrac{1}{s^2} \\ 0 & \dfrac{1}{s} \end{bmatrix}$$
>
> Therefore
>
> $$\mathbf{I} + \mathbf{K}^T \boldsymbol{\Phi}(s) = \begin{bmatrix} 1 + \dfrac{k_{11}}{s} & \dfrac{k_{11}}{s^2} + \dfrac{k_{21}}{s} \\ \dfrac{k_{12}}{s} & 1 + \dfrac{k_{12}}{s^2} + \dfrac{k_{22}}{s} \end{bmatrix}$$

Equation (7.5-11) then becomes

$$
\begin{bmatrix}
1 - \dfrac{k_{11}}{s} & -\dfrac{k_{12}}{s} \\[2ex]
\dfrac{k_{11}}{s^2} - \dfrac{k_{21}}{s} & 1 + \dfrac{k_{12}}{s^2} - \dfrac{k_{22}}{s}
\end{bmatrix}
\begin{bmatrix}
1 + \dfrac{k_{11}}{s} & \dfrac{k_{11}}{s^2} + \dfrac{k_{21}}{s} \\[2ex]
\dfrac{k_{12}}{s} & 1 + \dfrac{k_{12}}{s^2} + \dfrac{k_{22}}{s}
\end{bmatrix}
$$

$$
= \begin{bmatrix} 1 & 0 \\ 0 & 1 \end{bmatrix} +
\begin{bmatrix}
-\dfrac{1}{s} & 0 \\[2ex]
\dfrac{1}{s^2} & -\dfrac{1}{s}
\end{bmatrix}
\begin{bmatrix}
\dfrac{1}{s} & \dfrac{1}{s^2} \\[2ex]
0 & \dfrac{1}{s}
\end{bmatrix}
$$

Multiplying out both sides and equating coefficients of the powers of s, we find that it is necessary to solve the following algebraic equations:

$$k_{11}^2 + k_{12}^2 = 1 \qquad k_{12} - k_{21} = 0$$
$$k_{11} - k_{11}k_{21} - k_{12}k_{22} = 0 \qquad -2k_{12} + k_{21}^2 + k_{22}^2 = 1$$

Since these equations are nonlinear, the solution is not unique. However, if one enforces the requirement that the feedback coefficients be positive so that negative feedback results, the following unique answer is obtained:

$$k_{11} = 0.910 \qquad k_{12} = k_{21} = 0.414 \qquad k_{22} = 1.287$$

The resulting optimal system is shown in Fig. 7.5-1. The reader is urged to work this example by means of the reduced Riccati approach

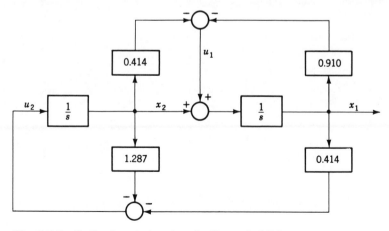

Fig. 7.5-1 Optimal-control system for Example 7.5-1.

of the previous section in order to see the relationship between the methods.

The above example has pointed out a very unfortunate feature of the Kalman equation approach. This approach also requires the solution of nonlinear algebraic equations, a task which is not easy to accomplish by hand or machine. Hence this approach has still not provided an easy solution to the linear optimal-control problem.

In the next chapters, the Kalman equation is used to form the basis of a new, effective, and practical approach to the design of linear control systems. In addition, several approximate procedures are discussed for solving the problem. However, before we discuss the more practical applications of the general theory of this chapter to the linear control problem, let us consider briefly a generalization of this linear control problem in which all the state variables are not available.

Exercises 7.5   *7.5-1.* Work Example 7.5-1 by means of the reduced Riccati equation.

7.5-2. Use the Kalman equation to find the optimal-feedback coefficients for the system

$$\dot{x} = \begin{bmatrix} 0 & 1 \\ -1 & -1 \end{bmatrix} x + \begin{bmatrix} 1 \\ 1 \end{bmatrix} u$$

if the performance index is

$$\text{PI} = \int_0^\infty (x_1{}^2 + x_2{}^2 + 2u^2)\, dt$$

answer:

$$\mathbf{k} = \text{col } (0.602, 0.333)$$

7.5-3. Repeat Exercise 7.5-2 using the reduced Riccati equation.

7.5-4. Find the feedback coefficients for the system

$$\dot{x} = \begin{bmatrix} 0 & 1 \\ -2 & -3 \end{bmatrix} x + \begin{bmatrix} 0 \\ 1 \end{bmatrix} u$$

by using the Kalman equation. The performance index is

$$\text{PI} = \int_0^\infty (x_1{}^2 + x_2{}^2 + pu^2)\, dt$$

where

(*a*) $p = 1.0$ (*b*) $p = 10.0$

answers:

(*a*) $\mathbf{k} = \text{col } (0.236, 0.236)$ (*b*) $\mathbf{k} = \text{col } (0.0248, 0.0248)$

7.5-5. Use the Kalman equation to find the optimal-feedback-coefficient matrix for the system

$$\dot{\mathbf{x}} = \begin{bmatrix} 0 & 1 & 0 \\ 0 & 0 & 1 \\ 0 & -3 & -2 \end{bmatrix} \mathbf{x} + \begin{bmatrix} 1 & 0 \\ 0 & 0 \\ 0 & 1 \end{bmatrix} \mathbf{u}$$

if the performance index is

$$\text{PI} = \int_0^\infty (x_1{}^2 + x_2{}^2 + 4u_1{}^2 + u_2{}^2) \, dt$$

answer:

$$\mathbf{K}^T = \begin{bmatrix} 0.459 & 0.262 & 0.099 \\ 0.394 & 0.438 & 0.199 \end{bmatrix}$$

7.6   *Kalman filter and inaccessible state variables*

Throughout this chapter we have assumed that all the state variables are directly measurable. While there are many practical systems for which this assumption is justified, there are many more for which it is not. It is with this latter class of systems that this section is concerned.

The approach we use in this section is an extension of the Wiener-Kolmogorov theory (Lee, 1960), commonly referred to as the *Kalman filter theory.* Since the concepts underlying this theory, e.g., orthogonal projection theory in Hilbert space, are beyond the scope of this book, our approach is, of necessity, rather formal, with little or no proof offered for the results presented. The emphasis is on the development of a manipulative understanding of the theory and its relation to practical design of control systems.

It is assumed that the reader has a basic knowledge of random-process theory, such as that contained in Truxal (1955), chap. 7, or

Schwartz and Friedland (1965), chap. 9.   If the reader does not have this background, it is suggested that this section be initially bypassed and that the reader wait until Chap. 9, where the same problem is treated without the use of random-process theory.

In simple terms, the Kalman filter is used to estimate, on the basis of noisy measurements, the values of the state variables of a system subject to stochastic input disturbances.   This approach requires that we take cognizance of the physical reality of random input disturbances and measurement noise, which we have neglected in our treatment so far.   Some modifications in the formulation of the control problem result.

First, the input disturbances are included by adding the noise input $\mathbf{v}(t)$ to the control input $\mathbf{u}(t)$, so that the system equations become

$$\dot{\mathbf{x}} = \mathbf{A}\mathbf{x} + \mathbf{B}(\mathbf{u} + \mathbf{v}) \tag{7.6-1}$$

In including the measurement noise, we add to the output expression a measurement-noise vector $\mathbf{w}(t)$, so that we have

$$\tilde{\mathbf{y}}(t) = \tilde{\mathbf{C}}\mathbf{x}(t) + \mathbf{w}(t) \tag{7.6-2}$$

Here, as above, we are treating the multiple-output system.   These outputs can be divided into two classes, control outputs and measurement outputs.   By control outputs we refer to the physical quantities that the system is to control, e.g., position in a positioning system or temperature in a thermal regulator.   Measurement outputs, on the other hand, are physical quantities which may be directly measured in the system but which are not the variables being controlled, e.g., velocity in a positioning system.

In order to indicate that we are using this more general concept of an output we have placed a tilde over both $\mathbf{y}$ and $\mathbf{C}$ in Eq. (7.6-2).   Hence we retain the output expression

$$\mathbf{y}(t) = \mathbf{C}\mathbf{x}(t) \tag{C}$$

for the original *control* outputs.

When we have previously referred to single-output systems, we have really meant single-*control*-output systems.   It was assumed that $n - 1$ measurement outputs also existed, so that the state variables of interest could be directly synthesized by linear combinations of these outputs.

In the present formulation one or both of the following items complicate the situation: (1) the total number of outputs, both control and measurement, may be less than n; (2) the measurements are corrupted by

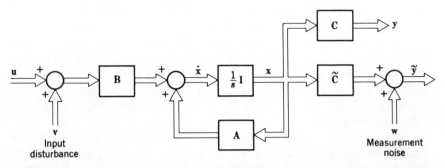

Fig. 7.6-1 System representation including input disturbance and measurement noise.

the noise signal $\mathbf{w}(t)$. Both of these conditions dictate further manipulations of the outputs before estimates of the state variables may be made. This is where the Kalman filter comes in; but first let us consider some further background.

It should be noted that we have assumed that both the input and output noise are additive. While this is not the only manner in which noise signals may affect a system, it is the most common. In addition, this additive-noise assumption is necessary to preserve the linearity and hence the mathematical tractability of the problem.

Our model of the system has now taken the form shown in Fig. 7.6-1. This model indicates that control may be exerted only through the noisy input channel and that observations may be made only through the noisy measurement channel.

The problem is then to find a closed-loop procedure for generating the optimal-control input $\mathbf{u}(t)$ in terms of the output $\tilde{\mathbf{y}}(t)$. The interesting and fortunate fact is that, under mild restrictions on the input and output disturbances, this problem can be separated into two simpler problems, referred to as *control* and *estimation*.

In the control phase of the solution one assumes that all the state variables are available, and hence one directly employs the techniques discussed in the preceding sections. In other words, we find the optimal-feedback coefficients just as before, assuming that all the state variables can be measured exactly.

In order to use these results it is necessary to reconstruct the state variables in some fashion from the noisy measurements which are the only actual outputs of the system. The device which accomplishes this job is the Kalman filter. Using the noisy measurements $\tilde{\mathbf{y}}(t)$ as inputs, the Kalman filter generates estimates of all the state variables. These estimates are symbolized by $\hat{\mathbf{x}}(t)$ to indicate that they are only estimates of the state variables rather than the true values of the state variables.

The amazing fact is that this Kalman filter takes on a particularly simple structure closely resembling the original system. In addition, the techniques used to solve the estimation problem by determining the Kalman filter are very closely related to the techniques used to solve the control problem. In fact, it is possible to cast the problem as a so-called "dual control problem."

These estimates are then used just as if they were the actual state variables in order to generate the optimal control, that is, $\mathbf{u}(t) = -\mathbf{K}^T\hat{\mathbf{x}}(t)$. The complete system is symbolically represented in Fig. 7.6-2. The validity of separating the problem into the two separate phases of control and estimation is a result of the linearity of the system, the nature of the performance index, and the character (as yet unspecified) of the input and output noise. While a rigorous proof of this fact is beyond the scope of this presentation, we shall discuss the point in a little more detail after a further characterization of the noise signals.

First of all, we assume that the noise signals $\mathbf{v}$ and $\mathbf{w}$ are stationary gaussian processes with zero mean. In addition, the signals $\mathbf{v}$ and $\mathbf{w}$ are assumed to be independent, that is,

$$E\{\mathbf{v}(t)\mathbf{w}(t+\tau)\} = 0$$

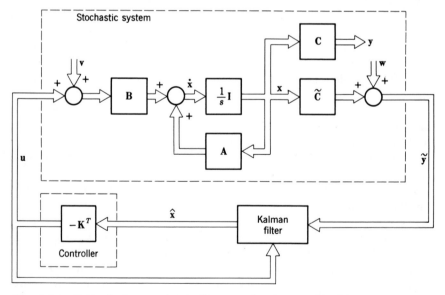

Fig. 7.6-2 Optimal structure for the linear stochastic control problem.

The last requirement is that the input and output disturbances be white noise so that the correlation functions may be written as

$$E\{\mathbf{v}(t)\mathbf{v}^T(t + \tau)\} = \bar{\mathbf{Q}}\delta(\tau) \quad \text{and} \quad E\{\mathbf{w}(t)\mathbf{w}^T(t + \tau)\} = \bar{\mathbf{P}}\delta(\tau)$$

where $\delta(\tau)$ is the Dirac delta function. For example, the element in the ith row and jth column of $\bar{\mathbf{Q}}$ is equal to $E\{v_i(t)v_j(t + \tau)\}$.

It is not uncommon for various elements of $\mathbf{v}$ and $\mathbf{w}$ also to be uncorrelated, so that $\bar{\mathbf{Q}}$ and $\bar{\mathbf{P}}$ become diagonal. In this case, the elements of $\bar{\mathbf{Q}}$ and $\bar{\mathbf{P}}$ may often be determined easily by experimental means. As added assistance, we shall see later that it is not necessary to know the absolute value of any of the elements but only the relative magnitude of the elements.

Of the requirements listed above for $\mathbf{v}$ and $\mathbf{w}$, the white-noise requirement is perhaps the most difficult to justify on a practical basis. No actual signal can ever satisfy the white-noise assumption, but if its frequency spectrum is appreciably flat out to a frequency one or more decades beyond the crossover frequency of the system, it may be approximated by white noise with no practical loss of accuracy. From this viewpoint it is particularly easy to justify the white-noise assumption for the typically low-frequency control systems.

Of primary importance in allowing the separation of the control and estimation problems is the gaussian nature of the input and output noise. This fact may be related to two features of gaussian signals: (1) any linear operation on a gaussian signal yields a gaussian signal, and (2) any gaussian signal is completely described by its means and variance. Since the Kalman filter provides an unbiased minimum-variance estimate of the state vector, it is the best filter that can be used for the estimation phase. We have already seen the optimality of the linear constant-gain feedback structure for the control phase. Hence, the optimal structure for the noisy problem consists of a combination of these two forms, as shown in Fig. 7.6-2.

With these definitions and comments as background, we are now prepared to discuss the solution of the estimation phase of the stochastic problem. This solution (Kalman, 1960; Kalman and Bucy, 1961) consists of the definition of a linear dynamic system, very similar to the original system, whose input is $\tilde{\mathbf{y}}(t)$ and whose output is $\hat{\mathbf{x}}(t)$,

$$\dot{\hat{\mathbf{x}}}(t) = \mathbf{A}\hat{\mathbf{x}}(t) + \bar{\mathbf{K}}[\tilde{\mathbf{y}}(t) - \tilde{\mathbf{C}}\hat{\mathbf{x}}(t)] + \mathbf{B}\mathbf{u}(t) \tag{7.6-3}$$

where

$$\bar{\mathbf{K}} = \bar{\mathbf{R}}_o\tilde{\mathbf{C}}^T\bar{\mathbf{P}}^{-1} \tag{7.6-4}$$

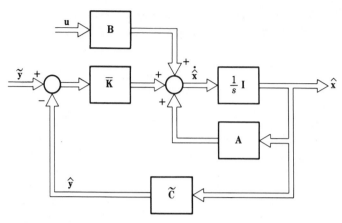

Fig. 7.6-3 Kalman filter.

and $\bar{\mathbf{R}}_o$ is the steady-state solution of a matrix Riccati differential equation

$$\dot{\bar{\mathbf{R}}} = \mathbf{A}\bar{\mathbf{R}} + \bar{\mathbf{R}}\mathbf{A}^T - \bar{\mathbf{R}}\tilde{\mathbf{C}}^T\bar{\mathbf{P}}^{-1}\tilde{\mathbf{C}}\bar{\mathbf{R}} + \mathbf{B}\bar{\mathbf{Q}}\mathbf{B}^T \qquad (7.6\text{-}5)$$

Here the steady-state value is found by integrating this equation forward in time from the initial condition $\bar{\mathbf{R}}(0) = E\{\mathbf{x}(0)\mathbf{x}^T(0)\}$. Here the initial state $\mathbf{x}(0)$ is treated as a random variable with gaussian distribution and $E\{\mathbf{x}(0)\} = 0$. The value of $\bar{\mathbf{R}}_o = \lim\limits_{t \to \infty} \bar{\mathbf{R}}(t)$ is independent of the initial conditions on $\bar{\mathbf{R}}$ and one may therefore set $\bar{\mathbf{R}}(0)$ to any value if only $\bar{\mathbf{R}}_o$ is of interest. The initial condition $\hat{\mathbf{x}}(0)$ is set equal to $E\{x(0)\} = 0$. This system is represented graphically in Fig. 7.6-3 for comparison with Fig. 7.6-1.

In simple terms an error signal is generated by subtracting the estimated output $\hat{\mathbf{y}}(t)$ from the actual output $\mathbf{y}(t)$, and then with $\bar{\mathbf{K}}$ as the input matrix this error signal is used as the input to a model of the original system. Hence we observe two features of the Kalman filter: (1) the structure of the system is simple and well defined, and (2) the filter structure closely resembles that of the original system. In addition, the mathematical techniques involved in determining the filter, e.g., solving a matrix Riccati equation, are similar to those used earlier for the solution of the optimal linear control problem.

This similarity can be further strengthened by a careful comparison of Eqs. (7.6-4) and (7.6-5) with Eqs. (7.3-16) and (7.3-9), repeated here,

$$\mathbf{K} = \mathbf{R}_o\mathbf{B}\mathbf{P}^{-1} \qquad (7.6\text{-}6)$$

$$-\dot{\mathbf{R}}(t) = \mathbf{A}^T\mathbf{R}(t) + \mathbf{R}(t)\mathbf{A} - \mathbf{R}(t)\mathbf{B}\mathbf{P}^{-1}\mathbf{B}^T\mathbf{R}(t) + \mathbf{Q} \qquad (7.6\text{-}7)$$

which yield the optimal control for the system

$$\dot{\mathbf{x}} = \mathbf{A}\mathbf{x} + \mathbf{B}\mathbf{u} \tag{AB}$$

with the performance index

$$\text{PI} = \int_0^\infty (\mathbf{x}^T\mathbf{Q}\mathbf{x} + \mathbf{u}^T\mathbf{P}\mathbf{u})\, dt$$

In order to illustrate the relationship between these two problems more clearly, let us consider the optimal control of a fictitious linear system

$$\dot{\mathbf{x}} = \mathbf{A}^T\mathbf{x} + \tilde{\mathbf{C}}^T\mathbf{u} \tag{7.6-8}$$

subject to the performance index

$$\text{PI} = \int_0^\infty [\mathbf{x}^T(\mathbf{B}\bar{\mathbf{Q}}\mathbf{B}^T)\mathbf{x} + \mathbf{u}^T\bar{\mathbf{P}}\mathbf{u}]\, dt \tag{7.6-9}$$

If we make the appropriate substitution into the original control problem then Eqs. (7.6-6) and (7.6-7) become

$$\mathbf{K} = \mathbf{R}_o\tilde{\mathbf{C}}^T\bar{\mathbf{P}}^{-1} \tag{7.6-10}$$

and

$$-\dot{\mathbf{R}} = \mathbf{A}\mathbf{R} + \mathbf{R}\mathbf{A}^T - \mathbf{R}\tilde{\mathbf{C}}^T\bar{\mathbf{P}}^{-1}\tilde{\mathbf{C}}\mathbf{R} + \mathbf{B}\bar{\mathbf{Q}}\mathbf{B}^T \tag{7.6-11}$$

These equations are identical to the Kalman filter equations (7.6-4) and (7.6-5) except for the negative sign on the left-hand side of the matrix Riccati equation. Therefore, in order to be able to equate the results, it is necessary to assume that Eq. (7.6-8) describes a system in which time runs backward. With this modification, Eqs. (7.6-5) and (7.6-11) become identical in mathematical meaning, since running time backward is equivalent to changing the sign in the left-hand side.

Another way to look at the situation is to realize that we normally integrate Eq. (7.6-11) backward in time from the known terminal condition $\mathbf{R}(\infty) = 0$; now we must integrate forward in time, using the initial condition $\mathbf{R}(0) = 0$. This makes the steady-state solution identical to that obtained by the use of Eq. (7.6-5).

Hence, we see that the $\bar{\mathbf{K}}$ matrix may be obtained as the feedback-coefficient matrix of a control problem with the system described by Eq. (7.6-8), time running backward, and the performance index of Eq. (7.6-9).

This control problem was referred to by Kalman as the *dual control problem* and the system (7.6-8) as the dual of the original system.   The concept of dual systems was mentioned briefly in Chap. 2 in the discussion of controllability and observability.

In terms of this dual control problem, it is now possible to use all the techniques of this chapter for the determination of the elements of $\bar{\mathbf{K}}$. Since we are seeking only the steady-state solution of Eq. (7.6-5), we may set $\dot{\bar{\mathbf{R}}}$ and $\dot{\mathbf{R}}$ in Eqs. (7.6-5) and (7.6-11) to zero, forming reduced Riccati equations.   It should be noted that, in this case, the reverse-time nature of the dual problem plays no role and may be eliminated.   From this reduced Riccati equation one may find a frequency-domain Kalman equation for the dual control problem.

In the light of this dual control problem, we can easily see why it is not important to know the absolute magnitude of each element in $\bar{\mathbf{Q}}$ and $\bar{\mathbf{P}}$. Since $\bar{\mathbf{Q}}$ and $\bar{\mathbf{P}}$ determine the performance index in the dual problem,

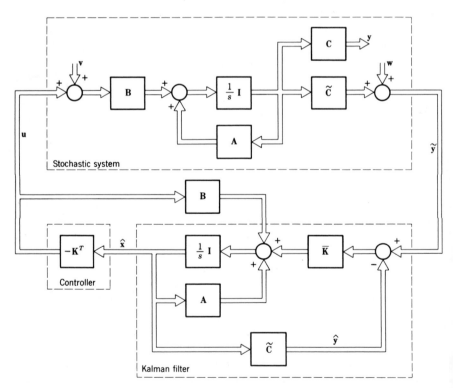

Fig. 7.6-4   Complete optimal structure for the stochastic control problem.

only their relative magnitudes are important, as we have seen before in terms of $\mathbf{Q}$ and $\mathbf{P}$.

The complete optimal structure for the stochastic control problem is shown in Fig. 7.6-4. The noisy measurements $\tilde{\mathbf{y}}(t)$ are used by the Kalman filter structure to generate $\hat{\mathbf{x}}(t)$. In terms of this estimate of the system state, the optimal control is formed by the use of the feedback-control matrix $\mathbf{K}$.

Although we have assumed in this brief treatment of Kalman filters that the plant and output equation are non-time-varying, this is not a necessary assumption. In addition, it is possible to allow the correlation matrices $\bar{\mathbf{P}}$ and $\bar{\mathbf{Q}}$ to be time-varying and for the control and hence observation interval to be finite. In all these cases the $\bar{\mathbf{K}}$ matrix becomes time-dependent, and one must solve and store the complete solution of interest. The interested reader is directed to the original papers of Kalman (1960, 1961).

In this section the Kalman filter approach to the problem of inaccessible state variables has been presented. While this approach provides a complete, rigorous, and optimal solution to the problem, it is often not practicable as a result of several factors. First, and possibly most important, the input and output noises are often not known in sufficient detail to justify the approach. Second, the approach requires the simulation of an nth-order system. In Chap. 9 the problem of inaccessible states is treated from another point of view, which attempts to remove some of these difficulties by taking an approach to the problem that is oriented more toward engineering factors.

Exercises 7.6 *7.6-1.* Determine the Kalman filter for the system shown in Fig. 7.6-5 if

$$E\{v^2\} = \bar{q}\delta(t) = \delta(t)$$

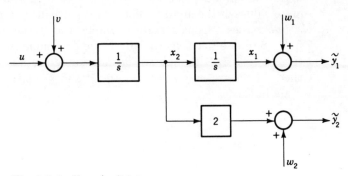

Fig. 7.6-5 Exercise 7.6-1.

and

$$E\{ww^T\} = \bar{\mathbf{P}}\delta(t) = \begin{bmatrix} 16 & 0 \\ 0 & 1 \end{bmatrix} \delta(t)$$

Draw the block diagram of the resulting filter.   Show that the dual control problem yields the same answer.

answer:

$$\bar{\mathbf{K}} = \begin{bmatrix} 0.125 & 0.470 \\ 0.015 & 1.00 \end{bmatrix}$$

7.6-2.   Repeat Exercise 7.6-1 assuming that only the $\tilde{\mathbf{y}}_1$ output is available.

answer:

$$\bar{\mathbf{k}} = \text{col } (0.707, 0.250)$$

7.6-3.   Find the transfer-function matrix $\mathbf{G}_f(s)$ for the Kalman filter assuming that $\mathbf{u} = 0$ where

$$\hat{\mathbf{x}}(s) = \mathbf{G}_f(s)\tilde{\mathbf{y}}(s)$$

answer:

$$\hat{\mathbf{x}}(s) = (s\mathbf{I} - \mathbf{A} - \bar{\mathbf{K}}\tilde{\mathbf{C}})^{-1}\bar{\mathbf{K}}\tilde{\mathbf{y}}(s)$$

7.6-4.   In terms of the dual control problem, we have observed that the Kalman filter depends only on the *relative* magnitude of the mean square values of the input and output disturbances and not on their *absolute* values.   Consider, for example, the system shown in Fig. 7.6-6.   Suppose that experimentally we determine that the $E\{v^2\}$ is twice the $E\{w^2\}$ although we do not know the absolute value of either.   Then we may select for the $\bar{\mathbf{P}}$ and $\bar{\mathbf{Q}}$ matrices, which are scalars in this case,

$$\bar{p} = 1 \quad \text{and} \quad \bar{q} = 2$$

or

$$\bar{p} = 5 \quad \text{and} \quad \bar{q} = 10$$

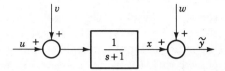

Fig. 7.6-6   Exercise 7.6-4.

as well as the general case

$$\bar{p} = \alpha \quad \text{and} \quad \bar{q} = 2\alpha$$

Show that the answer is identical for all these choices.   Note that this feature of the Kalman filter is of practical significance since it means that one need not make any absolute calibration of the noise measurements.   Draw a block diagram of the resulting Kalman filter.

answer:

$$\bar{k} = \sqrt{3} - 1$$

7.7 Summary and conclusion

From a theoretical standpoint, this chapter is vital to the logical development of this book.   The state function of Pontryagin was used in Sec. 7.2 to develop the Hamilton-Jacobi equation for the basic optimal-control problem.   The Hamilton-Jacobi equation is a nonlinear partial differential equation in the value function $V(\mathbf{x},t)$.   For the linear control problem with infinite control interval this value function may be considered to be a Liapunov function $V(\mathbf{x})$.   The matrix Riccati equation was developed from the point of view of the second method of Liapunov, as well as from the Hamilton-Jacobi equation.   The Kalman equation, a frequency-domain statement of the reduced Riccati equation, is the basis for the engineering synthesis methods discussed in the next chapters.

In a practical sense, this chapter may be something of a disappointment.   Many solutions to rather general problems are indicated, but few meaningful illustrations are provided.   The reason is that the solutions indicated throughout the chapter rely upon the solution of algebraic or differential matrix equations, which are just not suitable for hand calculations.   But the theory is general and amenable to machine computation and necessary for the material that follows.

The reader is urged to adopt the following approach.   First, master the more practical design methods of Chaps. 8 and 9 that are applicable to the single input–single output linear control problem. Then return to this chapter and write the digital-computer programs necessary to handle the multiple input–multiple output system. Not only will the experience gained with the simpler system prove invaluable in understanding the general case, but the solutions can serve as a check on the computer programs.

7.8 Problems

7.8-1. For the linear system

$$\dot{\mathbf{x}} = \begin{bmatrix} 0 & 1 \\ 0 & 1 \end{bmatrix} \mathbf{x} + \begin{bmatrix} 0 \\ K \end{bmatrix} u$$

$$y = \begin{bmatrix} 1 & 0 \end{bmatrix} \mathbf{x}$$

with $K = 10$ and the performance index

$$\mathrm{PI} = \int_0^\infty (x_1{}^2 + u^2)\, dt$$

(a) Find the optimal open-loop control $u^o(t)$ by using the minimum-principle approach for the initial condition $\mathbf{x}(0) = \mathrm{col}\,(1,0)$.

(b) Find the optimal closed-loop control law $u^o(\mathbf{x})$ by using the matrix Riccati equation.

(c) Compare the value of the performance index and the resulting trajectories if the initial condition is $\mathbf{x}(0) = \mathrm{col}\,(2,0)$.

Note the advantage of a closed-loop solution.

7.8-2. Repeat part c of the above problem but let $K = 20$ and $\mathbf{x}(0) = \mathrm{col}\,(1,0)$. Note once again the advantage of closed-loop control.

7.8-3. Find the closed-loop transfer function $y(s)/r(s)$ for the system shown in Fig. 7.8-1. There a Kalman filter is used to generate estimates of the state variables from noisy measurements of the output $\tilde{\mathbf{y}}$. Assume that the disturbances are zero in deriving the transfer function.

7.8-4. For the system

$$\dot{\mathbf{x}} = \begin{bmatrix} 0 & 1 \\ -1 & -1 \end{bmatrix} \mathbf{x} + \begin{bmatrix} 0 \\ 1 \end{bmatrix} u$$

$$y = \begin{bmatrix} 1 & 0 \end{bmatrix} \mathbf{x} \qquad \text{and} \qquad \tilde{\mathbf{y}} = \begin{bmatrix} 1 & 0 \\ 0 & 1 \end{bmatrix} \mathbf{x}$$

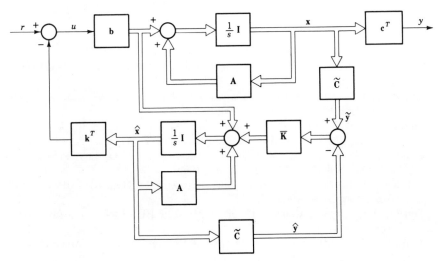

Fig. 7.8-1 Prob. 7.8-3.

with

$$E\{v^2\} = 1\delta(t) \qquad \text{and} \qquad E\{ww^T\} = \begin{bmatrix} 1 & 0 \\ 0 & 4 \end{bmatrix} \delta(t)$$

and the performance index

$$\text{PI} = \int_0^\infty (x_1{}^2 + u^2) \, dt$$

(a) Find the optimal-feedback coefficients assuming all states are available.

(b) Find the Kalman filter for the system.

(c) Use the results of Prob. 7.8-3 to find the closed-loop transfer function of the system.

7.8-5. Repeat the above problem, assuming that only $\tilde{y}_1$ is available.

References

Kalman, R. E.: A New Approach to Linear Filtering and Prediction Problems, *J. Basic Eng.*, ser. D, vol. 82, pp. 35–45, March, 1960.

———: New Methods in Wiener Filtering Theory in "Proceedings of First Symposium on Engineering Applications of Random Function Theory and Probability," John Wiley & Sons, Inc., New York, 1963.

————: When Is a Linear Control System Optimal? *J. Basic Eng.*, ser. D, vol. 86, pp. 51–60, March, 1964.

———— and R. S. Bucy: New Results in Linear Filtering and Prediction Theory, *J. Basic Eng.*, ser. D, vol. 83, pp. 95–108, March, 1961.

Lee, Y. W.: "Statistical Theory of Communication," John Wiley & Sons, Inc., New York, 1960.

Liu, R., and R. J. Leake: Inverse Liapunov Problem, *University of Notre Dame Tech. Rept.* EE-6510, August, 1965.

Merriam, C. W.: "Optimization Theory and the Design of Feedback Control Systems," McGraw-Hill Book Company, New York, 1964.

Pontryagin, L. S., et al.: "The Mathematical Theory of Optimal Processes," John Wiley & Sons, Inc., New York, 1962.

Schwartz, R. J., and B. Friedland: "Linear Systems," McGraw-Hill Book Company, New York, 1965.

Tou, J. T.: "Modern Control Theory," McGraw-Hill Book Company, New York, 1964.

Truxal, J. G.: "Automatic Feedback Control System Synthesis," McGraw-Hill Book Company, New York, 1955.

eight

linear system synthesis via performance indices

8.1 Introduction and outline of chapter

This chapter, like the last one, is concerned with the synthesis of linear control systems using state-variable feedback. The reader may find this disturbing, because just about all that can be said about design in terms of optimization procedures has already been said in Chap. 7. On the other hand, the reader may breathe a sigh of relief, in hope that the authors may have finally decided to drop the mathematical exercises and to start to talk about control systems. Either reaction is justifiable, depending on the reader's background.

It is the purpose of this chapter to relate the well-known frequency-domain methods, such as Bode diagrams and root locus, to the time-domain methods of modern control theory. The assumption here is that the reader is somewhat familiar with linear control theory at the undergraduate level from such texts as Kuo (1962), Savant (1964), or D'Azzo and Houpis (1965).

Because all basic courses concentrate almost exclusively on single input–single output systems, this chapter is limited to a discussion of that case.

The most basic feature in the formulation of the linear control problem, besides the system itself, is the choice of the performance index. The next section attempts to answer this question, at least in part, through the use of an approach known as modeling.

In Sec. 8.3 the synthesis problem is approached from the point of view of a designer who is not acquainted with modern control theory. The aim is to see what conclusions can be reached on the basis of conventional control theory, under the supposition that all the state variables are fed back. Simple manipulations on an example lead to interesting tentative conclusions. These conclusions are verified in the general case using matrix manipulations.

A method of design using Bode diagrams is discussed in Sec. 8.4. The motivation for this discussion is the point of view adopted in the previous section. The design procedure is based on the application of straight-line Bode approximations to one form of Kalman's equation, Eq. (7.5-10). Section 8.5 develops a root-locus technique for developing a less approximate method. The use of Kalman's frequency-domain equation in both the root-locus and Bode methods serves as the link between this chapter and the previous two. In Chap. 9, this link is discarded completely, and a design procedure is developed on the basis of closed-loop time- or frequency-domain specifications. That is, the criterion is no longer an integral type of performance index but conventional output specifications.

Throughout this chapter it is assumed that all the state variables are available for measurement, so that state-variable feedback can be accomplished using all the variables. If this is not the case, the unmeasurable state variables must be synthesized by using either the Kalman filter approach of the previous chapter or the methods presented in the next chapter.

8.2   Modeling and performance indices

As pointed out in the two previous chapters, one of the basic problems in designing a system by means of optimal-control theory is the choice of a performance index. Although the choice has been simplified somewhat by restricting our attention to integral quadratic performance indices, it is still necessary to select the matrices **P** and **Q**. While there is no complete or final solution to this problem, we develop a technique in this section which provides definite guidelines for the selection of **Q** and **P**.

In order to simplify the discussion, the assumption is made, as it is throughout this chapter, that the system is of the classical single input–single output type. In addition, we assume that the open-loop transfer function $y(s)/u(s)$ contains no zeros, so that

$$\frac{y(s)}{u(s)} = G(s) = \frac{K}{s^n + a_n s^{n-1} + \cdots + a_1}$$

In this case, as was shown in Chap. 2, the system may be written in phase-variable form as

$$\dot{x}_i = x_{i+1} \quad \text{for } i = 1, 2, \ldots, n-1$$
$$\dot{x}_n = -a_1 x_1 - a_2 x_2 - \cdots - a_n x_n + Ku \tag{8.2-1}$$

with the output given by $y = x_1$. For the scalar-input case the performance index becomes

$$\text{PI} = \int_0^\infty (\mathbf{x}^T \mathbf{Q} \mathbf{x} + p u^2) \, dt \tag{8.2-2}$$

In terms of this performance index, we show first that of the $n(n+1)/2$ elements in **Q** only n combinations are critical in determining the optimal system. In order to do this it is necessary to show that $\mathbf{x}^T \mathbf{Q} \mathbf{x}$ may be written as

$$\mathbf{x}^T \mathbf{Q} \mathbf{x} = (\boldsymbol{\gamma}^T \mathbf{x})^2 + \frac{d}{dt} \mathbf{x}^T \mathbf{S} \mathbf{x} \tag{8.2-3}$$

where, as usual, **S** is assumed to be symmetric and constant. In doing this it would be desirable for such a decomposition to be independent of the particular system at hand. In order to realize this desire it is necessary only to require that $\dot{x}_n$ not appear. This is due to the phase-variable representation chosen for the system, since all the other derivatives are independent of the system.

However, $\dot{x}_n$ appears unless the quadratic form $\mathbf{x}^T \mathbf{S} \mathbf{x}$ does not contain terms involving x_n. This may be accomplished by requiring that the last row and column of **S** be zero, thereby in effect reducing **S** to an $n-1 \times n-1$ matrix. Because of this requirement on **S**, it is convenient to carry out the following development with Eq. (8.2-3) rewritten in summation form as

$$\sum_{j=1}^{n}\sum_{i=1}^{n} q_{ij}x_ix_j = \sum_{j=1}^{n}\sum_{i=1}^{n} \gamma_i\gamma_jx_ix_j + \frac{d}{dt}\sum_{j=1}^{n-1}\sum_{i=1}^{n-1} s_{ij}x_ix_j \qquad (8.2\text{-}4)$$

where the fact that the last row and column of **S** are zero has been recognized by letting the summation run only to $n-1$.

Let us consider this last term more closely. If the differentiation is carried out, it then becomes

$$\frac{d}{dt}\sum_{j=1}^{n-1}\sum_{i=1}^{n-1} s_{ij}x_ix_j = \sum_{j=1}^{n-1}\sum_{i=1}^{n-1} s_{ij}(x_i\dot{x}_j + \dot{x}_ix_j) \qquad (8.2\text{-}5)$$

The system is represented in phase variables, and therefore $\dot{x}_i = x_{i+1}$ since $i \le n-1$. Similarly, $\dot{x}_j = x_{j+1}$, and Eq. (8.2-5) therefore becomes

$$\frac{d}{dt}\sum_{j=1}^{n-1}\sum_{i=1}^{n-1} s_{ij}x_ix_j = \sum_{j=1}^{n-1}\sum_{i=1}^{n-1} s_{ij}(x_ix_{j+1} + x_{i+1}x_j)$$

$$= 2\sum_{j=1}^{n-1}\sum_{i=1}^{n-1} s_{ij}x_ix_{j+1}$$

where this second reduction may be made since **S** is symmetric. Substituting this expression into Eq. (8.2-4), we obtain

$$\sum_{j=1}^{n}\sum_{i=1}^{n} q_{ij}x_ix_j = \sum_{j=1}^{n}\sum_{i=1}^{n} \gamma_i\gamma_jx_ix_j + 2\sum_{j=1}^{n-1}\sum_{i=1}^{n-1} s_{ij}x_ix_{j+1} \qquad (8.2\text{-}6)$$

If the summations are carried out on both sides of this equation and the coefficients of the various x_ix_j terms are equated, $n(n+1)/2$ equations involving the elements of **Q**, **γ**, and **S** are generated.

There are n unknown elements of **γ** and $(n-1)n/2$ unknown elements of **S**, making a total of $n(n+1)/2$ unknowns; therefore it is possible to solve for the elements of **γ** and **S** from these equations. In fact, since the elements of **γ** appear in these equations in a quadratic manner, there is, in general, more than one solution to the equations. In order to make the solution unique, we require that all the elements of **γ** be positive. The logic behind this restriction is explained later.

Example 8.2-1 In order to illustrate this decomposition procedure, let us consider the general second-order case. Writing Eq. (8.2-6) in full, for this case we have

$$q_{11}x_1^2 + 2q_{12}x_1x_2 + q_{22}x_2^2 = \gamma_1^2 x_1^2 + 2\gamma_1\gamma_2 x_1 x_2 + \gamma_2^2 x_2^2 + 2s_{11}x_1x_2$$

If the coefficients of the various $x_i x_j$ terms are equated, the following three equations result:

$$q_{11} = \gamma_1^2 \qquad q_{12} = \gamma_1\gamma_2 + s_{11} \qquad q_{22} = \gamma_2^2$$

Therefore, we find that

$$\gamma_1 = \sqrt{q_{11}} \qquad \gamma_2 = \sqrt{q_{22}} \qquad s_{11} = q_{12} - \sqrt{q_{11}q_{22}}$$

If, for example, **Q** had been

$$\mathbf{Q} = \begin{bmatrix} 4 & 0 \\ 0 & 1 \end{bmatrix}$$

then

$$\gamma_1 = 2 \qquad \gamma_2 = 1 \qquad s_{11} = -2$$

In other words, we have shown that

$$4x_1^2 + x_2^2 = (2x_1 + x_2)^2 + \frac{d}{dt}(-2x_1^2)$$

which may be easily verified by making use of the fact that $\dot{x}_1 = x_2$.

Example 8.2-2 For the third-order case, six equations are obtained:

$$q_{11} = \gamma_1^2 \qquad q_{12} = \gamma_1\gamma_2 + s_{11} \qquad q_{13} = \gamma_1\gamma_3 + s_{12}$$

$$q_{22} = \gamma_2^2 + 2s_{12} \qquad q_{23} = \gamma_2\gamma_3 + s_{22} \qquad q_{33} = \gamma_3^2$$

If these equations are solved, the following results are obtained:

$$\gamma_1 = \sqrt{q_{11}} \qquad \gamma_2 = \sqrt{q_{22} + 2(\sqrt{q_{11}q_{33}} - q_{13})} \qquad \gamma_3 = \sqrt{q_{33}}$$

and

$$s_{11} = q_{12} - \gamma_1\gamma_2 \qquad s_{12} = q_{13} - \gamma_1\gamma_3 \qquad s_{22} = q_{23} - \gamma_2\gamma_3$$

Consider, for example, the matrix

$$\mathbf{Q} = \begin{bmatrix} 1 & 0 & 0 \\ 0 & 1 & 0 \\ 0 & 0 & 1 \end{bmatrix}$$

For this matrix $\boldsymbol{\gamma}$ and $\mathbf{S}$ become

$$\boldsymbol{\gamma} = \begin{bmatrix} 1 \\ \sqrt{3} \\ 1 \end{bmatrix} \quad \text{and} \quad \mathbf{S} = \begin{bmatrix} -\sqrt{3} & -1 & 0 \\ -1 & -\sqrt{3} & 0 \\ 0 & 0 & 0 \end{bmatrix}$$

Hence the quadratic form $\mathbf{x}^T\mathbf{Q}\mathbf{x}$ may be written as

$$\mathbf{x}^T\mathbf{Q}\mathbf{x} = (x_1 + \sqrt{3}\,x_2 + x_3)^2 + \frac{d}{dt}(-\sqrt{3}\,x_1{}^2 - 2x_1x_2 - \sqrt{3}\,x_2{}^2)$$

which may be easily verified by carrying out the differentiation. The reader is reminded that the system is assumed to be represented in phase variables, so that $\dot{x}_1 = x_2$ and $\dot{x}_2 = x_3$.

By means of the above development, we have demonstrated that the quadratic form $\mathbf{x}^T\mathbf{Q}\mathbf{x}$ can be decomposed into the sum of a perfect square $(\boldsymbol{\gamma}^T\mathbf{x})^2$ plus a perfect derivative $d(\mathbf{x}^T\mathbf{S}\mathbf{x})/dt$ by a procedure which is independent of the given system. In addition, the two examples have illustrated the general procedure for accomplishing this decomposition for the second- and third-order cases. All this is well and good, but the reader may, with reason, question why we have carried out such algebraic gymnastics. In order to answer this question, let us consider once again the performance index, Eq. (8.2-2). In terms of our new result this may be written as

$$\text{PI} = \int_0^\infty \left[(\boldsymbol{\gamma}^T\mathbf{x})^2 + \frac{d}{dt}\mathbf{x}^T\mathbf{S}\mathbf{x} + pu^2 \right] dt \tag{8.2-7}$$

Since the middle term represents a perfect derivative, it may be directly integrated to obtain

$$\text{PI} = \int_0^\infty [(\boldsymbol{\gamma}^T\mathbf{x})^2 + pu^2]\,dt + \mathbf{x}^T\mathbf{S}\mathbf{x}\Big|_0^\infty$$

$$= \int_0^\infty [(\boldsymbol{\gamma}^T\mathbf{x})^2 + pu^2]\,dt + \mathbf{x}^T(\infty)\mathbf{S}\mathbf{x}(\infty) - \mathbf{x}^T(0)\mathbf{S}\mathbf{x}(0)$$

If we assume that the optimal system is asymptotically stable, then $\mathbf{x}(\infty) = 0$, and $\mathbf{x}^T(\infty)\mathbf{S}\mathbf{x}(\infty) = 0$.

In addition, we note that the $\mathbf{x}^T(0)\mathbf{S}\mathbf{x}(0)$ term is in no way affected by the choice of the optimal-feedback law, since it depends only on the given initial state. Therefore the minimization of the initial performance index, Eq. (8.2-2), may be equivalently stated as the minimization of a *reduced performance index*

$$\text{PI} = \int_0^\infty [(\gamma^T\mathbf{x})^2 + pu^2]\, dt \qquad (8.2\text{-}8)$$

Since there are only n elements in γ, we have established our conjecture that of the $n(n + 1)/2$ elements in $\mathbf{Q}$ only n combinations are critical in determining the optimal system. This result was first introduced and proved in the control literature by Wonham and Johnson (1964).

Example 8.2-3 Consider, for example, the following $\mathbf{Q}$ matrices,

$$\mathbf{Q}_1 = \begin{bmatrix} 1 & 0 & 0 \\ 0 & 1 & \frac{1}{2} \\ 0 & \frac{1}{2} & 1 \end{bmatrix} \qquad \mathbf{Q}_2 = \begin{bmatrix} 1 & \frac{1}{2} & 0 \\ \frac{1}{2} & 1 & 0 \\ 0 & 0 & 1 \end{bmatrix}$$

$$\mathbf{Q}_3 = \begin{bmatrix} 1 & 0 & \frac{1}{2} \\ 0 & 2 & 0 \\ \frac{1}{2} & 0 & 1 \end{bmatrix}$$

While these matrices appear to be quite different, one can show, using the results of Example 8.2-2, that they all yield the same γ vector, namely,

$$\gamma = \begin{bmatrix} 1 \\ \sqrt{3} \\ 1 \end{bmatrix}$$

Therefore, if one used the performance index (8.2-2), each of these $\mathbf{Q}$ matrices would result in exactly the same optimal system, since they all have the same reduced performance index.

Since the reduced performance index and γ contain no redundancy, it is obvious that one should not pick $\mathbf{Q}$ and then find γ but rather that γ should be chosen directly. By selecting the more complicated $\mathbf{Q}$ form of the performance index one is able to gain nothing in terms of added generality. In addition to its obvious advantage of simplicity and conciseness, this reduced performance index has another very important feature with regard to the selection of a performance index. This feature is related to a concept known as *modeling*.

In order to illustrate this concept most easily, let us suppose for the moment that p equals zero in the reduced performance index. In this case it is obvious that the performance index has an absolute minimum value of zero if and only if

$$\boldsymbol{\gamma}^T \mathbf{x} = \gamma_1 x_1(t) + \gamma_2 x_2(t) + \cdots + \gamma_n x_n(t) = 0 \tag{8.2-9}$$

for all $0 \le t < \infty$. In order to interpret the meaning of this expression, let us remember that the system is expressed in phase variables, so that $x_i(t) = d^{i-1} x_1(t)/dt^{i-1}$ for $i \le n$. Therefore Eq. (8.2-9) becomes

$$\gamma_1 x_1(t) + \gamma_2 \frac{dx_1(t)}{dt} + \gamma_3 \frac{d^2 x_1(t)}{dt^2} + \cdots + \gamma_n \frac{d^{n-1} x_1(t)}{dt^{n-1}} = 0$$

Since $y(t)$, the output, equals $x_1(t)$, this equation may be written as

$$\gamma_1 y(t) + \gamma_2 \frac{dy(t)}{dt} + \gamma_3 \frac{d^2 y(t)}{dt^2} + \cdots + \gamma_n \frac{d^{n-1} y(t)}{dt^{n-1}} = 0 \tag{8.2-10}$$

It should be noted that once again only the fact that the system is represented in phase variables has been used and the actual system parameters have not been involved.

Equation (8.2-10) represents an $(n-1)$st-order differential equation which the output $y(t)$ must satisfy if the performance index is to achieve its absolute minimum of zero. A time response which satisfies this equation is referred to as the ideal or *model time response*. Equivalently, one often speaks of the *model* as the system which has Eq. (8.2-10) as its describing differential equation.

Since the system being optimized is nth-order and the model is $(n-1)$st, it is obviously impossible for $y(t)$ to satisfy Eq. (8.2-10) exactly. On the other hand, in order for the performance index to be minimized, it is obvious that $y(t)$ must approximate the model response as closely as possible. The model response, in turn, is determined by the selection of the elements of $\boldsymbol{\gamma}$. One therefore may choose $\boldsymbol{\gamma}$ in such a fashion that the model or its response satisfies specifications such as rise time, overshoot, damping ratio, M peak, phase margin, and so forth. The use of the modeling concept allows one to apply the classical rules of thumb to the specifications of a performance index and thereby the design of the optimal system.

Example 8.2-4 Let us consider, in terms of this modeling concept, the performance index of Example 8.2-2. Since $\gamma = \text{col}\,(1,\sqrt{3},1)$, the differential equation of the model is given by

$$y(t) + \sqrt{3}\,\frac{dy(t)}{dt} + \frac{d^2y(t)}{dt^2} = 0$$

A unity-ratio feedback system with this describing differential equation is shown in Fig. 8.2-1a. By conventional methods it is quite easy to determine that this model has a phase margin of approximately 70°, a damping ratio of $\sqrt{3}/2$, and a bandwidth of approximately $\sqrt{3}/3$, indicating a somewhat sluggish system. The resulting optimal system therefore also has, in a general sense, these same properties.

While such a model might be adequate and, in fact, highly desirable for some purposes, a more responsive model might be desired in other cases. If, for example, we wish to decrease the damping ratio and the phase margin, this can be accomplished by decreasing the value of γ_2 to, say, $\sqrt{2}$. The resulting model is shown in Fig. 8.2-1b. This system has a phase margin of approximately 60°, a damping ratio of $\sqrt{2}/2$, and a bandwidth of approximately $\sqrt{2}/2$.

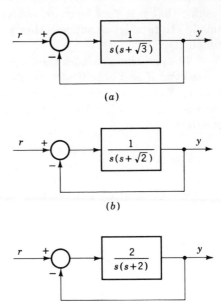

(a)

(b)

Fig. 8.2-1 Unity-ratio feedback models. (a) $\gamma = \text{col}\,(1,\sqrt{3},1)$; ($b$) $\gamma = \text{col}\,(1,\sqrt{2},1)$; ($c$) $\gamma = \text{col}\,(2,2,1)$.

(c)

If we wished further to increase the speed of response while maintaining the same phase margin and damping ratio, this could be done by increasing the bandwidth by selecting γ as col (2,2,1), which yields the model shown in Fig. 8.2-1c.

While our discussion has centered on the $(n - 1)$st-order model, it is obvious that a lower-order model may be selected by letting some of the elements in γ be zero. For example, to obtain an mth-order model, where $m \leq n - 1$, we simply let $\gamma_{m+2}, \gamma_{m+3}, \ldots, \gamma_n$ be zero. Since most classical concepts of desirable performance, phase margin and rise time, for example, are based on low-order systems, one often chooses a second- or third-order model even for high-order systems. In addition, models beyond the third order are so difficult to analyze that they are not convenient to use.

The reason for specifying that only positive values be selected for the elements of γ is now obvious. If negative values were selected, the resulting model would be unstable and hence meaningless.

In an actual performance index it is not possible for p to be zero since the matrix $\mathbf{P}$ was required to be positive definite. In the scalar-control case, this means that p must be strictly positive, and therefore while it may be made small, it cannot be zero. In order to see the influence of this factor on the modeling concept presented above, let us assume that p is very large or, equivalently, that the magnitude of γ is small. In fact, let us suppose that γ is equal to zero just for the sake of simplicity.

The performance index then has an absolute minimum of zero, which is achieved if and only if $u(t)$ equals zero for all $0 \leq t < \infty$. The time response of the optimal system therefore becomes the unforced response of the system. In other words, the model in this case is the unforced plant equation

$$\dot{\mathbf{x}} = \mathbf{A}\mathbf{x}$$

In terms of the output $y(t)$, this may be written as the nth-order differential equation

$$\frac{d^n y(t)}{dt^n} + a_n \frac{d^{n-1}y(t)}{dt^{n-1}} + a_{n-1}\frac{d^{n-2}y(t)}{dt^{n-2}} + \cdots + a_1 y(t) = 0 \quad (8.2\text{-}11)$$

If γ is now made nonzero, the optimal time response is somewhere between the response described by Eq. (8.2-10) and the unforced response of Eq. (8.2-11). Depending on the exact weighting of the two factors γ and p, the optimal response is closer to one or the other.

Since the important feature is the relative magnitude of γ and p, let us normalize γ by letting $\gamma_1 = 1$. In this way the exact weighting may be interpreted in terms of p alone. As p becomes large, the optimal response tends toward the unforced response (8.2-11), and as p is made small, the model response (8.2-10) is approached.

One might reasonably ask, "Why not just make p very small in all cases and let the optimal response become essentially equal to the ideal model response?" The problem with making p very small is that this allows u to become large without affecting the value of the performance index. In order to generate these large values of u it is necessary to have excessive amounts of gain in the system. Hence it is necessary to settle on an optimal performance which only approximates the model but at the same time does not require excessive gain in the system.

As a rule of thumb one can generally conclude that if p is less than 0.1, the optimal response approximates reasonably well the model response specified by γ. On the other hand, if p is greater than 10, the response is approximately equal to the unforced response.

Example 8.2-5 Consider, for example, the system

$$\dot{\mathbf{x}} = \begin{bmatrix} 0 & 1 & 0 \\ 0 & 0 & 1 \\ 0 & -2 & -3 \end{bmatrix} \mathbf{x} + \begin{bmatrix} 0 \\ 0 \\ 1 \end{bmatrix} u \qquad y = x_1$$

The performance index is

$$\text{PI} = \int_0^\infty [(x_1 + \sqrt{3}\, x_2 + x_3)^2 + p u^2]\, dt$$

The resulting optimal time response for this system is shown in Fig. 8.2-2 for various values of p. In addition, the model response ($p = 0$) and the unforced response ($p = \infty$) are shown for comparison. We see that as the value of p decreases, the optimal response approaches the model response, as predicted. All the time-response values were obtained by assuming that $y(0) = 1$ and $d^i y(t)/dt^i = 0$ for $i = 1, 2, \ldots, n - 1$.

With one minor modification, the above modeling approach can also be applied to systems which have zeros in the open-loop transfer function

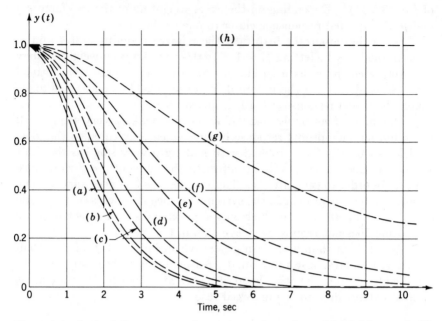

Fig. 8.2-2   Optimal time response for various values of p.   (a) Model, $p = 0$; (b) $p = 0.01$;   (c) $p = 0.1$;   (d) $p = 0.25$;   (e) $p = 1.0$;   (f) $p = 2.0$;   (g) $p = 10.0$; (h) unforced system, $p = \infty$.

$y(s)/u(s)$, such as

$$\frac{y(s)}{u(s)} = G(s) = \frac{K(s^m + c_m s^{m-1} + \cdots + c_2 s + c_1)}{s^n + a_n s^{n-1} + \cdots + a_1}$$

If we make use of the phase-variable representation, the zeros of $G(s)$ affect only the output expression, which now becomes

$$y = c_1 x_1 + c_2 x_2 + \cdots + c_m x_m + x_{m+1} \qquad (8.2\text{-}12)$$

while the equations for $\mathbf{x}$ remain unchanged.   In order to simplify the following argument let us suppose that there is only one zero, so that the above expression becomes

$$y = c_1 x_1 + x_2 \qquad (8.2\text{-}13)$$

Once again the specifications on the optimal time response are translated into an $(n - 1)$st-order differential-equation model which the optimal system is to approximate.   This model equation is written in terms of the coefficients α_i as

$$\alpha_1 y(t) + \alpha_2 \frac{dy(t)}{dt} + \alpha_3 \frac{d^2 y(t)}{dt^2} + \cdots + \alpha_n \frac{d^{n-1} y(t)}{dt^{n-1}} = 0 \qquad (8.2\text{-}14)$$

In order to change this model equation into the desired $\boldsymbol{\gamma}^T \mathbf{x}$ form we substitute the output expression (8.2-13) for y to obtain

$$\alpha_1 (c_1 x_1 + x_2) + \alpha_2 \frac{d(c_1 x_1 + x_2)}{dt} + \cdots + \alpha_n \frac{d^{n-1}(c_1 x_1 + x_2)}{dt^{n-1}} = 0$$

Using the fact that the system is represented in phase variables, we rewrite this equation as

$$\alpha_1 c_1 x_1 + (\alpha_1 + \alpha_2 c_1) x_2 + (\alpha_2 + \alpha_3 c_1) x_3 + \cdots$$
$$+ (\alpha_{n-2} + \alpha_n c_1) x_n + \alpha_n \dot{x}_n = 0$$

The last term appears because $d^{n-1} x_2 / dt^{n-1} = d^n x_1 / dt^n = \dot{x}_n$.   Therefore in order to keep the model independent of the initial system parameters, it is necessary that α_n be zero, thereby reducing the model to $(n - 2)$nd order.   Now comparing this equation with Eq. (8.2-9), we see that

$$\boldsymbol{\gamma} = \begin{bmatrix} c_1 \alpha_1 \\ \alpha_1 + \alpha_2 c_1 \\ \alpha_2 + \alpha_3 c_1 \\ \cdot \\ \cdot \\ \cdot \\ \alpha_{n-1} \end{bmatrix}$$

and the performance index is chosen except for the weighting on p.

By a similar argument, it is easy to see that if there are m zeros, the order of the model can be no greater than $n - m - 1$.   Hence we see that a zero in the open-loop transfer function actually presents a performance limitation.

Example 8.2-6   In order to illustrate this approach, let us consider a fourth-order system with one zero.   Suppose, for example, that the zero is at $s = -1$, so that the output expression is

$$y = x_1 + x_2$$

For.this problem, the order of the model must be less than or equal to $n - m - 1 = 4 - 1 - 1 = 2$.   Let us assume that the following second-order model adequately represents the desired system performance,

$$y(t) + \frac{dy(t)}{dt} + 2\frac{d^2y(t)}{dt^2} = 0$$

Now substituting the output expression for $y(t)$, we obtain

$$(x_1 + x_2) + \frac{d(x_1 + x_2)}{dt} + 2\frac{d^2(x_1 + x_2)}{dt^2} = 0$$

which becomes

$$x_1 + x_2 + (x_2 + x_3) + 2(x_3 + x_4) = 0$$

Grouping terms, we have

$$x_1 + 2x_2 + 3x_3 + 2x_4 = 0$$

so that $\gamma = \text{col}\ (1,2,3,2)$.

The modeling approach can be applied to systems which are not represented in phase variables by one of two techniques:

1. Consider the system in phase-variable form to select the performance index and to obtain the optimal-control law.   Then use the transformation relation to translate the control law into the desired state variables.
2. Use the phase-variable representation to find the performance index. Then use the transformation relation to translate the performance index and hence obtain the optimal control directly in the desired state variables.

In this section, we have investigated a procedure known as the modeling concept for determining the performance index in the linear control problem.   In the following sections, we use this modeling approach in the development of practical techniques for solving the linear control problem.

Exercises 8.2 *8.2-1.* Find the models associated with each of the following **Q** matrices by direct application of Eq. (8.2-6). Assume that the system is represented in phase variables and that $G(s)$ has no zeros.

$$(a) \begin{bmatrix} 9 & 5 \\ 5 & 16 \end{bmatrix} \quad (b) \begin{bmatrix} 9 & 0 \\ 0 & 16 \end{bmatrix} \quad (c) \begin{bmatrix} 1 & 0 & 0 \\ 0 & 2 & 0 \\ 0 & 0 & 1 \end{bmatrix}$$

$$(d) \begin{bmatrix} 1 & 0 & 1 \\ 0 & 7 & 0 \\ 1 & 0 & 4 \end{bmatrix}$$

answers:

(a) $3y + 4\dot{y} = 0$ (b) $3y + 4\dot{y} = 0$
(c) $y + 2\dot{y} + \ddot{y} = 0$ (d) $y + 3\dot{y} + 2\ddot{y} = 0$

8.2-2. Repeat the above problem but in this case use the results of Examples 8.2-1 and 8.2-2 to find the models.

8.2-3. Find two more **Q** matrices which have the same model as the following **Q** matrix:

$$\mathbf{Q} = \begin{bmatrix} 4 & 0 & 1 \\ 0 & 3 & 1 \\ 1 & 1 & 4 \end{bmatrix}$$

8.2-4. Find the $\boldsymbol{\gamma}$ vector for the system whose transfer function is

$$G(s) = \frac{K(s + 2)}{s^2(s + 1)(s + 3)}$$

such that the model for the system is

$$3y(t) + \dot{y}(t) = 0$$

Assume that the system is represented in phase variables.

answer:

$\boldsymbol{\gamma} = \text{col } (6,5,1,0)$

8.3 A block-diagram look at state-variable feedback

This section examines the overall effect of state-variable feedback through
the use of simple block-diagram manipulations. As a vehicle for this
discussion, consider a specific example of a simple positioning servomechanism, indicated in Fig. 8.3-1. The power element in this system is a dc
motor with constant armature current, so that control is achieved through
field control. Assume that the plant transfer function is given as

$$\frac{y(s)}{u(s)} = G(s) = \frac{10K}{s(s+1)(s+5)} \tag{8.3-1}$$

Here the pole at -1 is due to the mechanical portions of the system, the
motor inertia, reflected load inertia, and the viscous damping. The pole
at -5 is associated with the motor field circuit, and the amplifier is
assumed to be a pure gain K.

The natural physical state variables in this system are the output x_1,
its derivative x_2, and the motor field current x_3. Figure 8.3-1 indicates
that the x_2 variable is generated with a tachometer and that the motor
field current is also being measured across the resistor R and fed back to
the input. Thus control in this case is being achieved by feedback of all
the state variables.

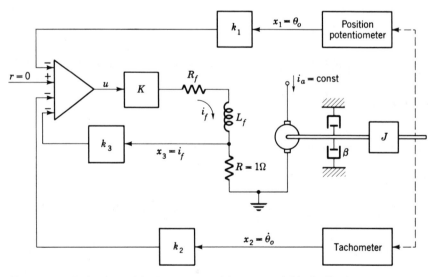

Fig. 8.3-1 A simple positioning system with state-variable feedback.

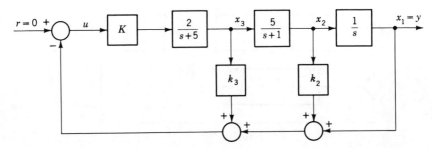

Fig. 8.3-2 Block diagram of the positioning system of Fig. 8.3-1 with $k_1 = 1$.

Since this is a simple positioning system with one integration in the forward path, zero steady-state position error is readily achieved by a direct feedback of the output, or by making $k_1 = 1$. A block diagram of the system of Fig. 8.3-1 is given in Fig. 8.3-2 with $k_1 = 1$. Note that on this block diagram values of gain are associated with each of the individual blocks that separate the state variables. These values of gain are assumed to be fixed by the physical constants of the system and are therefore relatively inflexible. In the forward path the amplifier gain K may be easily adjustable. If K is considered as an adjustable parameter rather than as a fixed value of gain, the number of adjustable parameters, which was reduced to two by fixing $k_1 = 1$, is now restored to three. The other two parameters available for adjustment are k_2 and k_3 in the feedback paths of x_2 and x_3.

Two basic configurations into which the block diagram of Fig. 8.3-2 may be reduced are indicated in Fig. 8.3-3. For obvious reasons these

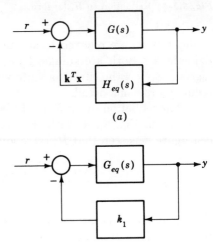

Fig. 8.3-3 Two possible reductions of the state-variable feedback configuration. (*a*) $H_{eq}(s)$ form; (*b*) $G_{eq}(s)$ form.

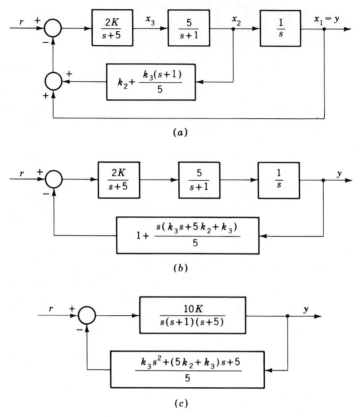

Fig. 8.3-4 Reduction to $H_{eq}(s)$ form.

configurations are referred to as the H-equivalent and the G-equivalent reductions. Both are standard block-diagram forms, and it is advantageous to view the effects of state-variable feedback by considering each reduction in some detail.

The reduction to the form of Fig. 8.3-3a is accomplished by the steps indicated in Fig. 8.3-4, with the final result as Fig. 8.3-4c. From this last figure it is seen that $H_{eq}(s)$ is given by

$$H_{eq}(s) = \frac{k_3 s^2 + s(k_3 + 5k_2) + 5}{5} \qquad (8.3\text{-}2)$$

Note that the numerator of $H_{eq}(s)$ is a quadratic in s, of the form $As^2 + Bs + C$. Thus $H_{eq}(s)$ contains two zeros, whose locations on the s plane may be determined as desired by a suitable choice of k_2 and k_3. From a root-locus point of view this is a highly desirable result. Now $G(s)H_{eq}(s)$ has three poles and two zeros, with the zero locations arbitrary. Note particularly that the amplifier gain K does not enter into the determination of the zero locations. The asymptote on the root-locus diagram goes to ∞ at $-180°$, so that it is possible to pick zero locations to ensure stability for *all* values of amplifier gain. This is considerable improvement over conventional lead-lag type of compensation, where the angles of the asymptotes remain unchanged.

It is possible to demonstrate that, in the general case, $H_{eq}(s)$ has $n-1$ arbitrary zeros. It can also be shown that the open-loop transfer function $G(s)H_{eq}(s)$ has poles only where $G(s)$ has poles and has zeros at the arbitrary zero locations of $H_{eq}(s)$. This demonstration is most easily accomplished in terms of phase variables. Assume that $G(s)$ is a ratio of polynomials, as

$$G(s) = \frac{K(c_{m+1}s^m + c_m s^{m-1} + \cdots + c_2 s + c_1)}{s^n + a_n s^{n-1} + \cdots + a_2 s + a_1} \tag{8.3-3}$$

If this system is represented in phase variables, the equations of motion become[1]

$$\dot{\mathbf{x}} = \begin{bmatrix} 0 & 1 & \cdots & 0 \\ 0 & 0 & \cdots & 0 \\ \multicolumn{4}{c}{\dotfill} \\ -a_1 & -a_2 & \cdots & -a_n \end{bmatrix} \mathbf{x} + \begin{bmatrix} 0 \\ 0 \\ \cdots \\ K \end{bmatrix} u \tag{8.3-4}$$

and

$$y = [c_1 \quad c_2 \quad \cdots \quad c_{m+1} \quad 0 \quad \cdots \quad 0]\mathbf{x} \tag{8.3-5}$$

From Fig. 8.3-3a we see that

$$H_{eq}(s) = \frac{\mathbf{k}^T \mathbf{x}}{y(s)} = \frac{\mathbf{k}^T \mathbf{x}(s)}{\mathbf{c}^T \mathbf{x}(s)} = \frac{k_1 x_1(s) + k_2 x_2(s) + \cdots + k_n x_n(s)}{c_1 x_1(s) + c_2 x_2(s) + \cdots + c_{m+1} x_{m+1}(s)}$$

Since the system is represented in phase variables, $x_i(s) = s^{i-1}x_1(s)$, and

---

[1] Since our basic interest at present is in transfer-function properties, the choice of state variables is unimportant. Note, however, that we have assumed that the transfer function $x_n(s)/u(s)$ contains no zero so that the system may be represented in state-variable form as Eqs. (**Ab**) and (**c**). The more general situation when this assumption is violated is discussed in Chap. 9.

$H_{eq}(s)$ becomes

$$H_{eq}(s) = \frac{(k_1 + k_2 s + \cdots + k_n s^{n-1}) x_1(s)}{(c_1 + c_2 s + \cdots + c_{m+1} s^m) x_1(s)}$$

or

$$H_{eq}(s) = \frac{k_1 + k_2 s + \cdots + k_n s^{n-1}}{c_1 + c_2 s + \cdots + c_{m+1} s^m} \qquad (8.3\text{-}6)$$

Here it is seen that the numerator of $H_{eq}(s)$ is a polynomial of order $n - 1$ in s and that all the coefficients of the various powers of s in this polynomial are arbitrary. That is, $\mathbf{k}$ may be chosen at the discretion of the designer. Thus $H_{eq}(s)$ has $n - 1$ arbitrary zero locations as predicted. In addition, we note that the poles of $H_{eq}(s)$ are exactly equal to the zeros of $G(s)$, that is, the denominator of $H_{eq}(s)$ is equal to the numerator of $G(s)$ except for the gain K. Therefore the open-loop transfer function $G(s)H_{eq}(s)$ is given by

$$G(s)H_{eq}(s) = \frac{K(k_n s^{n-1} + k_{n-1} s^{n-2} + \cdots + k_2 s + k_1)}{s^n + a_n s^{n-1} + \cdots + a_2 s + a_1}$$

It is seen that the arbitrary zeros of $H_{eq}(s)$ become the only zeros in the loop transfer function. In terms of a root-locus diagram, these $n - 1$ arbitrary zeros may be placed anywhere on the s plane, and $n - 1$ of the n poles of $G(s)$ must terminate on these zeros. Thus, in the general case, the only asymptote is at $-180°$, and if the zeros are all located in the left-half s plane, stability is ensured for high values of the gain K.

The above statement is important and open to possible misinterpretation. Note that the K under discussion is the gain that precedes the dynamics of the system, as an ideal amplifier gain. The fact that the system may have other internal gains is placed in evidence by allowing a coefficient for s^m in the numerator of $G(s)$. A change in any of the inherent system gains would change the zero locations in $H_{eq}(s)$ as well as the loop gain.

The discussion until now has been concerned with the open-loop transfer function $G(s)H_{eq}(s)$, where $H_{eq}(s)$ does not exist as such but is the consequence of a block-diagram reduction to the configuration of Fig. 8.3-3a. Since the closed-loop transfer function $y(s)/r(s)$ is given by

$$\frac{y(s)}{r(s)} = \frac{G_{eq}(s)}{1 + k_1 G_{eq}(s)} = \frac{G(s)}{1 + G(s)H_{eq}(s)}$$

the discussion of the closed-loop transfer function can be carried out in terms of either the G_{eq} or the H_{eq} forms. However, the discussion is most easily carried out in terms of the $G_{eq}(s)$ configuration of Fig. 8.3-3b. As above, we consider the specific example of the positioning control system and then generalize to the nth-order case.

The reduction of the positioning system of Fig. 8.3-2 to the form of Fig. 8.3-3b is carried out in Fig. 8.3-5. Examine carefully the first reduction from Fig. 8.3-5a to b. Since k_3 is a constant, k_3 affects only the position of the pole that had been at $s = -5$. If the forward transfer function had been $K(s + a)/(s + 5)$ rather than just $2K/(s + 5)$, the zero at a would be unaffected. Thus the effect of feedback through constant elements is to change pole position and to leave the zeros, if any, unaltered. *No new zeros are introduced.* This fact is true regardless of the complication involved in the forward transfer function. Thus the second block-diagram reduction involving k_2, as given from Fig. 8.3-5b to c, also has no effect on zeros. A similar statement is true for the final reduction to $y(s)/r(s)$ in Fig. 8.3-5d.

So much for the zeros of the final *closed-loop* system. Now look at the poles. The closed-loop transfer function $y(s)/r(s)$ as given in Fig. 8.3-5d is

$$\frac{y(s)}{r(s)} = \frac{10K}{s^3 + (6 + 2k_3K)s^2 + (5 + 2k_3K + 10k_2K)s + 10k_1K}$$

$$(8.3\text{-}7)$$

The denominator of $y(s)/r(s)$ is a cubic in s, and three coefficients are available for adjustment by varying k_1, k_2, and k_3. Thus the poles of the closed-loop system may be placed anywhere that is desired. As before, k_1 will most likely be chosen to be unity to ensure zero steady-state position error, but this still leaves a choice of three pole locations if K is not fixed.

The tentative conclusion that is reached from the block-diagram reduction of the specific example to the form of Fig. 8.3-3b is that any desired pole locations can be obtained, but open-loop zeros of $G(s)$ are unaffected and appear as closed-loop zeros. It remains to be shown that this is true in the nth-order case.

The argument for zeros given is adequate for the general case, since regardless of the complexity of a forward transfer function, a constant feedback affects only pole locations. From classical control theory it is known that the closed-loop transfer function $y(s)/r(s)$ has zeros where $G(s)$ has zeros and where $H(s)$ has poles. Here $H(s) = k_1$ is a constant and

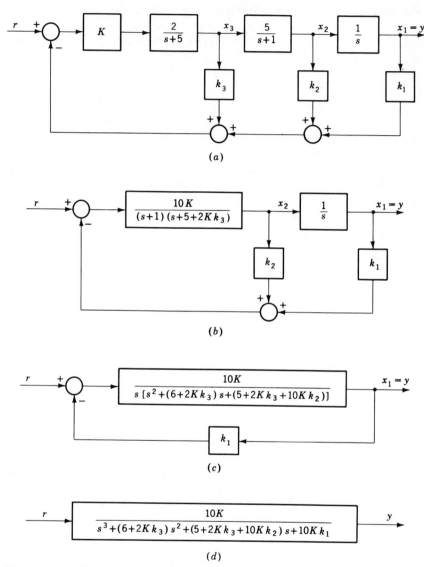

Fig. 8.3-5 Reduction to $G_{eq}(s)$ form.

therefore has no poles. Thus $H(s)$ introduces no zeros in the closed-loop transfer function.

That the pole locations may be chosen arbitrarily in the nth-order case can be shown by considering once again the general system with the transfer function given in Eq. (8.3-3). As before, we represent the system by means of phase variables as

$$\dot{\mathbf{x}} = \begin{bmatrix} 0 & 1 & \cdots & 0 \\ 0 & 0 & \cdots & 0 \\ \cdots & \cdots & \cdots & \cdots \\ -a_1 & -a_2 & \cdots & -a_n \end{bmatrix} \mathbf{x} + \begin{bmatrix} 0 \\ 0 \\ \cdots \\ K \end{bmatrix} u \qquad (8.3\text{-}4)$$

$$y = [c_1 \quad c_2 \quad \cdots \quad c_{m+1} \quad 0 \quad \cdots \quad 0]\mathbf{x} \qquad (8.3\text{-}5)$$

In the closed-loop case u becomes

$$u = r - \mathbf{k}^T\mathbf{x} = r - (k_1x_1 + k_2x_2 + \cdots + k_nx_n)$$

If this result is substituted into Eq. (8.3-4), we obtain

$$\dot{\mathbf{x}} = \begin{bmatrix} 0 & 1 & \cdots & 0 \\ 0 & 0 & \cdots & 0 \\ \cdots & \cdots & \cdots & \cdots \\ -(a_1 + Kk_1) & -(a_2 + Kk_2) & \cdots & -(a_n + Kk_n) \end{bmatrix} \mathbf{x}$$

$$+ \begin{bmatrix} 0 \\ 0 \\ \cdots \\ K \end{bmatrix} r$$

$$y = [c_1 \quad c_2 \quad \cdots \quad c_{m+1} \quad 0 \quad \cdots \quad 0]\mathbf{x}$$

The closed-loop transfer function may then be obtained by inspection from the phase-variable representation

$$\frac{y(s)}{r(s)} = \frac{K(c_{m+1}s^m + c_ms^{m-1} + \cdots + c_1)}{s^n + (a_n + Kk_n)s^{n-1} + \cdots + (a_1 + Kk_1)} \qquad (8.3\text{-}8)$$

From this result we see that the coefficients of the denominator polynomial of $y(s)/r(s)$ may be adjusted at will by proper selection of **k**. In addition, if k_1 is fixed, this result may still be achieved if K is adjustable. The freedom of the choice of pole locations also provides a means by which unwanted zeros of $G(s)$ which appear in the closed-loop transfer function may be canceled. The transfer function of Eq. (8.3-8) also illustrates the fact that the zeros of $y(s)/r(s)$ are the zeros of $G(s)$.

This section has discussed the characteristics of state-variable feedback from both an open-loop and a closed-loop point of view. The discussion of the open-loop characteristics was carried out in terms of the $H_{eq}(s)$ reduction of the original state-feedback configuration. The conclusion was that the *open-loop system has poles where G(s) has poles and n — 1 arbitrary zeros*, as determined by the values of **k**. This conclusion was verified in the general case through the use of phase variables. The discussion of the closed-loop system was carried out in terms of $G_{eq}(s)$ by reducing the original block diagram to the form of Fig. 8.3-3b. The conclusion reached here was that the *closed-loop system has zeros where G(s) has zeros and poles as determined by K and k*. One might view these two conclusions jointly and say that the ability to select the locations of the open-loop zeros ensures that the closed-loop poles can be located at will.

This section introduced no new design procedures, though perhaps some ideas may have occurred to the reader. The remainder of this chapter and the next chapter are devoted to design considerations and techniques.

Exercises 8.3   *8.3-1*.   For each of the two systems shown in Fig. 8.3-6, find $G_{eq}(s)$, $H_{eq}(s)$, and $y(s)/r(s)$ by means of block-diagram manipulations.   Verify that

$$\frac{y(s)}{r(s)} = \frac{G_{eq}(s)}{1 + k_1 G_{eq}(s)} = \frac{G(s)}{1 + G(s) H_{eq}(s)}$$

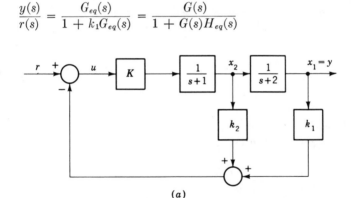

(a)

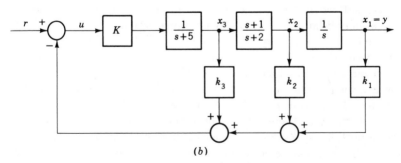

(b)

Fig. 8.3-6   Exercise 8.3-1.

answers:

$$G_{eq}(s) = \frac{K}{(s+2)(s+1+Kk_2)}$$

(a) $H_{eq}(s) = k_2 s + (k_1 + 2k_2)$

$$\frac{y(s)}{r(s)} = \frac{K}{s^2 + s(3 + Kk_2) + [2 + K(k_1 + 2k_2)]}$$

(b)

$$G_{eq}(s) = \frac{K(s+1)}{s^3 + s^2(7 + Kk_2 + Kk_3) + s(10 + Kk_2 + 2Kk_3)}$$

$$H_{eq}(s) = \frac{s^2(k_2 + k_3) + s(k_1 + k_2 + 2k_3) + k_1}{s+1}$$

$$\frac{y(s)}{r(s)}$$

$$= \frac{K(s+1)}{s^3 + s^2(7 + Kk_2 + Kk_3) + s(10 + Kk_1 + Kk_2 + 2Kk_3) + Kk_1}$$

8.3-2. Use the expression $H_{eq}(s) = \mathbf{k}^T \mathbf{x}(s)/\mathbf{c}^T \mathbf{x}(s)$ to find $H_{eq}(s)$ for both of the systems of Exercise 8.3-1.

8.3-3. Show that $H_{eq}(s)$ may be written as

$$H_{eq}(s) = \frac{\mathbf{k}^T \mathbf{\Phi}(s) \mathbf{b}}{\mathbf{c}^T \mathbf{\Phi}(s) \mathbf{b}}$$

by substituting $\mathbf{x}(s) = \mathbf{\Phi}(s)\mathbf{b}u(s)$ in the expression

$$H_{eq}(s) = \mathbf{k}^T \mathbf{x}(s)/\mathbf{c}^T \mathbf{x}(s)$$

Use the above result to find $H_{eq}(s)$ for the system

$$\dot{\mathbf{x}} = \begin{bmatrix} 0 & 1 & 0 \\ 0 & -1 & 1 \\ 0 & 0 & -3 \end{bmatrix} \mathbf{x} + \begin{bmatrix} 0 \\ 0 \\ 10 \end{bmatrix} u$$

$$y = \begin{bmatrix} 2 & 1 & 0 \end{bmatrix} \mathbf{x}$$

answer:

$$H_{eq}(s) = \frac{k_3 s^2 + (k_2 + k_3)s + k_1}{s+2}$$

8.3-4. Find $H_{eq}(s)$ for the system of Exercise 8.3-3 by drawing a block diagram of the system and making block-diagram manipulations.

8.3-5. Show that the closed-loop transfer function $y(s)/r(s)$ is given by the equation

$$\frac{y(s)}{r(s)} = \mathbf{c}^T[s\mathbf{I} - (\mathbf{A} - \mathbf{b}\mathbf{k}^T)]^{-1}\mathbf{b}$$

Use this expression to find the closed-loop transfer functions of the two systems of Exercise 8.3-1.

8.4   State-variable feedback and Bode diagrams

The Bode diagram procedures of this section are based on a particular form of the Kalman equation

$$|1 + \mathbf{k}^T\mathbf{\Phi}(s)\mathbf{b}|^2 = 1 + |\boldsymbol{\gamma}^T\mathbf{\Phi}(s)\mathbf{b}|^2 \qquad (7.5\text{-}10)$$

The reader will recall that this equation is applicable for the case of scalar control where the performance index is of the form

$$\text{PI} = \int_0^\infty (\mathbf{x}^T\boldsymbol{\gamma}\boldsymbol{\gamma}^T\mathbf{x} + u^2)\, dt$$

As demonstrated in the discussion of modeling in Sec. 8.2, except for the fact that $p = 1$, this is the most general form for the performance index.

In this section, we restrict the form of the performance index severely by selecting $\boldsymbol{\gamma} = \mathbf{c}$, so that

$$\text{PI} = \int_0^\infty (\mathbf{x}^T\mathbf{c}\mathbf{c}^T\mathbf{x} + u^2)\, dt = \int_0^\infty (y^2 + u^2)\, dt \qquad (8.4\text{-}1)$$

This is done to simplify the present discussion; later, techniques for restoring the full generality of this performance index are developed. In terms of this choice for $\boldsymbol{\gamma}$, the Kalman equation becomes

$$|1 + \mathbf{k}^T\mathbf{\Phi}(s)\mathbf{b}|^2 = 1 + |\mathbf{c}^T\mathbf{\Phi}(s)\mathbf{b}|^2 \qquad (8.4\text{-}2)$$

In order to interpret this equation in terms of transfer functions of the system, we make use of Fig. 8.3-3a, which is repeated here as Fig. 8.4-1

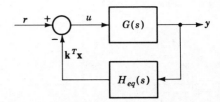

Fig. 8.4-1 $H_{eq}(s)$ form.

for convenience. In terms of this figure we have shown previously that the transfer function of the plant $G(s)$ is

$$G(s) = \frac{y(s)}{u(s)} = \mathbf{c}^T \boldsymbol{\Phi}(s) \mathbf{b} \qquad (8.4\text{-}3)$$

while the return-path transfer function $H_{eq}(s)$ is

$$H_{eq}(s) = \frac{\mathbf{k}^T \mathbf{x}(s)}{y(s)} = \frac{\mathbf{k}^T \mathbf{x}(s)}{\mathbf{c}^T \mathbf{x}(s)} \qquad (8.4\text{-}4)$$

However, since $\mathbf{x}(s) = \boldsymbol{\Phi}(s)\mathbf{b}u(s)$, the last transfer function may also be written as

$$H_{eq}(s) = \frac{\mathbf{k}^T \boldsymbol{\Phi}(s) \mathbf{b}}{\mathbf{c}^T \boldsymbol{\Phi}(s) \mathbf{b}}$$

Then the open-loop transfer function $G(s)H_{eq}(s)$ becomes

$$G(s)H_{eq}(s) = \mathbf{c}^T \boldsymbol{\Phi}(s) \mathbf{b} \frac{\mathbf{k}^T \boldsymbol{\Phi}(s) \mathbf{b}}{\mathbf{c}^T \boldsymbol{\Phi}(s) \mathbf{b}} = \mathbf{k}^T \boldsymbol{\Phi}(s) \mathbf{b} \qquad (8.4\text{-}5)$$

In terms of the results of Eqs. (8.4-3) and (8.4-5), the Kalman equation (8.4-2) may then be written in terms of more familiar transfer functions as

$$|1 + G(s)H_{eq}(s)|^2 = 1 + |G(s)|^2 \qquad (8.4\text{-}6)$$

Before discussing a design procedure based on Eq. (8.4-6), it is instructive to consider an inequality based on this equation. Since $|G(s)|^2$ is always a positive number for all $s = j\omega$, $\omega < \infty$,

$$|1 + G(j\omega)H_{eq}(j\omega)| > 1 \qquad (8.4\text{-}7)$$

A polar plot of $G(j\omega)H_{eq}(j\omega)$ illustrates this inequality, as in Fig. 8.4-2. Note that the polar plot of $G(j\omega)H_{eq}(j\omega)$, that is, a Nyquist diagram, never enters the interior of the circle of unit radius about the -1 point. Thus

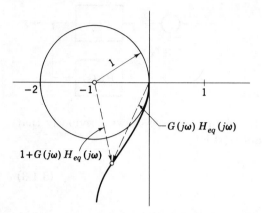

Fig. 8.4-2   Property of optimal $G(s)H_{eq}(s)$.

it is easily seen that many control systems that have been designed in the past by conventional series-equalization methods have not been optimum in the integral sense.

In the design procedure using the Bode diagram approach (Leake, 1965), three properties of Eq. (8.4-6) are used:

1. For small ω, $|1 + G(j\omega)H_{eq}(j\omega)| \sim |G(j\omega)|$
2. For large ω, $|1 + G(j\omega)H_{eq}(j\omega)| \sim 1$
3. For $|G(j\omega)| = 1$, $|1 + G(j\omega)H_{eq}(j\omega)| = \sqrt{2}$

The approximations of properties 1 and 2 are valid whenever $|G(j\omega)| \gg 1$ for small ω and $|G(j\omega)| \ll 1$ for large ω. These conditions are almost always satisfied for real control systems. In particular, we note that if the plant has an open-loop integration and a pole-zero excess of one or more, then these conditions are met. The last property provides the link between the asymptotic behavior described by properties 1 and 2. This last property is used as part of the design procedure listed below. The step-by-step procedure is as follows.

Step 1.   Sketch the Bode diagram of $G(j\omega)$. Here it is assumed for convenience that straight-line approximations are used.

Step 2.   For values of ω less than the crossover frequency of $G(j\omega)$, that is, for $\omega < \omega_c$, match the Bode diagram of $1 + G(j\omega)H_{eq}(j\omega)$ with that of $G(j\omega)$.

Step 3.   For values of $\omega > \omega_c$, let $1 + G(j\omega)H_{eq}(j\omega) = 1$. This can be accomplished by multiplying $G(j\omega)$ by a Butterworth polynomial with a characteristic frequency ω_c of the order of the pole-zero excess of $G(j\omega)$.

Step 4.   Use the results of the three previous steps to determine an approximate expression of $1 + G(j\omega)H_{eq}(j\omega)$.   Also determine an exact expression for $1 + G(j\omega)H_{eq}(j\omega)$ on the basis of the known $G(s)$ and the form of $H_{eq}(s)$, as given in Eq. (8.4-4).   Equate the exact and approximate expressions for $1 + G(s)H_{eq}(s)$ and solve for the unknown values of **k**.

Note that by choosing a Butterworth polynomial at the crossover frequency, it is ensured that property 3 is satisfied, since the magnitude of the Butterworth polynomial at crossover is $\sqrt{2}$.   A list of Butterworth polynomials is given in Table 8.4-1.

Table 8.4-1   *A List of Butterworth Polynomials with Break Frequency at ω_c*

Order	Butterworth Polynomial
1	$\dfrac{s}{\omega_c} + 1$
2	$\left(\dfrac{s}{\omega_c}\right)^2 + \sqrt{2}\,\dfrac{s}{\omega_c} + 1$
3	$\left(\dfrac{s}{\omega_c}\right)^3 + 2\left(\dfrac{s}{\omega_c}\right)^2 + 2\,\dfrac{s}{\omega_c} + 1$
n	$\left(\dfrac{s}{\omega_c}\right)^n + B_{n-1}\left(\dfrac{s}{\omega_c}\right)^{n-1} + \cdots + B_1\,\dfrac{s}{\omega_c} + 1$

$$\text{where } B_{n-1} = \frac{1}{\sin(\pi/2n)}$$

$$B_{n-2} = \frac{B_{n-1}\cos(\pi/2n)}{\sin(\pi/n)}$$

$$B_{n-k} = \frac{B_{n-k+1}\cos[(k-1)(\pi/2n)]}{\sin(k\pi/2n)}$$

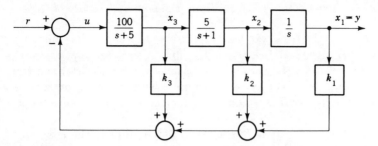

Fig. 8.4-3 Block diagram of a simple positioning system.

Example 8.4-1 The above procedure is illustrated by means of the simple positioning system shown in Fig. 8.4-3.

Step 1. From the block diagram $G(s)$ is

$$G(s) = \frac{500}{s(s+1)(s+5)} = \frac{100}{s(s+1)(s/5+1)}$$

The straight-line Bode diagram for $G(s)$ is plotted in Fig. 8.4-4. Note that on this Bode diagram the amplitude of $G(j\omega)$ is plotted directly rather than in terms of decibels. The slopes of the elements of the Bode plot are then -1, -2, etc., instead of -20 db per decade, -40 db per decade, etc. This is actually an unimportant feature as far as the method is concerned, but it does aid in plotting.

Steps 2 and 3. The approximate value of $1 + G(j\omega)H_{eq}(j\omega)$ is also indicated in Fig. 8.4-4 by the dashed line. Since $G(s)$ has three more poles than zeros, the appropriate Butterworth filter is third-order. The approximate expression for $1 + G(s)H_{eq}(s)$ is therefore

$$1 + G(s)H_{eq}(s) = \frac{500}{s(s+1)(s+5)}\left[\left(\frac{s}{\omega_c}\right)^3 + 2\left(\frac{s}{\omega_c}\right)^2 + 2\frac{s}{\omega_c} + 1\right]$$

$$= \frac{(500/\omega_c{}^3)(s^3 + 2\omega_c s^2 + 2\omega_c{}^2 s + \omega_c{}^3)}{s(s+1)(s+5)} \qquad (8.4\text{-}8)$$

Step 4. It is necessary to obtain an exact expression for $1 + G(s)H_{eq}(s)$. From Eq. (8.4-4), $H_{eq}(s)$ is

$$H_{eq}(s) = \frac{\mathbf{k}^T\mathbf{x}(s)}{\mathbf{c}^T\mathbf{x}(s)}$$

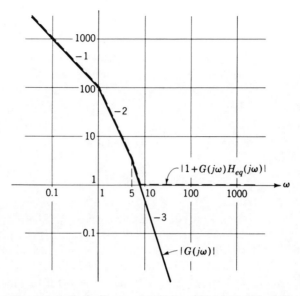

Fig. 8.4-4 Bode diagram for $G(s) = 500/s(s + 1)(s + 5)$.

In this example, $y = x_1$, or $\mathbf{c} = \mathrm{col}\,(1,0,0)$. Thus

$$H_{eq}(s) = \frac{k_1 x_1(s) + k_2 x_2(s) + k_3 x_3(s)}{x_1(s)}$$

From the block diagram of Fig. 8.4-3, we see that

$$x_2(s) = s x_1(s) \qquad x_3(s) = \frac{s+1}{5}\,x_2(s) = \frac{s(s+1)}{5}\,x_1(s)$$

Substituting these results into the above expression for $H_{eq}(s)$ and canceling the common $x_1(s)$ term yields

$$H_{eq}(s) = \frac{k_3 s^2 + (k_3 + 5k_2)s + 5k_1}{5}$$

Since $G(s)$ is given, $1 + G(s)H_{eq}(s)$ is simply

$$\begin{aligned}
1 &+ G(s)H_{eq}(s) \\
&= \frac{s^3 + (6 + 100k_3)s^2 + (5 + 100k_3 + 500k_2)s + 500k_1}{s(s + 1)(s + 5)}
\end{aligned}$$

This exact expression for $1 + G(s)H_{eq}(s)$ is set equal to the approximate expression in order to evaluate the k_i's. Note that this is possible in this example because the denominators are equal and the numerators are of the same order. If equal powers of s in the numerators are equated, the following four linear algebraic equations result:

$$\frac{500}{\omega_c{}^3} = 1 \qquad \frac{1,000}{\omega_c{}^2} = 6 + 100k_3$$

$$\frac{1,000}{\omega_c} = 5 + 100k_3 + 500k_2 \qquad 500 = 500k_1$$

If these four equations are solved for the four unknowns, k_1, k_2, k_3, and ω_c, we obtain $k_1 = 1.00$; $k_2 = 0.221$; $k_3 = 0.099$; and $\omega_c = 7.93$. Here all the k_i are ≤ 1, so no gain is needed in any of the feedback paths. The exact feedback coefficients for this problem are $k_1 = 1.00$; $k_2 = 0.228$; and $k_3 = 0.109$. The approximate answers obtained by the Bode approximation agree quite favorably with these exact results.

Note that although k_1 is equal to 1, the value necessary to provide zero steady-state error in this example, this is generally not the case. Since the computation is done in terms of an initial-condition disturbance, without input, zero steady-state error is not guaranteed. In order to achieve this feature, it is necessary to be able to adjust the forward-path gain.

A fact that should be stressed in regard to the use of this Bode method is that the technique works only if the two equations for the exact and approximate expressions for $1 + G(s)H_{eq}(s)$ have the same form. The exact and approximate expression for $1 + G(s)H_{eq}(s)$ must agree in form in both numerator and denominator. The example problem worked only because all the breaks in the Bode diagram occurred above the unit-amplitude line. Had the open-loop gain been lower, for instance, 10 rather than 100, the break at $s = 5$ would have occurred below the unit-amplitude line, as in Fig. 8.4-5. Now for small ω, $1 + G(j\omega)H_{eq}(j\omega) \approx G(j\omega)$ or

$$1 + G(s)H(s) \approx \frac{10}{s(s + 1)}$$

If $10/s(s + 1)$ is multiplied by a Butterworth polynomial of any order in the numerator, this can never be equal to the analytic expression for

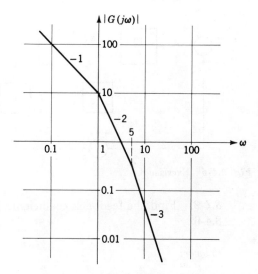

Fig. 8.4-5 Bode diagram for

$$G(s) = \frac{50}{s(s + 1)(s + 5)}$$

$1 + G(s)H_{eq}(s)$, since this expression has poles where $G(s)$ has poles, or it has poles at s, $s + 1$, and $s + 5$. The two are simply not equal for all ω.

This concludes the discussion of the Bode diagram approach. In summary it can be said that the method is easy to use and gives a good approximation to the exact answer. The approximation is better as the gain is increased. Thus this approach has much to recommend it.

Exercises 8.4 *8.4-1.* Find the feedback coefficients for each of the systems below. Assume that phase variables are used to represent the system.

(a) $G(s) = \dfrac{1{,}438}{s(s^2 + 3.2s + 3.56)}$ (b) $G(s) = \dfrac{1}{s^3}$

(c) $G(s) = \dfrac{100(s^2 - s + 1)}{s^2(s + 10)}$ (d) $G(s) = \dfrac{10}{s^2(s - 1)}$

answers:

(a) $\mathbf{k} = \text{col }(1, 0.175, 0.013)$
(b) $\mathbf{k} = \text{col }(1, 2, 2)$
(c) $\mathbf{k} = \text{col }(1, 1.01, 0.91)$
(d) $\mathbf{k} = \text{col }(1, 0.93, 0.53)$

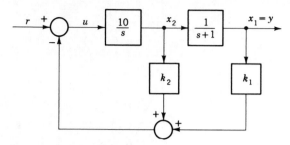

Fig. 8.4-6   Exercise 8.4-2.

8.4-2.   Find the feedback coefficients for the system shown in Fig. 8.4-6.

answer:

k = col (0.652,0.348)

8.4-3.   Find the feedback coefficients for the system

$$\dot{\mathbf{x}} = \begin{bmatrix} 0 & 1 & 0 \\ 0 & -1 & 1 \\ 0 & 0 & -3 \end{bmatrix} \mathbf{x} + \begin{bmatrix} 0 \\ 0 \\ 10 \end{bmatrix} u$$

$$y = \begin{bmatrix} 2 & 1 & 0 \end{bmatrix} \mathbf{x}$$

answer:

k = col (2,1.35,0.247)

8.5   *State-variable feedback and root-locus methods*

The basic assumptions and restrictions of this section are identical with those of the previous section.   The performance index is assumed to be

$$\text{PI} = \int_0^\infty (y^2 + u^2)\, dt$$

This is, of course, a restrictive performance index, but once again this fact does not concern us for the present.   The point of this section is to explain the root-locus technique within the framework of the familiar. Generalization of the performance index is left to Sec. 8.6.

The root-locus techniques described here are based on the restricted form of Kalman's equation developed in Sec. 8.4. This restricted form of Kalman's equation is repeated here for convenience in terms of the system transfer functions,

$$|1 + G(s)H_{eq}(s)|^2 = 1 + |G(s)|^2 \tag{8.5-1}$$

where $G(s)$ is assumed to be given and known and $H_{eq}(s)$ is

$$H_{eq}(s) = \frac{\mathbf{k}^T \mathbf{x}(s)}{\mathbf{c}^T \mathbf{x}(s)} \tag{8.5-2}$$

Consider the left-hand side of Eq. (8.5-1) first. Since $1 + G(s)H_{eq}(s)$ is a complex quantity, the square of its magnitude is simply the product of itself and its complex conjugate, or

$$|1 + G(s)H_{eq}(s)|^2 = [1 + G(s)H_{eq}(s)][1 + G(-s)H_{eq}(-s)] \tag{8.5-3}$$

In Sec. 8.3, it was demonstrated that the poles of $G(s)H_{eq}(s)$ are the poles of $G(s)$, and thus the poles of $1 + G(s)H_{eq}(s)$ are also restricted to being poles of $G(s)$. For simplicity it is assumed in the following development that $G(s)$ is stable so that the poles of $1 + G(s)H_{eq}(s)$ are in the left-half s plane.[1]

The zeros of $1 + G(s)H_{eq}(s)$ are the poles of the closed-loop system $y(s)/r(s)$. If it is assumed that the closed-loop system is stable, then all the poles of the closed-loop system, that is, the zeros of $1 + G(s)H_{eq}(s)$, are in the left half plane. Consequently $1 + G(s)H_{eq}(s)$ has all its poles and zeros in the left-half s plane.

Let us now turn our attention to the right-hand side of Eq. (8.5-1); since $G(s)$ is a complex quantity

$$|G(s)|^2 = G(s)G(-s)$$

and therefore

$$1 + |G(s)|^2 = 1 + G(s)G(-s) \tag{8.5-4}$$

---

[1] For the purpose of this discussion, $G(s)$ is considered as stable even if it has poles on the $j\omega$ axis. If $G(s)$ is unstable, the procedure discussed here may still be used. However, the denominator of $G(s)$ is not equal to the denominator of $[1 + G(s)G(-s)]^+$ although the denominators of $|1 + G(s)H_{eq}(s)|^2$ and $1 + |G(s)|^2$ are still identical.

The function $1 + G(s)G(-s)$ is also a ratio of polynomials. Both the numerator polynomial and the denominator polynomial can be factored into terms that lie only in the left-half s plane and terms that lie only in the right-half s plane. We use the notation

$$[1 + G(s)G(-s)]^+$$

to indicate those poles and zeros of $1 + G(s)G(-s)$ that lie in the left-half s plane and

$$[1 + G(s)G(-s)]^-$$

to indicate those poles and zeros of $1 + G(s)G(-s)$ that lie in the right-half s plane. This technique is known as *spectrum factorization* and is common in Wiener filter applications. The right side of Eq. (8.5-1) then becomes

$$1 + |G(s)|^2 = [1 + G(s)G(-s)]^+[1 + G(s)G(-s)]^- \qquad (8.5\text{-}5)$$

It is important to note here that the poles of $[1 + G(s)G(-s)]^+$ are just the poles of $G(s)$ if $G(s)$ is open-loop stable.

In terms of the results of Eqs. (8.5-3) and (8.5-5), Eq. (8.5-1) may be rewritten as

$$[1 + G(s)H_{eq}(s)][1 + G(-s)H_{eq}(-s)]$$
$$= [1 + G(s)G(-s)]^+[1 + G(s)G(-s)]^- \quad (8.5\text{-}6)$$

Since $1 + G(s)H_{eq}(s)$ has its poles and zeros only in the left half plane and the same is true for $[1 + G(s)G(-s)]^+$, the two may be equated, or

$$1 + G(s)H_{eq}(s) = [1 + G(s)G(-s)]^+ \qquad (8.5\text{-}7)$$

The denominators of these two expressions are identical. The numerator of the left-hand side is known in terms of the unspecified k_i's. Once the numerator of the right-hand side of Eq. (8.5-7) is known, the k_i's may be determined by equating the coefficients of equal powers in s, as in the Bode technique. This can be viewed either as a factoring problem or as a root-locus problem; it is simply necessary to find the left-half-plane zeros of $1 + G(s)G(-s)$. We shall refer to the function $G(s)G(-s)$ as the *associated transfer function* since although it is not a transfer function, we shall treat it as one, e.g., by plotting its root locus.

Here we view the problem as a root-locus problem, but the factoring approach should not be overlooked. Polynomial-factoring routines are commonly available even with modest computing equipment. Note also that because of the symmetry of the problem, it is necessary only to solve an nth-order polynomial rather than $2n$. On the other hand, the graphical root-locus approach has the advantage that approximate answers can be obtained quickly, and trends are easily seen, i.e., the usual advantages of the root-locus method are still applicable.

In plotting the root locus we consider $G(s)G(-s)$ as a single transfer function and look for

$$G(s)G(-s) = -1 = 1\underline{/180°}$$

as always. There is one point that must be observed, however. If the pole-zero excess of $G(s)$ is odd, then $G(-s)$ will contain a negative gain. In this case, the negative sign is removed, and one must plot a root locus with a 0° phase angle, rather than 180°.

Example 8.5-1 The root-locus procedure is illustrated with the same problem that was used in Sec. 8.4. The transfer function $G(s)$ is given as

$$G(s) = \frac{500}{s(s + 1)(s + 5)}$$

In Example 8.4-1, we found that

$$
\begin{aligned}
&1 + G(s)H_{eq}(s) \\
&= \frac{s^3 + (6 + 100k_3)s^2 + (5 + 100k_3 + 500k_2)s + 500k_1}{s(s + 1)(s + 5)}
\end{aligned}
\tag{8.5-8}
$$

The right-hand side of Eq. (8.5-7) has poles at $s = 0$, -1, and -5 and zeros where $1 + G(s)G(-s)$ has zeros in the left half plane. We use the root locus for determining these left-half-plane zeros. Since the pole-zero excess of $G(s)$ is odd, a 0° locus must be plotted. This is shown in Fig. 8.5-1.

The actual drawing of the root locus is quite simple, even though $2n$ branches of the locus are involved. Here $2n = 6$, as the given $G(s)$ is third-order. The origin of the asymptotes is always the origin, and the locus is always symmetrical about both the σ and $j\omega$ axes. This simplifies the drawing considerably. Only those branches which lie along the negative real axis and in the second

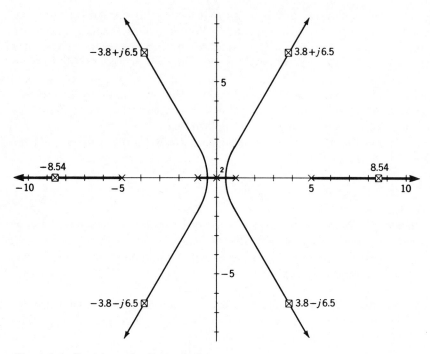

Fig. 8.5-1   Root locus for Example 8.5-1.

quadrant of the s plane need be drawn, although all branches are indicated in Fig. 8.5-1.

One other point is often helpful.   Here, for instance, the open-loop gain is 500, so that the open-loop gain of the associated transfer function $G(s)G(-s)$ is 500^2, a big number.   The roots for which we are looking must therefore lie an appreciable distance along the branches of the root locus and away from the initial closed-loop poles.   A quick approximation is to assume that the roots actually lie on the asymptotes.   This was done in this problem, as the branch of the root locus in the second quadrant is so close to the asymptote at the gain 500^2 that no distinction could be made in a graphical construction.   As indicated in Fig. 8.5-1, the zeros of $[G(s)G(-s)]^+$ are located at $s = -8.54$, $s = -3.8 \pm j6.5$.   Hence

$$[1 + G(s)G(-s)]^+ = \frac{(s + 8.54)[(s + 3.8)^2 + 6.5^2]}{s(s + 1)(s + 5)}$$

$$= \frac{s^3 + 16.14s^2 + 121.5s + 484}{s(s + 1)(s + 5)} \qquad (8.5\text{-}9)$$

If the numerators of Eqs. (8.5-8) and (8.5-9) are equated, the following identities result,

$$6 + 100k_3 = 16.14 \qquad 5 + 100k_3 + 500k_2 = 121.5$$
$$500k_1 = 484$$

Therefore $k_1 = 0.969$, $k_2 = 0.213$, and $k_3 = 0.101$. The answers obtained for this same problem using the Bode technique were $k_1 = 1$, $k_2 = 0.221$, $k_3 = 0.099$, while the exact answers are $k_1 = 1.00$, $k_2 = 0.228$, and $k_3 = 0.109$.

The values of the k_i's do not agree exactly, nor are they expected to agree exactly, since both the Bode method and the graphical root locus are approximate. If an exact answer is needed, the left-half-plane zeros of $1 + G(s)G(-s)$ can be determined by machine to more significant figures than is necessary for engineering purposes. In this sense the root-locus technique is exact and is essentially a method of solving the matrix Riccati equation by factoring and solving linear algebraic equations for the k_i's.

The previous paragraphs are somewhat academic, in view of the very restricted performance index which has been considered thus far. Section 8.6 generalizes this performance index, and the root-locus picture is then very helpful in aiding in the choice of the performance index, as well as in the indication of the closed-loop response.

Exercises 8.5 *8.5-1.* Use the root-locus method to find the feedback coefficients for each of the systems shown below. Assume that the systems are represented in phase variables.

(a) $G(s) = \dfrac{10}{s^2 + 3s + 2}$ (b) $G(s) = \dfrac{100(s + 1)}{s(s + 2)}$

(c) $G(s) = \dfrac{10(s + 2)}{s(s + 1)(s + 3)}$

answers:

(a) $\mathbf{k} = \text{col } (0.82, 0.20)$
(b) $\mathbf{k} = \text{col } (0.98, 0.97)$
(c) $\mathbf{k} = \text{col } (2.00, 1.68, 0.304)$

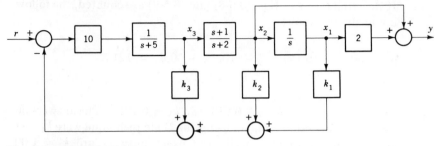

Fig. 8.5-2   Exercise 8.5-3.

8.5-2.   Find the feedback coefficients for the system

$$\dot{\mathbf{x}} = \begin{bmatrix} -1 & 1 \\ 0 & 0 \end{bmatrix} \mathbf{x} + \begin{bmatrix} 0 \\ 10 \end{bmatrix} u$$

$$y = x_1$$

answer:

$\mathbf{k} = \text{col } (0.640, 0.360)$

8.5-3.   Find the feedback coefficients for the third-order system shown in Fig. 8.5-2.

answer:

$\mathbf{k} = \text{col } (2.00, 1.00, -0.296)$

8.6   *Generalized performance indices*

The two previous sections utilized the Bode and root-locus diagrams to emphasize methodology rather than generality.   In both these instances we assumed that $\boldsymbol{\gamma} = \mathbf{c}$, such that the performance index was simply

$$\text{PI} = \int_0^\infty (\mathbf{x}^T \mathbf{c} \mathbf{c}^T \mathbf{x} + u^2)\, dt = \int_0^\infty (y^2 + u^2)\, dt \tag{8.6-1}$$

There are two obvious ways in which this performance index may be generalized.   In Eq. (8.6-1) the term representing the cost of control

u^2 has a coefficient of unity. In some particular cases, e.g., satellite attitude control, the cost of control energy is indeed high, and a designer may wish to weight the cost of control with a factor ρ. For the attitude-control case, ρ would be greater than 1 but in other instances ρ might be much less than 1.

The other term in Eq. (8.6-1), $x^T cc^T x$, represents the cost of error. Once a particular choice of state variables is made, c is fixed, and hence the cost-of-error term in the performance index is also fixed. If one is thinking in terms of the modeling approach mentioned in Sec. 8.2, the problem specifies the model. Obviously this is not a desirable situation.

It is a relatively simple matter to adjust the weighting on the cost of control through the introduction of a parameter ρ. This is done by replacing c in the performance index by $\hat{c} = c/\rho$. Thus the performance index analogous to Eq. (8.6-1) is

$$\text{PI} = \int_0^\infty \left(x^T \hat{c}\hat{c}^T x + u^2 \right) dt = \int_0^\infty \left(\frac{x^T cc^T x}{\rho^2} + u^2 \right) dt \qquad (8.6\text{-}2)$$

Both sides of Eq. (8.6-2) may be multiplied by ρ^2 to give

$$\text{PI} = \int_0^\infty \left(x^T cc^T x + \rho^2 u^2 \right) dt = \int_0^\infty \left(y^2 + \rho^2 u^2 \right) dt \qquad (8.6\text{-}3)$$

The substitution of c/ρ for c in the Kalman equation (8.4-2) produces the following result:

$$\left| 1 + k^T \Phi(s) b \right|^2 = 1 + \left| \frac{1}{\rho} c^T \Phi(s) b \right|^2$$

In terms of the transfer functions $G(s)$ and $H_{eq}(s)$, this result may be written as

$$\left| 1 + G(s) H_{eq}(s) \right|^2 = 1 + \left| \frac{G(s)}{\rho} \right|^2 \qquad (8.6\text{-}4)$$

Thus the only change that we need to make if we wish to weight the control cost other than as unity is to modify the gain of $G(s)$ on the right side of Eq. (8.4-6). Note, however, that the left side of the equation remains unchanged.

If the cost of control is weighted heavily, $\rho > 1$, the gain of the *modified transfer function* $G(s)/\rho$ is lower than the open-loop gain of the given system. On the other hand, if the cost of control is weighted very low, the open-loop gain of the modified transfer function is higher than that of the given system.   If one thinks in terms of a Bode diagram, the bandwidth of both the open- and closed-loop systems increases as the gain is increased.   As ρ approaches zero, the gain and the bandwidth both tend toward infinity.   The reader is reminded that we are discussing only the performance index of Eq. (8.6-3) here.   When we consider a more general performance index, it is necessary to modify these comments.

In terms of the root-locus method, a variation of ρ simply alters the location of the zeros of $1 + G(s)G(-s)/\rho^2$ on the original root locus. In other words, we may think of the root locus as being plotted for the parameter $1/\rho$.   Because of this fact the root-locus method provides a very convenient tool for studying the effect of control-cost weighting on the closed-loop system.   In both cases we see that weighting u^2 less heavily is analogous to increasing the open-loop gain of the system. More is said on this point later in this section.

Note that for $\rho < 1$ the accuracy of the Bode approximation is increased, while for $\rho > 1$ the Bode method may not apply at all, as some of the break points may occur below the unity line.   Since the root-locus approach is exact in the sense that the accuracy depends only upon the care with which the diagram is drawn, the root-locus method is not affected, regardless of the choice of ρ.

Example 8.6-1   In order to illustrate the above comments, let us consider once again the problem of Examples 8.4-1 and 8.5-1. Only the Bode method will be used here; the reader is urged to determine the answer by means of the root-locus method also.   Let us assume that we wish to reduce the weighting on the control so that we select ρ as 0.1.   The performance index is now

$$\text{PI} = \int_0^\infty (y^2 + 0.01u^2)\, dt$$

and $G(s)/\rho$ is

$$\frac{G(s)}{\rho} = \frac{5{,}000}{s(s + 1)(s + 5)} = \frac{1{,}000}{s(s + 1)(s/5 + 1)}$$

Using the Bode diagram for this modified transfer function, as shown in Fig. 8.6-1, the approximate expression for $1 + G(s)H_{eq}(s)$ is easily determined to be

$$1 + G(s)H_{eq}(s) = \frac{(5{,}000/\omega_c{}^3)(s^3 + 2\omega_c s^2 + 2\omega_c{}^2 s + \omega_c{}^3)}{s(s + 1)(s + 5)}$$

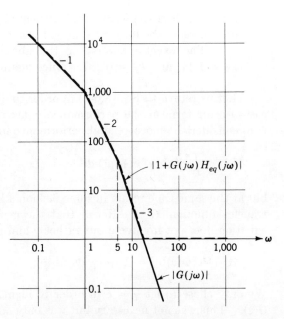

Fig. 8.6-1 Bode diagram for Example 8.6-1, $G(s) = 5,000/s(s + 1)(s + 5)$.

The exact expression for $1 + G(s)H_{eq}(s)$ is unchanged:

$$1 + G(s)H_{eq}(s)$$
$$= \frac{s^3 + (6 + 100k_3)s^2 + (5 + 100k_3 + 500k_2)s + 500k_1}{s(s + 1)(s + 5)}$$

If we equate coefficients in these two forms, we find that the following four equations must be satisfied:

$$\frac{5,000}{\omega_c^3} = 1 \qquad \frac{10,000}{\omega_c^2} = 6 + 100k_3$$

$$\frac{10,000}{\omega_c} = 5 + 100k_3 + 500k_2 \qquad 5,000 = 500k_1$$

From these equations, we find $k_1 = 10$, $k_2 = 1.1$, $k_3 = 0.28$, and $\omega_c = 17.1$.

   As predicted, we see that the bandwidth has increased from 7.93 to 17.1. In addition, each of the feedback coefficients has increased. Note that this system no longer has zero steady-state error since $k_1 = 10$. If we wish to restore this property, we must divide each of the feedback coefficients by 10, thus making $k_1 = 1$, and increase the forward-path gain by 10, so that it becomes 5,000.

The exact answers for the above problem are $k_1 = 10.0$, $k_2 = 1.11$, and $k_3 = 0.287$. Once again we note good agreement.

Let us return to Eq. (8.6-1) in order to discuss means by which the cost-of-error term in the performance index may be altered. Our goal is to consider the more general performance index

$$PI = \int_0^\infty (\mathbf{x}^T \boldsymbol{\gamma} \boldsymbol{\gamma}^T \mathbf{x} + u^2) \, dt \tag{8.6-5}$$

but at the same time retain in some fashion a link with the initial system transfer function, $G(s)$. Recall that the general form of the Kalman equation does not involve $\mathbf{c}$ but rather $\boldsymbol{\gamma}$ and is written as

$$|1 + \mathbf{k}^T \boldsymbol{\Phi}(s)\mathbf{b}|^2 = 1 + |\boldsymbol{\gamma}^T \boldsymbol{\Phi}(s)\mathbf{b}|^2 \tag{8.6-6}$$

We only chose to let $\boldsymbol{\gamma} = \mathbf{c}$ in order to identity the term $\boldsymbol{\gamma}^T \boldsymbol{\Phi}(s)\mathbf{b}$ with $G(s)$. This was not necessary but was only an aid to our thinking and a means of relating the matrix approach to well-known frequency-domain methods.

An examination of Eq. (8.6-6) reveals that the left side of the equation is unchanged and can still be written as $|1 + G(s)H_{eq}(s)|^2$. In order to put the right side of this equation into a transfer-function form we recall the definition of the *synthetic output* $\bar{y}$ made in Sec. 7.4,

$$\bar{y} = \boldsymbol{\gamma}^T \mathbf{x} \tag{8.6-7}$$

In terms of this synthetic output we may define a *synthetic transfer function* $\Gamma(s)$ by the relation

$$\Gamma(s) = \frac{\bar{y}(s)}{u(s)} = \boldsymbol{\gamma}^T \boldsymbol{\Phi}(s)\mathbf{b} \tag{8.6-8}$$

In other words, the synthetic transfer function relates the plant input $u(s)$ and the synthetic output $\bar{y}(s)$. We have used the word *synthetic* here because neither $\bar{y}$ nor $\Gamma(s)$ exists in the real system but is synthesized mathematically.

By using $\Gamma(s)$ the general form of the Kalman equation (8.6-6) may be written as

$$|1 + G(s)H_{eq}(s)|^2 = 1 + |\Gamma(s)|^2 \tag{8.6-9}$$

Since this equation is identical to Eq. (8.4-6) except that $\Gamma(s)$ has replaced $G(s)$ on the right, both the Bode and root-locus methods may be applied to this equation by simply replacing $G(s)$ by $\Gamma(s)$. In the Bode method, therefore, we plot the Bode diagram of $\Gamma(s)$ rather than $G(s)$. In using the root-locus method, we must plot the root locus of the *associated synthetic transfer function* $\Gamma(s)\Gamma(-s)$ rather than $G(s)G(-s)$. The left side of Eq. (8.6-9) is used just as before to find the expression for $1 + G(s)H_{eq}(s)$ in terms of the feedback coefficients. Once again by equating coefficients of the two sides of Eq. (8.6-9), we may solve for the feedback coefficients.

In order to relate the synthetic transfer function $\Gamma(s)$ to the original plant transfer function, it is necessary to recall some of the procedure used in the modeling approach of Sec. 8.2. There the model response was defined in terms of an $(n - m - 1)$st-order differential equation of the form

$$\alpha_1 y(t) + \alpha_2 \frac{dy(t)}{dt} + \cdots + \alpha_{n-m}\frac{d^{n-m-1}y(t)}{dt^{n-m-1}} = 0 \qquad (8.6\text{-}10)$$

In terms of this desired model, the performance index is

$$\text{PI} = \int_0^\infty \left[\left(\alpha_1 y + \alpha_2 \frac{dy}{dt} + \cdots + \alpha_{n-m}\frac{d^{n-m-1}y}{dt^{n-m-1}} \right)^2 + u^2 \right] dt$$

However, in terms of the definition of the synthetic output (8.6-7), the performance index may be written as

$$\text{PI} = \int_0^\infty (\bar{y}^2 + u^2)\, dt$$

Comparing these two performance indices, we see that the synthetic output is given by

$$\bar{y}(t) = \alpha_1 y(t) + \alpha_2 \frac{dy(t)}{dt} + \cdots + \alpha_{n-m}\frac{d^{n-m-1}y(t)}{dt^{n-m-1}} \qquad (8.6\text{-}11)$$

In the frequency domain this result becomes

$$\bar{y}(s) = (\alpha_1 + \alpha_2 s + \cdots + \alpha_{n-m}s^{n-m-1})y(s) \qquad (8.6\text{-}12)$$

Therefore the synthetic transfer function is

$$\Gamma(s) = \frac{\bar{y}(s)}{u(s)} = (\alpha_1 + \alpha_2 s + \cdots + \alpha_{n-m}s^{n-m-1})\frac{y(s)}{u(s)}$$

or

$$\Gamma(s) = (\alpha_1 + \alpha_2 s + \cdots + \alpha_{n-m}s^{n-m-1})G(s) \qquad (8.6\text{-}13)$$

This result indicates that the synthetic transfer function is formed from $G(s)$ by multiplying $G(s)$ by the characteristic polynomial of the model.

Note that in computing the synthetic transfer function by means of the above procedure it was not necessary to compute the γ vector. While this is not a considerable computational saving, it does allow the synthetic transfer function to be computed without a knowledge of the set of state variables chosen for the system representation. Hence we see the advantage of using the transfer-function approach to study input-output properties. This knowledge forms the basis of the design procedure of the next chapter.

Before going on to a specific example, consider a slight change in the performance index of Eq. (8.6-5) to include the factor ρ, so that the performance index becomes

$$\mathrm{PI} = \int_0^\infty (\mathbf{x}^T \gamma \gamma^T \mathbf{x} + \rho^2 u^2)\, dt = \int_0^\infty (\bar{y}^2 + \rho^2 u^2)\, dt \qquad (8.6\text{-}14)$$

For this case, the Kalman equation becomes

$$|1 + G(s)H_{eq}(s)|^2 = 1 + \left| \frac{\Gamma(s)}{\rho} \right|^2 \qquad (8.6\text{-}15)$$

and once again we see that varying ρ has the same effect as altering the gain of $\Gamma(s)$.

Now, however, as the value of ρ is reduced, the closed-loop system approaches the model system. As ρ is reduced, m of the closed-loop poles tend toward the zeros of $G(s)$, thereby canceling them; other poles approach the zeros created by the model while the one or more remaining poles of $y(s)/r(s)$ move toward infinity in the left half plane, and so their effect becomes negligible. In the limit when ρ equals zero, the closed-loop system equals the model. These points are illustrated by the following example.

Example 8.6-2 In this example, we wish to find the feedback coefficients for the system shown in Fig. 8.6-2, whose transfer function is

$$G(s) = \frac{10(s + 1)}{s(s + 2)(s + 5)}$$

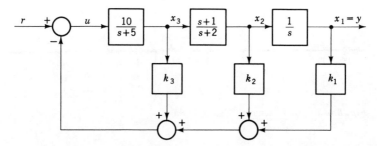

Fig. 8.6-2 Block diagram of the system for Example 8.6-2.

Since this system is third-order and has one zero,

$$n - m - 1 = 3 - 1 - 1 = 1$$

and we may select at most a first-order model. Correspondingly, let us choose the following model,

$$3y(t) + \dot{y}(t) = 0$$

In other words, the behavior of the system is to approximate that of a first-order system with a time constant of $\frac{1}{3}$ sec. In addition, the value of ρ is assumed to be unity, so that the performance index is

$$\text{PI} = \int_0^\infty [(3y + \dot{y})^2 + u^2]\, dt$$

We shall use the root-locus approach to determine the answer.

The synthetic transfer function as given by Eq. (8.6-13) is

$$\Gamma(s) = \frac{10(s + 1)(s + 3)}{s(s + 2)(s + 5)}$$

The added zero in $\Gamma(s)$ is the pole of the model, $s + 3$. The root locus of $1 + \Gamma(s)\Gamma(-s)$ is shown in Fig. 8.6-3. However, as a result of scaling problems, the zeros of $1 + \Gamma(s)\Gamma(-s)$ in the left-hand plane were determined by factoring as $s = -0.958, -2.86,$ and -10.95. Therefore $[1 + \Gamma(s)\Gamma(-s)]^+$ is given by

$$[1 + \Gamma(s)\Gamma(-s)]^+ = \frac{s^3 + 14.8s^2 + 44.6s + 30}{s(s + 2)(s + 5)}$$

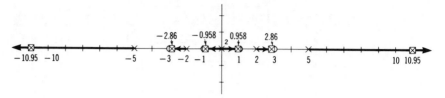

Fig. 8.6-3   Root locus for Example 8.6-2.

By the use of block-diagram manipulations on Fig. 8.6-2 $H_{eq}(s)$ was determined to be

$$H_{eq}(s) = \frac{s^2(k_2 + k_3) + s(k_1 + k_2 + 2k_3) + k_1}{s + 1}$$

so that $1 + G(s)H_{eq}(s)$ becomes

$$\begin{aligned} &1 + G(s)H_{eq}(s) \\ &= \frac{s^3 + s^2(7 + 10k_2 + 10k_3) + s(10 + 10k_1 + 10k_2 + 20k_3) + 10k_1}{s(s + 2)(s + 5)} \end{aligned}$$

If the coefficients of the various powers of s in $[1 + \Gamma(s)\Gamma(-s)]^+$ and $1 + G(s)H_{eq}(s)$ are equated, the following values are determined for **k**:

$$\mathbf{k} = \text{col}\ (3.0, 1.1, -0.32)$$

The closed-loop transfer function is then

$$\frac{y(s)}{r(s)} = \frac{10(s + 1)}{(s + 0.958)(s + 2.86)(s + 10.95)}$$

As predicted, one of the poles of $y(s)/r(s)$ approximately cancels the zero, while a second pole has become relatively unimportant. The third pole has approximately reached the position of the model's pole.   Note that if ρ were made less than unity these approximations would become even closer, since one may view the root locus of Fig. 8.6-3 as being plotted against $1/\rho$.

Note that once again the system does not have zero steady-state position error.   In order to achieve this result it is necessary to divide **k** by 3 and increase the gain to 30 so that $y(s)/r(s)$ becomes

$$\frac{y(s)}{r(s)} = \frac{30(s + 1)}{(s + 0.958)(s + 2.86)(s + 10.95)}$$

The results of this section present a paradox. The purpose of the section was to investigate how the procedures of the last two sections might be modified to encompass a general performance index. Surprisingly, the conclusion of this investigation is that one does not really need a performance index. All one needs to do is to specify a model for the system and then select the appropriate value for ρ. While the performance index, that is, γ, could be found, it is not necessary, since no use is made of it. Since a performance index is not used, one need no longer restrict the representation to phase variables but can work in terms of real physical variables, as was done in Example 8.6-2.

The realization that one can work in terms of a model performance rather than an integral performance index is important. The next chapter adopts this approach at the beginning with some very interesting consequences.

From the above comments it may appear that the extensive development of the modeling procedure in Sec. 8.2 was not necessary. This conclusion is false for two reasons: (1) in order to develop the frequency-domain methods of these last three sections it was necessary to work with the reduced performance index of the form

$$\text{PI} = \int_0^\infty (\mathbf{x}^T \boldsymbol{\gamma} \boldsymbol{\gamma}^T \mathbf{x} + u^2)\, dt$$

and (2) if we wish to make use of any of the approaches for solving the linear control problem discussed in the previous chapter, it is necessary to have a performance index. Hence the modeling approach of Sec. 8.2 provides a valuable link in relating the frequency- and time-domain approaches to the linear control problem.

Exercises 8.6   *8.6-1.*   Rework Example 8.6-1 using the root-locus method.

8.6-2.   Rework Example 8.6-2 using the Bode method.

8.6-3.   Find the values of the feedback coefficients for the system

$$\dot{\mathbf{x}} = \begin{bmatrix} 0 & 1 & 0 \\ 0 & 0 & 1 \\ 0 & -10 & -7 \end{bmatrix} \mathbf{x} + \begin{bmatrix} 0 \\ 0 \\ 10 \end{bmatrix} u$$

$$y = [1 \quad 1 \quad 0]\mathbf{x}$$

The model for the system is

$$3y(t) + \dot{y}(t) = 0$$

and $\rho = 1$.

answer:

$\mathbf{k} = \text{col} \ (3.00, 3.46, 0.777)$

8.6-4.   Find the feedback coefficients for the system

$$\dot{\mathbf{x}} = \begin{bmatrix} 0 & 1 & 0 \\ 0 & 0 & 1 \\ 0 & -2 & -3 \end{bmatrix} \mathbf{x} + \begin{bmatrix} 0 \\ 0 \\ 1 \end{bmatrix} u$$

$$y = [1 \quad 0 \quad 0]\mathbf{x}$$

if the model is

$$y(t) + \sqrt{3} \ \dot{y}(t) + \ddot{y}(t) = 0$$

and if

(a) $\rho = 1.0$
(b) $\rho = 0.5$
(c) $\rho = 0.1$

In addition, find the closed-loop transfer function for each case. Observe that a ρ is decreased as $y(s)/r(s)$ approaches the model transfer function $1/(s^2 + \sqrt{3} \ s + 1)$.

answers:

(a) $\mathbf{k} = \text{col} \ (1.0, 1.49, 0.604)$

$$\frac{y(s)}{r(s)} = \frac{1}{(s + 2.25)(s + 0.55)(s + 0.80)}$$

(b) $\mathbf{k} = \text{col} \ (2.0, 3.04, 1.37)$

$$\frac{y(s)}{r(s)} = \frac{1}{(s + 2.84)(s^2 + 1.53s + 0.704)}$$

(c) $\mathbf{k} = \text{col } (10.0, 16.5, 8.92)$

$$\frac{y(s)}{r(s)} = \frac{1}{(s + 10.2)(s^2 + 1.72s + 0.98)}$$

8.7 Summary and conclusion

The purpose of this chapter has been to relate the Bode and root-locus frequency-domain techniques to the solution of the linear control problem. The vehicle for this discussion was the Kalman equation of Sec. 7.6. The results of this investigation have been very fruitful, both in terms of new methods for solving the linear control problem and in added insight into the problem.

The methods developed in this chapter provide valuable tools for solving the linear control problem. In particular, these methods allow relatively simple graphical procedures to be used to obtain approximate solutions. More important than the computational labor that they save, these graphical procedures, especially the root locus, allow one to acquire a better understanding of the meaning of designing to an integral performance index.

As we have seen in the last section, once one has gained a working knowledge of these frequency-domain transfer-function procedures, one can work without ever determining a performance index. Performance specifications are translated into a model response and then directly into the form of the synthetic transfer function, completely bypassing the determination of a performance index.

This procedure has two serious shortcomings, however: (1) The procedure always leads to the approximate cancellation of the zeros of $G(s)$. There is simply no way to avoid the result even if one would like to preserve the zeros. (2) The procedure never adds to the order of the system, although one knows from classical design methods that the introduction of a lead-lag network often improves performance. In order to circumvent these problems it is necessary to drop completely the artifice of an integral performance index. This is the approach taken in the next chapter.

We have assumed throughout this chapter that all the state variables were available for measurement and control. If this is not true, as it often is not in a practical problem, one must generate these unmeasurable state variables. This may be done either by using the Kalman filter approach of the last chapter or by using the technique discussed in the next chapter.

8.8   Problems

8.8-1.   For the system

$$\dot{x} = \begin{bmatrix} 0 & 1 & 0 \\ 0 & -2 & 2 \\ 0 & 0 & -4 \end{bmatrix} x + \begin{bmatrix} 0 \\ 0 \\ 10 \end{bmatrix} u$$

$$y = x_1$$

find the feedback coefficients if the performance index is

$$PI = \int_0^\infty (y^2 + u^2)\, dt$$

8.8-2.   For the system of Prob. 8.8-1, find the feedback coefficients and the response of the closed-loop system for the initial-condition disturbance $x(0) = $ col $(1,0,0)$ if the performance index is

$$PI = \int_0^\infty [(y + \dot{y} + \ddot{y})^2 + \rho^2 u^2]\, dt$$

and ρ is

(*a*) $\rho = 2$
(*b*) $\rho = 1$
(*c*) $\rho = 0.5$

8.8-3.   Find the feedback coefficients for the system

$$\dot{x} = \begin{bmatrix} 0 & 1 & 1 \\ 0 & -2 & 1 \\ 0 & 0 & -4 \end{bmatrix} x + \begin{bmatrix} 0 \\ 0 \\ 10 \end{bmatrix} u$$

$$y = x_1$$

using both the root-locus and the Bode diagram method. Assume that the performance index is

$$PI = \int_0^\infty [(y + \dot{y})^2 + u^2]\, dt$$

8.8-4. Represent the system of Prob. 8.8-3 in phase variables and determine the feedback coefficients directly using both the root-locus and Bode methods. Show that this answer could have been obtained by determining the transformation matrix relating the two sets of state variables.

8.8-5. Show that the two following expressions for $y(s)/r(s)$ are equivalent by the use of matrix algebra.

$$\frac{y(s)}{r(s)} = \frac{G(s)}{1 + G(s)H_{eq}(s)} = \frac{\mathbf{c}^T\mathbf{\Phi}(s)\mathbf{b}}{1 + \mathbf{k}^T\mathbf{\Phi}(s)\mathbf{b}}$$

and

$$\frac{y(s)}{r(s)} = \mathbf{c}^T[s\mathbf{I} - (\mathbf{A} - \mathbf{bk}^T)]^{-1}\mathbf{b}$$

HINT: Use the matrix identity $(\mathbf{MN}^T + \mathbf{I})^{-1} = [\mathbf{I} - \mathbf{M}(\mathbf{N}^T\mathbf{M} + I)^{-1}N^T]$.

8.8-6. Determine an expression for $G_{eq}(s)$ in terms of the state-variable representation.

$$\dot{\mathbf{x}} = \mathbf{Ax} + \mathbf{b}u$$
$$y = \mathbf{c}^T\mathbf{x} \quad \text{and} \quad u = r - \mathbf{k}^T\mathbf{x}$$

References

Brockett, R. W.: Poles, Zeros and Feedback: State Space Interpretation, *IEEE Trans. Autom. Control*, vol. AC-10, no. 2, pp. 129–135, April, 1965.

D'Azzo, J. J., and C. H. Houpis: "Feedback Control System Analysis and Synthesis," 2d ed., McGraw-Hill Book Company, New York, 1965.

Wonham, W. M., and C. D. Johnson, Optimal Bang-Bang Control with Quadratic Index of Performance, *J. Basic Engr*, ser D, vol. 86, pp. 107–115, March, 1964.

Kuo, B. C.: "Automatic Control Systems," Prentice-Hall, Inc., Englewood Cliffs, N.J., 1962.

Leake, R. J.: Analytical Controller Design and the Servomechanism Problem, *Syracuse Univ., Dept. Elec. Eng. Tech. Rept.*, 64-4, July, 1964.

————: Return Difference Bode Diagram for Optimal System Design, *IEEE Trans. Autom. Control*, vol. AC-10, no. 3, pp. 342–344, July, 1965.

Savant, C. J.: "Control System Design," 2d ed., McGraw-Hill Book Company, New York, 1964.

Slivinsky, C. R.: "Linear System Design Using State Variable Feedback," M.S. thesis, University of Arizona, Tucson, Ariz., 1966.

nine   *linear system synthesis via desired closed-loop response*

9.1   Introduction and outline of chapter

This chapter, like the previous two, is concerned with the synthesis of linear control systems by means of state-variable feedback.   The trend in the last two chapters has been away from the theoretical and toward the practical and more familiar classical control techniques.   In Chap. 7 synthesis procedures were discussed that depended entirely on the solution of the matrix Riccati or Kalman equation to minimize a given integral performance index, while Chap. 8 attacked the same problem but made use of the more familiar frequency-domain methods of Bode and root locus to provide graphical approaches to the same optimization problem.

Here we abandon completely the design on the basis of integral performance indices. By doing so we eliminate the need of solving the matrix Riccati equation as well as the need of choosing a suitable performance index. The approach of this chapter is based almost completely on conventional control concepts, and even the matrix notation used up to this point is almost entirely absent. The design criterion used throughout this chapter is the desired closed-loop transfer function, and the mathematics required to design to this criterion is simply algebra, which may be accomplished largely in terms of block-diagram manipulations.

In a sense this chapter attempts to remove the need for any modern control theory in the linear single input–single output system. The only important fact retained from the previous chapters is the desirability of feeding back all the state variables.

Since the mathematical tool used here is algebra, this chapter could have been written 20 years ago. But the fact that it was not written 20 years ago, or at any previous time, is significant. Authors have been preoccupied with the conventional unity-ratio-feedback system and have largely ignored the feedback of variables other than the output. The realization that all state variables must be fed back is a direct consequence of modern control theory. In this chapter we attempt to exploit this contribution without recourse to other formalisms of the modern approach.

This chapter also serves to relate the synthesis procedures in terms of state-variable feedback to the more conventional synthesis procedures utilizing series-compensation networks, such as lead or lag networks. The use of a series equalizer has the effect of increasing the order of the closed-loop transfer function $y(s)/r(s)$. Thus far we have never changed the order of the system by feeding back all the state variables; there is clearly a gap between the synthesis methods that we have discussed up to now and the synthesis methods using series equalizers.

Section 9.2 presents a brief review of the Guillemin-Truxal method of series compensation along with a discussion of the choice of the closed-loop transfer function $y(s)/r(s)$. In addition, the design approach of this chapter is related to the performance-index approach of the previous chapters.

Sections 9.3 and 9.4 develop the $H_{eq}(s)$ method of design to a particular closed-loop transfer function $y(s)/r(s)$ for the simplest case in which $y(s)/r(s)$ has no zeros. In Sec. 9.3, $G(s)$ is also assumed to have no zeros, while Sec. 9.4 considers the case when $G(s)$ does have inherent zeros. If the given open-loop transfer function $G(s)$ has zeros, it is necessary to increase the order of the system in order to be able to specify an nth-order response. Thus Sec. 9.4 illustrates the first instance in which it is necessary to add series compensation in addition to state-variable feedback.

The discussion of design in the face of inaccessible state variables in Sec. 9.5 is intended to complement the more elegant Kalman filter approach of Chap. 7.

Section 9.6 presents the extension of the $H_{eq}(s)$ method to the general case. The method is further developed in Sec. 9.7, where some special procedures are discussed. These procedures, when applicable, allow one to achieve truly amazing system behavior.

9.2   Design in terms of desired closed-loop response

The idea of designing closed-loop control systems to conform to a given closed-loop transfer function was introduced by Guillemin in 1947 and popularized by Truxal in his book "Automatic Feedback Control System Synthesis" (1955). Chapter 5 of that book, titled Synthesis through Pole-Zero Configurations, is particularly significant. The use of series equalizers to realize a specific closed-loop transfer function is known as the Guillemin-Truxal method.

In this chapter we illustrate an alternate approach to the realization of a desired closed-loop response through the use of state-variable feedback. In doing so, we adopt the basic arguments and philosophy set forth by Truxal, but the realization is in terms of state-variable feedback rather than series compensation. Before proceeding to the actual methods of realization, it is well to review the arguments for and against the Guillemin-Truxal approach and to contrast this method of design with design methods utilizing the frequency domain and integral performance indices.

The Guillemin-Truxal procedure is based upon a closed-loop-system realization, as pictured in Fig. 9.2-1. Here $G(s)$ is, as usual, the unalter-

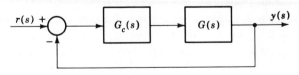

Fig. 9.2-1   Basic system configuration of the Guillemin-Truxal method.

able fixed plant, and $G_c(s)$ is the required compensating network. The design procedure involves the following three steps:

1. The desired closed-loop transfer function $y(s)/r(s)$ is determined from the specifications as a ratio of polynomials in s.
2. The required $G_c(s)$ is determined by solving the equation

$$\frac{y(s)}{r(s)} = \frac{G_c(s)G(s)}{1 + G_c(s)G(s)} \qquad (9.2\text{-}1)$$

for $G_c(s)$.
3. The required $G_c(s)$ is synthesized, usually with passive elements, in particular resistors and capacitors.

Let us comment briefly on each of these three steps. The determination of the desired closed-loop transfer function from the given specifications may be no easy problem. Often the initial design specifications are transmitted to the engineer in rather vague terms by nontechnical people. It is then the engineer's job to transform these specifications into analytical expressions. Here it is impossible to probe this general problem in any depth. Rather we invert the problem and examine what can be accomplished in terms of system specification if it is possible to design to a specific closed-loop response. This approach also allows a comparison between conventional methods of design and design to a desired closed-loop response.

A wide variety of synthesis techniques now exist, and it is possible to proceed from any given design method directly to a specification of $y(s)/r(s)$. In a sense, this begs the question, since we are suggesting the designer proceed in his own preferred way to specify $y(s)/r(s)$. It does not seem desirable to suggest that the designer abandon his years of experience and proceed by a new recipe. The express purpose of this entire chapter is to tie in the methods of state-variable feedback with conventional design.

Suppose the designer's method of approach is, for example, phase-margin design by the use of straight-line Bode approximations. Phase margin is a rather questionable design criterion, and the knowledgeable designer will no doubt check the resulting system either by examining the closed-loop frequency response or by doing a closed-loop transient analysis. On the basis of either method of evaluation the closed-loop behavior may be found to be deficient in one respect or another. Once these deficiencies are known, in terms of either frequency response or transient response, a more desirable $y(s)/r(s)$ is determined. The state-variable-feedback methods to be outlined in the following sections enable the designer to realize this more desirable $y(s)/r(s)$ *exactly.*

The choice of $y(s)/r(s)$ may be made on the basis of a time response alone with no reference to the frequency domain. One of the most general ways of specifying $y(t)$ is as the solution of an nth-order differential equation to a particular input $r(t)$. The Laplace transformation of this nth-order equation then leads to a frequency-domain specification of $y(s)/r(s)$.

The completion of step 2 of the Guillemin-Truxal procedure requires only algebra. Once the closed-loop transfer $y(s)/r(s)$ is specified as a ratio of polynomials, $G_c(s)$ may be determined, by solving Eq. (9.2-1), as

$$G_c(s) = \frac{y(s)/r(s)}{G(s)[1 - y(s)/r(s)]} \tag{9.2-2}$$

The synthesis techniques necessary to realize a given $G_c(s)$ in step 3 are more network problems than control-system problems, and they are not considered here. The subject is also well covered in Truxal. Note that the open-loop transfer function of the Guillemin-Truxal method is just $G_{eq}(s)$, that is,

$$G_{eq}(s) = G_c(s)G(s)$$

As an illustration of the Guillemin-Truxal method, consider the control of the plant shown in Fig. 9.2-2. Let us assume that the desired closed-loop transfer function is given as

$$\frac{y(s)}{r(s)} = \frac{160}{[(s + 2)^2 + 2^2](s + 20)} = \frac{160}{s^3 + 24s^2 + 88s + 160}$$

The resulting $G_c(s)$ from Eq. (9.2-2) is

$$G_c(s) = \frac{(80/3)(s + 3)(s + 10)}{(s + 4.6)(s + 19.4)}$$

The final closed-loop configuration is pictured in Fig. 9.2-3a. The outstanding feature of the final result is the cancellation of the poles of $G(s)$

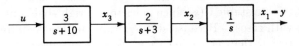

Fig. 9.2-2 Plant to be controlled.

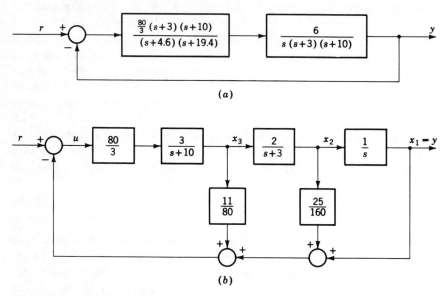

Fig. 9.2-3   Closed-loop system.   (*a*) The Guillemin-Truxal realization; (*b*) a state-variable-feedback realization.

by the zeros of $G_c(s)$.   In the ideal case this cancellation would be perfect, and the order of the closed-loop system is the same as the order of the plant being controlled.   In this sense, the Guillemin-Truxal approach is much like that of optimal-control theory and different from those series-compensation methods which do not rely on pole-zero cancellation.   It will be shown later that in some cases it is highly desirable to increase the order of the system over that of the unalterable plant.

The realization of the same closed-loop transfer function through the use of state-variable feedback is shown in Fig. 9.2-3*b*.   The use of state-variable feedback alters pole locations through the use of feedback rather than by canceling them with zeros.   Because the mechanism by which new pole locations are realized is basically different, one might suspect that the state-variable-feedback design procedure would not suffer from the limitations imposed upon the Guillemin-Truxal method. This is indeed the case.

One obvious restriction of the Guillemin-Truxal method is a limitation to stable $G(s)$ since poles in the right-half s plane cannot be canceled with zeros.   Because state-variable feedback simply alters pole locations rather than canceling them, $G(s)$ is not restricted to being stable when state-variable feedback is used.

The Guillemin-Truxal method requires that $y(s)/r(s)$ be chosen not only to meet desired system specifications but also to ensure that all the poles of the open-loop transfer function $G_c(s)G(s)$ lie on the negative real axis. The following is a quotation from Truxal, page 297:

> The imposition of the additional constraint that all poles of the open-loop transfer function lie on the negative real axis is not only necessary if the synthesis [of $G_c(s)$] is to be simple, but also frequently desirable to ensure that the transfer functions of the compensation networks be realizable by RC networks.

Thus it is seen that the difficulty in the Guillemin-Truxal method stems largely from the necessity to realize a rather complicated $G_c(s)$. This practical difficulty does not arise in the use of state-variable feedback. Therefore the problem of realizing the transfer function $G_c(s)$, step 3 of the design procedure, is replaced by the problem of determining the values of the feedback coefficients. It is shown in the following sections of this chapter that not only is it simpler to determine the k_i's, but the resulting overall system configuration is substantially improved from the point of view of stability and sensitivity.

The basic theoretical limitation of the state-variable feedback method is the same as that of the Guillemin-Truxal method. The closed-loop transfer function $y(s)/r(s)$ cannot have a smaller pole-zero excess than that originally existing in $G(s)$.

It is interesting to relate the closed-loop design procedure of this chapter to the integral-performance-index approach of the previous chapter. This may be done by considering once again the general form of the Kalman equation involving the synthetic transfer function $\Gamma(s)$,

$$|1 + G(s)H_{eq}(s)|^2 = 1 + \left| \frac{\Gamma(s)}{\rho} \right|^2$$

The reader will recall from the discussion of Sec. 8.6 that $\Gamma(s)$ is given by

$$\Gamma(s) = \frac{N(s)}{\Delta(s)} \tag{9.2-3}$$

where the polynomial $N(s)$ is the product of the characteristic polynomial of the model and the numerator polynomial of $G(s)$ while $\Delta(s)$ is the denominator polynomial of $G(s)$.

On the other hand, in Sec. 8.5, $1 + G(s)H_{eq}(s)$ was shown to be

$$1 + G(s)H_{eq}(s) = \frac{\Delta_k(s)}{\Delta(s)} \tag{9.2-4}$$

where $\Delta_k(s)$ is the denominator polynomial of the closed-loop transfer function $y(s)/r(s)$.

If Eqs. (9.2-3) and (9.2-4) are substituted into the Kalman equation, it becomes

$$\left| \frac{\Delta_k(s)}{\Delta(s)} \right|^2 = 1 + \left| \frac{N(s)}{\rho \, \Delta(s)} \right|^2$$

or

$$\frac{\Delta_k(s) \, \Delta_k(-s)}{\Delta(s) \, \Delta(-s)} = 1 + \frac{N(s)N(-s)}{\rho^2 \, \Delta(s) \, \Delta(-s)}$$

The result may be solved for $N(s)N(-s)$ to obtain

$$N(s)N(-s) = \rho^2[\Delta_k(s) \, \Delta_k(-s) - \Delta(s) \, \Delta(-s)]$$

so that

$$N(s) = \rho[\Delta_k(s) \, \Delta_k(-s) - \Delta(s) \, \Delta(-s)]^+ \tag{9.2-5}$$

where the symbol [ ]$^+$ indicates, as before, the roots in the left half plane.

If the closed-loop transfer function is specified, then $\Delta_k(s)$ is known, and Eq. (9.2-5) may be solved for $N(s)$ and hence the model. From the model the performance index may be found. In other words, if the performance index determined in the above procedure is used with the system described by $G(s)$, the resulting optimal closed-loop transfer function will be $y(s)/r(s)$.

Equation (9.2-5) may be exactly solved by hand for low-order systems or factored by computer for higher-order systems. In addition, the left-plane roots may be found by plotting the root locus of the function $\Delta(s) \, \Delta(-s)/\Delta_k(s) \, \Delta_k(-s)$ for *negative* gain and finding the roots when the gain equals -1.

Example 9.2-1 In order to illustrate this procedure, let us determine the performance index for the system shown in Fig. 9.2-4 if the

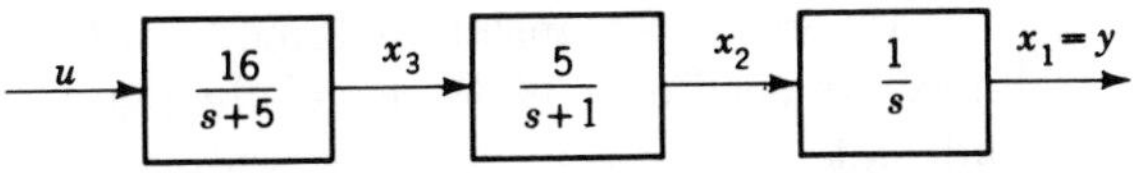

Fig. 9.2-4 Example 9.2-1.

closed-loop transfer function is

$$\frac{y(s)}{r(s)} = \frac{80}{s^3 + 14s^2 + 48s + 80}$$

For this problem

$$\Delta(s) = s^3 + 6s^2 + 5s$$

and

$$\Delta_k(s) = s^3 + 14s^2 + 48s + 80$$

Therefore Eq. (9.2-5) becomes

$$N(s) = \rho[(-s^6 + 100s^4 - 64s^2 + 6{,}400) - (-s^6 + 26s^4 - 25s^2)]^+$$
$$= \rho[74s^4 - 39s^2 + 6{,}400]^+$$

Because of its symmetry, this polynomial may be easily factored to obtain

$$N(s) = \rho(8.6s^2 + 37.1s + 80)$$

Since the numerator of $G(s)$ consists of only a gain of 80, the characteristic polynomial for the model is given by

$$\alpha_1 + \alpha_2 s + \alpha_3 s^2 = \frac{\rho}{80}(80 + 37.1s + 8.6s^2)$$
$$= \rho(1 + 0.464s + 0.108s^2)$$

For simplicity, let us assume that $\rho = 1$, so that the model for this problem is

$$y(t) + 0.464\dot{y}(t) + 0.108\ddot{y}(t) = 0$$

In order to translate the model into an integral performance index, we need only make use of the plant and output equations to find that

$$y(t) = x_1(t)$$
$$\dot{y}(t) = \dot{x}_1(t) = x_2(t)$$
$$\ddot{y}(t) = \dot{x}_2(t) = -x_2 + 5x_3$$

If these results are substituted into the model equation, we find that the performance index is

$$PI = \int_0^\infty [(x_1 + 0.356x_2 + 0.538x_3)^2 + u^2]\, dt$$

Hence if the above performance index is used with the system of Fig. 9.2-4, the desired closed-loop transfer function will result.

The reader will note that we have made no mention of the numerator polynomial of $y(s)/r(s)$. This omission is easy to explain, since, as we have seen in Sec. 8.3, the zeros of $y(s)/r(s)$ must be the same as the zeros of $G(s)$. Since there is no freedom in choosing the zeros of $y(s)/r(s)$, it is not amazing that they do not influence the performance index. However, by augmenting the order of the system, we shall show later how it is possible to select arbitrary zeros for $y(s)/r(s)$. This procedure, in effect, creates a new $G(s)$, and one must find the performance index in terms of the state variables of this augmented system.

The purpose of the above discussion was not to imply that one should translate a closed-loop transfer function into a performance index and then determine the feedback coefficients by the methods of Chap. 7 or 8; on the contrary, the authors do not recommend that procedure.

In a sense, the above material can be considered as an extension and clarification of the modeling approach of Sec. 8.2. There we were able to talk only in terms of asymptotically approaching the model as the weighting on u^2 was reduced to zero. Here we speak in terms of exact realization of desired closed-loop behavior.

Note, however, that not all $y(s)/r(s)$'s have an associated performance index since it was assumed in the derivation above that the given $y(s)/r(s)$ satisfies the Kalman equation. It is possible to select a $\Delta_k(s)$ for which the Kalman equation is not satisfied. This means that the polar plot of $G(s)H_{eq}(s)$ penetrates the unit circle about the minus-one point in violation of the property illustrated in Chap. 8 as Fig. 8.4-2. This violation of the Kalman equation is manifested by the occurrence of complex values for the coefficients of $N(s)$. What this means, in a physical sense, is that the given $y(s)/r(s)$ is not optimal for any quadratic integral performance index. This, however, does not mean that such a $y(s)/r(s)$ is necessarily undesirable and in that sense the approach of this chapter is more general than that of Chaps. 7 and 8 since here we may realize a closed-loop transfer function for which no quadratic integral performance index exists.

Exercises 9.2 *9.2-1.* Determine the performance index for the problem of Example 9.2-1 by using root-locus methods to find $N(s)$.

9.2-2. Using the performance index found in Example 9.2-1 with the system shown in Fig. 9.2-4, find the optimal-feedback coefficients using any of the procedures of Chap. 7 or 8. Show that the resulting closed-loop system is as desired.

9.2-3. Find the performance index associated with the following system (see Fig. 9.2-2):

$$\dot{\mathbf{x}} = \begin{bmatrix} 0 & 1 & 0 \\ 0 & -3 & 2 \\ 0 & 0 & -10 \end{bmatrix} \mathbf{x} + \begin{bmatrix} 0 \\ 0 \\ 3 \end{bmatrix} u$$

$$y = x_1$$

in order to achieve the closed-loop transfer function

$$\frac{y(s)}{r(s)} = \frac{160}{s^3 + 24s^2 + 88s + 160}$$

Assume that $\rho = 1$.

answer:

$$\int_0^\infty [(26.6x_1 + 5.94x_2 + 5.68x_3)^2 + u^2]\, dt$$

9.3 *H-equivalent method: the simplest case*

Before discussing a design procedure, let us review the conclusion drawn at the end of Sec. 8.3 concerning the characteristic features of state-variable feedback. First, it was established that in an nth-order system the poles of the closed-loop transfer function $y(s)/r(s)$ may be located anywhere on the s plane by suitable choice of the n feedback coefficients k_i. In practice k_1 is usually specified to ensure zero steady-state error.

The ability to position all n poles is retained if the amplifier gain K is assumed to be adjustable.

In addition, the following properties of $H_{eq}(s)$ are of interest here:

1. $H_{eq}(s)$ has $n - 1$ zeros whose locations are determined by the feedback coefficients.
2. $H_{eq}(s)$ is not a function of K, the input amplifier gain.
3. The poles of $H_{eq}(s)$ are equal to the zeros of $G(s)$, and the transfer function $G(s)H_{eq}(s)$ has $n - 1$ zeros and n poles.

Property 3 is true unless the transfer function of $x_n(s)/u(s)$ contains one of the zeros of $G(s)$. In this case the denominator of $H_{eq}(s)$ does not contain that zero, and the transfer function $G(s)H_{eq}(s)$ has n poles and zeros. This last case was not discussed in Sec. 8.3 and will not be needed until Sec. 9.6. It is included here for completeness; Sec. 9.7 contains a detailed discussion of the situation.

As we shall see, the only limitation on the closed-loop transfer function $y(s)/r(s)$ is that its pole-zero excess not be less than the pole-zero excess of $G(s)$. In this section we discuss means by which the feedback coefficients k_i are determined to realize a given $y(s)/r(s)$. Both the open-loop and closed-loop transfer functions are assumed to have no zeros. This situation is referred to as the *simplest case*. The more general situation when $y(s)/r(s)$ and $G(s)$ may have zeros is treated in the following sections.

The H-equivalent method is based on the block-diagram reduction of the form indicated in Fig. 8.3-3a. Here the state variables are assumed to have physical meaning, and the resulting k_i are the values that would be inserted into the actual system. Actually there is no new theory to be introduced in this section. All that remains to be done is to demonstrate by example that it is possible to realize any $y(s)/r(s)$ that contains no zeros. On the basis of this demonstration, a general design procedure is formulated.

As a specific case, consider the system which has served as a running example throughout the previous chapter. This plant is indicated in block-diagram form in Fig. 9.3-1a, and the means by which this plant is to be controlled are indicated in Fig. 9.3-1b. Note that in both figures we have associated with the transfer function $1/(s + 1)$ the gain of 5 and with $1/(s + 5)$ the gain of 2. It is assumed that these gains are inherent and are dictated by the components that comprise the system. In Fig. 9.3-1b the feedback coefficient k_1 has been set equal to 1 in order to ensure zero steady-state error for position inputs. This reduces the number of feedback elements that may be chosen arbitrarily from three to two. In

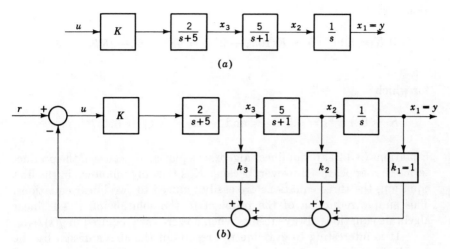

Fig. 9.3-1 The simplest case. (a) Plant to be controlled; (b) method of control.

order to compensate for this reduction the forward-path gain is made adjustable. If this gain is not adjustable and k_1 is set equal to 1, then the number of poles of $y(s)/r(s)$ that can be located as desired is reduced from n to $n - 1$, or in this case from three to two.

One element of the closed-loop response has already been specified by choosing $k_1 = 1$, namely, zero steady-state error for step inputs. This is a specification that is often desirable, but it is not necessary to the method. Assume that a desired closed-loop frequency response is given by

$$\frac{y(s)}{r(s)} = \frac{80}{[(s + 2)^2 + 2^2](s + 10)} = \frac{80}{s^3 + 14s^2 + 48s + 80} \qquad (9.3\text{-}1)$$

In order to realize this closed-loop specification, it is necessary to express the system of Fig. 9.3-1b as an input-output relationship and to solve for the values of k_2, k_3, and K. Figure 9.3-1b may be reduced by either one of the two methods discussed in Sec. 8.3. That is, the inner loops may be combined to yield an equivalent open-loop system with unity feedback, as in Fig. 9.3-2a, or the feedback elements may be combined to form $H_{eq}(s)$, as in Fig. 9.3-2b. Either method, of course, gives the same closed-loop transfer function, and each method gives an opportunity to evaluate the results from a different point of view.

By comparing the closed-loop transfer function as given in Fig. 9.3-2c with the required statement of $y(s)/r(s)$, three following algebraic equations result:

$$10K = 80 \qquad 5 + K(10k_2 + 2k_3) = 48 \qquad 6 + 2Kk_3 = 14$$

$$(9.3\text{-}2)$$

for which

$$K = 8 \qquad k_3 = 0.500 \qquad \text{and} \qquad k_2 = {}^{35}\!/_{80} = 0.437$$

Equations (9.3-2) are not linear algebraic equations because of the product terms that appear. However, because K is the only unknown in the first equation, the three equations are easily reduced to two linear equations. This simple reduction of the problem to the solution of $n - 1$ linear algebraic equations always results when no zeros are required in $y(s)/r(s)$.

It is interesting to examine the results of the above design by the root-locus technique. A root locus may be drawn only for the $G(s)H_{eq}(s)$ structure since the poles of $G_{eq}(s)$ are functions of the gain K. On the basis of the now-known values of K, k_2, and k_3, $G(s)H_{eq}(s)$ and $G_{eq}(s)$ are

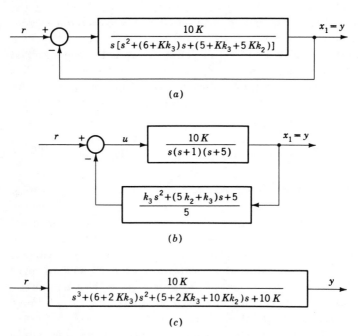

(a)

(b)

(c)

Fig. 9.3-2 System of Fig. 9.3-1. *(a)* $G_{eq}(s)$ form; *(b)* $H_{eq}(s)$ form; *(c)* closed-loop system.

$$G(s)H_{eq}(s) = \frac{80}{s(s+1)(s+5)} \frac{0.5s^2 + 2.85s + 5}{5}$$

$$= \frac{8[(s+2.685)^2 + 1.68^2]}{s(s+1)(s+5)} \qquad (9.3\text{-}3)$$

and

$$G_{eq}(s) = \frac{80}{s(s^2 + 14s + 48)} = \frac{80}{s(s+6)(s+8)} \qquad (9.3\text{-}4)$$

The root locus of $G(s)H_{eq}(s)$ shown in Fig. 9.3-3 is interesting from both a stability and a sensitivity point of view. As K is increased from its design value of 8 to infinity, the complex conjugate poles of $y(s)/r(s)$ move but a relatively slight amount along the root locus to the zeros of $H_{eq}(s)$ located at $s = -2.685 \pm j1.68$. The real pole moves toward negative infinity, and the overall closed-loop response not only is stable but exhibits an even lower damping ratio than when K is equal to the design value of 8. In other words, the system is amazingly stable.

The root locus shown in Fig. 9.3-4 represents the situation which would exist if a Guillemin-Truxal series-type equalizer had been used. In terms of $G_{eq}(s)$, $G_c(s)G(s) = G_{eq}(s)$, so that the equivalent series equalizer would be

$$G_c(s) = \frac{(s+1)(s+5)}{(s+6)(s+8)}$$

From Fig. 9.3-4 we see that the asymptotes of the resulting root-locus diagram remain unaltered and go into the right half plane at $\pm 60°$ for

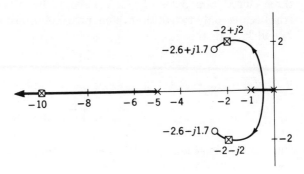

Fig. 9.3-3 Root-locus diagram for $H_{eq}(s)$ system.

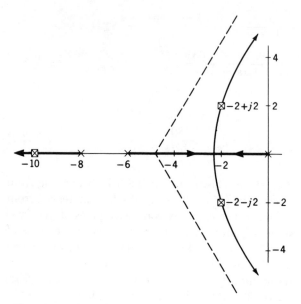

Fig. 9.3-4   Root-locus diagram for Guillemin-Truxal realization.

the compensated system, since it still has three more poles than zeros. Thus the series-compensated system would be unstable for high gain.

On the basis of this one example alone the reader may expect that the sensitivity of the system closed-loop poles to changes in gain is substantially better than in cases where series compensation is used. We shall see that this is basically a correct conclusion.

In the above example, if K had been set at a value of 50 and k_1 set equal to unity to ensure zero steady-state position error, only two of the three closed-loop poles of $y(s)/r(s)$ could have been specified. This is true because only two of the system parameters are available for variation, k_2 and k_3. In this case it is necessary to specify $y(s)/r(s)$ as

$$\frac{y(s)}{r(s)} = \frac{8\rho}{[(s + 2)^2 + 2^2](s + \rho)}$$

$$= \frac{8\rho}{s^3 + (4 + \rho)s^2 + (8 + 4\rho)s + 8\rho} \quad (9.3\text{-}5)$$

Here the closed-loop gain has been set equal to 8ρ to ensure the zero steady-state position error. By a block-diagram reduction to an equivalent feedback type of system, the expression for $y(s)/r(s)$ is determined in terms of the k_i's to be

$$\frac{y(s)}{r(s)} = \frac{500}{s^3 + (6 + 100k_3)s^2 + (5 + 500k_2 + 100k_3)s + 500} \quad (9.3\text{-}6)$$

By equating coefficients in similar powers of s in Eqs. (9.3-5) and (9.3-6) the k_i's and ρ are found to be $\rho = 62.5$, $k_2 = 0.369$, and $k_3 = 0.605$, and $H_{eq}(s)$ is therefore

$$H_{eq}(s) = 0.121[(s + 2.015)^2 + 2.05^2]$$

while $G(s)H_{eq}(s)$ is

$$G(s)H_{eq}(s) = \frac{60.5[(s + 2.015)^2 + 2.05^2]}{s(s + 1)(s + 5)}$$

Note that the zeros toward which the closed-loop poles are moving as K is increased are almost identical with the desired closed-loop poles for the complex conjugate poles. The pole at $s = -62.5$ has a real part more than 10 times the real part of the complex conjugate poles and hence may be effectively ignored.

This concludes the discussion and interpretation of the simplest case, i.e., when $y(s)/r(s)$ and $G(s)$ have no zeros. The simplest case is quite easy to handle, because $y(s)/r(s)$ and $G(s)$ are assumed to be compatible, and no series compensation need be added. The specific steps in the design procedure are as follows:

1. Assume that all the state variables are available and represent the system in the usual state-variable-feedback configuration.
2. Choose the desired closed-loop transfer function $y(s)/r(s)$.
3. Find $y(s)/r(s)$ in terms of the k_i's, preferably by the use of the $H_{eq}(s)$ block-diagram reduction.
4. Equate the expressions for $y(s)/r(s)$ from steps 2 and 3 and solve for the k_i's by equating coefficients of like powers of s.
5. If all the state variables are not available, use the known values of the k_i's to determine suitable series or minor-loop compensation.

The implementation of step 5 is not discussed until Sec. 9.5. In step 2, above, it is recommended that $y(s)/r(s)$ be determined from the $H_{eq}(s)$ reduction. In the simplest case this does not appear to be necessary; however, the $H_{eq}(s)$ representation proves to be of considerable use in the general case, when series compensation must be added. In addition, a knowledge of $H_{eq}(s)$ provides a systematic method of evaluation of the final design. The following steps indicate the systematic evaluation that was used on the example:

1. Use the values of the k_i's to find $H_{eq}(s)$.
2. Determine the zeros of $H_{eq}(s)$.
3. Locate the poles and zeros of $G(s)H_{eq}(s)$ on the s plane. Also locate on the s plane the closed-loop poles of $y(s)/r(s)$ as an aid in drawing the root locus.
4. Sketch the root locus to ensure that the desired stability and sensitivity benefits that can be achieved through state-variable feedback actually have been realized.

This evaluation procedure becomes more important as we consider some of the more general situations.

In cases where the plant contains an integration at the output, it is usually assumed at the outset that $k_1 = 1$ so that zero steady-state position error for step inputs is ensured, and the above procedures are carried out in terms of the k_i, $i = 2, 3, \ldots , n$, and K.

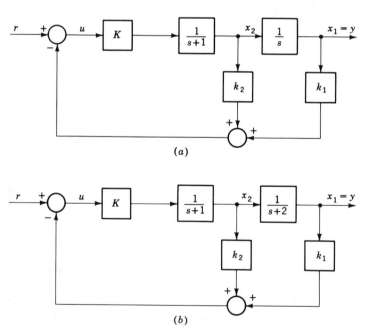

(a)

(b)

Fig. 9.3-5   Exercise 9.3-1.

Before proceeding to the more general case of allowable or desired zeros in $y(s)/r(s)$, it is necessary to consider the situation in which the given plant $G(s)$ has one or more inherent zeros and $y(s)/r(s)$ is to have no zeros.

Exercises 9.3   *9.3-1.* Find the feedback coefficients of the two systems shown in Fig. 9.3-5 such that the closed-loop transfer function for each is

$$\frac{y(s)}{r(s)} = \frac{5}{s^2 + 2s + 5}$$

Plot the root locus for $G(s)H_{eq}(s)$ for each of the systems.

answers:

(a) $\mathbf{k} = \text{col } (1,0.2)$ $K = 5$
(b) $\mathbf{k} = \text{col } (1,-0.2)$ $K = 5$

9.3-2. Find the feedback coefficients for the system shown in Fig. 9.3-6 such that the closed-loop transfer function is

$$\frac{y(s)}{r(s)} = \frac{160}{[(s + 2)^2 + 2^2](s + 20)}$$

Using the feedback coefficients found above, show that this system is stable for all positive gain. Find the locus of the closed-loop poles if the transfer function $x_2(s)/x_3(s)$ is allowed to vary from $2/(s + 1)$ to $2/(s + 5)$.

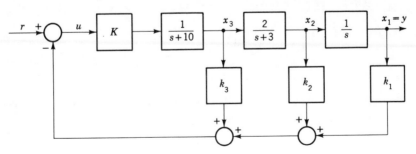

Fig. 9.3-6 Exercise 9.3-2.

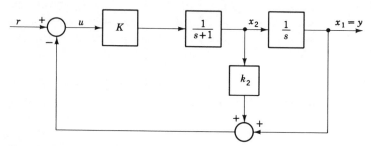

Fig. 9.3-7 Exercise 9.3-3.

answer:

$$\mathbf{k} = \text{col} \left(1, {}^{25}\!\!/_{160}, {}^{11}\!\!/_{80}\right) \qquad K = 80$$

9.3-3. For the system shown in Fig. 9.3-7, find the values of K and k_2 such that the closed-loop transfer function is

(a) $\dfrac{y(s)}{r(s)} = \dfrac{2}{(s + 1)^2 + 1^2}$ (b) $\dfrac{y(s)}{r(s)} = \dfrac{8}{(s + 2)^2 + 2^2}$

(c) $\dfrac{y(s)}{r(s)} = \dfrac{18}{(s + 3)^2 + 3^2}$

Note that the damping ratio remains fixed in these systems but that the natural frequency is increasing linearly.   Plot the root locus of $G(s)H_{eq}(s)$ for each of the three cases.

answers:

(a) $K = 2$, $k_2 = 0.5$ (b) $K = 8$, $k_2 = 0.375$
(c) $K = 18$, $k_2 = 0.277$

9.3-4. For the open-loop system

$$\dot{\mathbf{x}} = \begin{bmatrix} 0 & 1 \\ 0 & \alpha \end{bmatrix} \mathbf{x} + \begin{bmatrix} 0 \\ K \end{bmatrix} u$$

$$y = x_1$$

find the values of α such that the state-variable feedback system whose closed-loop transfer function is

$$\frac{y(s)}{r(s)} = \frac{2}{s^2 + 2s + 2}$$

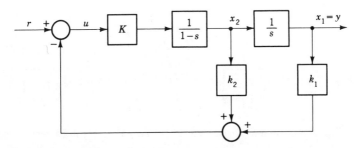

Fig. 9.3-8 Exercise 9.3-5.

is stable for all gain. Also find k_2 as a function of α.

answer:

$$0 < \alpha < 2, \; k_2 = 1 - \alpha/2$$

9.3-5. For the system shown in Fig. 9.3-8 find the feedback coefficients and the gain such that the closed-loop transfer function is

$$\frac{y(s)}{r(s)} = \frac{2}{(s+1)^2 + 1^2}$$

answer:

$$\mathbf{k} = \text{col} \ (1, \tfrac{3}{2}) \qquad K = -2$$

9.4 A modification of the simplest case

In the simplest case of the preceding section both $y(s)/r(s)$ and $G(s)$ were assumed to have no zeros. In this section we consider the case in which $G(s)$ has m zeros while $y(s)/r(s)$ has none. If no special precautions are taken, the zeros of $G(s)$ appear also as zeros of $y(s)/r(s)$. These zeros may be canceled by either an open-loop or a closed-loop procedure. Both procedures are considered below, as well as a combination of the two.

The process of canceling an unwanted zero in the open-loop system is indicated in Fig. 9.4-1. There a zero associated with the ith state variable is eliminated by placing a pole of the same value *directly in front* of the box containing the unwanted zero. In this way the identity of the

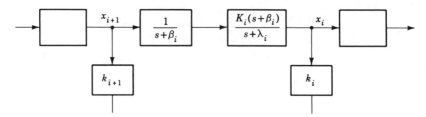

Fig. 9.4-1 Removal of an unwanted zero at $s = -\beta_i$ by series compensation in the open loop.

initial state variable is not lost, and the k_i's may be determined in the manner described above when $G(s)$ had no zeros.

If the given plant has m zeros, and m poles are added in the manner indicated in Fig. 9.4-1, it is possible to view the system as being of order $n + m$.   In fact, the resulting system is of order $n + m$, but if treated this way, m of the feedback coefficients are zero.   The m zero feedback coefficients are those associated with the m variables that are introduced by the cancellation compensation.   Hence the algebra is simplified by treating the system as though $G(s)$ has no zeros, as advocated above.   As a consequence of this procedure, the $(n + m)$th-order system is unobservable; i.e., if $x(t)$ is determined, this vector is only of order n, not $n + m$. In this case, this fact is not important, since the magnitudes of the unobservable variables are always smaller than the magnitudes of the state variables at the inputs to the cancellation blocks.

Although the above procedure is simple, it is somewhat academic, since it is usually impossible to insert the compensation wherever desired in a practical system.   Hence it is usually impossible to insert the cancellation pole directly in front of the undesired zero.   For this reason, we shall not consider the approach any further.

An alternate approach must then be used; m of the n poles of $y(s)/r(s)$ may be positioned at exactly the same locations as the m unwanted zeros, canceling them in the overall system response.   As a consequence of this action, the resulting $y(s)/r(s)$ will have $n - m$ poles rather than the original n.   If an nth-order response is desired rather than the $(n - m)$th-order response, this can be achieved by introducing m new poles, with their associated state variables, into the original plant to be controlled, making the order of the open-loop plant $n + m$.   If m of the poles of $y(s)/r(s)$ are used to cancel m unwanted zeros in $y(s)/r(s)$, then n poles are left to be placed as desired.

In some cases it may be desirable to add fewer than m new poles if sufficient flexibility in the choice of $y(s)/r(s)$ is still available.   Consider,

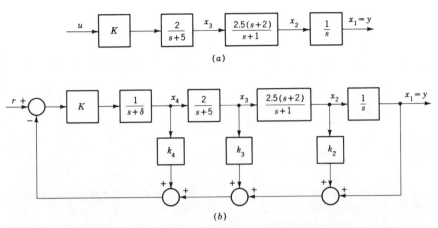

(a)

(b)

Fig. 9.4-2 Zero cancellation in the closed loop. (a) Plant to be controlled; (b) final system.

for example, a third-order system with two zeros in $G(s)$. With no added series elements, only one pole of $y(s)/r(s)$ could be positioned arbitrarily. However, if only one new pole were added rather than two, we would still be able to achieve any second-order response. Such flexibility might be adequate, and hence we would add only one pole. For simplicity, we shall assume that m poles are added in order to make the following discussion specific.

This latter approach is important because it is the first time that we have attempted to *increase the system order* by introducing series elements preceding $G(s)$. For each new pole added, a new state variable is added, and at the same time two unknowns are introduced. These unknowns are the location of the newly added pole and the value of the feedback coefficient associated with this new state variable. A certain degree of arbitrariness is now involved, since twice as many new unknowns are being added as new state variables. This point is discussed further in the following example.

Assume that the linear plant we have been considering in the examples thus far is altered to include a zero at $s = -2$, as shown in Fig. 9.4-2a. Assume further that this zero is an unalterable feature of the plant and that it is physically impossible to insert a pole immediately preceding this unwanted zero, as suggested by Fig. 9.4-1. In Fig. 9.4-2b a pole is added in the electronic portion of the system which introduces a new state variable x_4 located at the output of the combined lag circuit and amplifier. Since we have no idea as yet of what value to assign to this new pole location at δ, let us choose the convenient value of zero.

Later it becomes clear that this is not the best choice, but that is unimportant for the present.

Since we wish to cancel in the closed-loop system, the closed-loop transfer function that must be realized in order to eliminate the unwanted zero at $s = -2$ is

$$\frac{y(s)}{r(s)} = \frac{80(s + 2)}{(s + 2)(s + 10)(s^2 + 4s + 8)}$$

$$= \frac{80(s + 2)}{s^4 + 16s^3 + 76s^2 + 176s + 160} \tag{9.4-1}$$

Here, as before, the closed-loop gain of 80 is chosen to ensure zero steady-state position error.

If the block diagram of Fig. 9.4-2b is reduced to the equivalent feedback configuration, then $H_{eq}(s)$ is

$$H_{eq}(s) = [k_4s^3 + (5k_2 + 2k_3 + 6k_4)s^2 + (10k_2 + 2k_3 + 5k_4 + 5)s + 10]/5(s + 2)$$

and $G(s)$ is

$$G(s) = \frac{5K(s + 2)}{s^2(s + 1)(s + 5)}$$

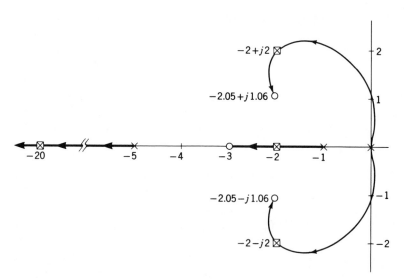

Fig. 9.4-3 The root locus for the system of Fig. 9.4-2b, with $\delta = 0$.

With these values of $G(s)$ and $H_{eq}(s)$, $y(s)/r(s)$ is determined to be

$$\frac{y(s)}{r(s)} = 5K(s+2)/\{s^4 + (6+k_4K)s^3 + [5 + K(5k_2 + 2k_3 + 6k_4)]s^2 + (10k_2 + 2k_3 + 5k_4 + 5)Ks + 10K\}$$

If the coefficients of the various powers of s in the numerator and denominator of $y(s)/r(s)$ are equated to the desired coefficients of Eq. (9.4-1), the following equations result:

$$6 + k_4K = 16 \qquad 5 + K(5k_2 + 2k_3 + 6k_4) = 76$$
$$(10k_2 + 2k_3 + 5k_4 + 5)K = 176 \qquad 10K = 160$$

From these equations K is determined to be 16, thereby reducing the three remaining equations to three linear algebraic equations in three unknowns. The values of the resulting k_i's are

$$k_2 = \tfrac{7}{16} \qquad k_3 = -\tfrac{3}{4} \qquad k_4 = \tfrac{5}{8}$$

The transfer function $H_{eq}(s)$ is now known, and after some numerical reduction $H_{eq}(s)$ is found to be

$$H_{eq}(s) = \frac{s^3 + 7.15s^2 + 17.6s + 16}{8(s+2)} = \frac{(s+3)[(s+2.05)^2 + 1.06^2]}{8(s+2)}$$

The reader may wonder why we even bother to calculate $H_{eq}(s)$, since the problem is completely solved once the k_i are known. The answer is that we wish to verify that the design is adequate, since we initially made a rather arbitrary choice of the added pole location δ. A root locus of $G(s)H_{eq}(s)$ is plotted in Fig. 9.4-3, and it is apparent that the arbitrary choice of the added pole location at zero was not a good one. Because of the two poles of $G(s)$ located at the origin, the root locus moves into the right half plane for low values of gain. The stability advantage of state-variable feedback is thus lost if the added pole is at zero.

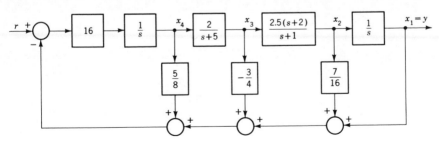

Fig. 9.4-4 Final system configuration if $\delta = 0$.

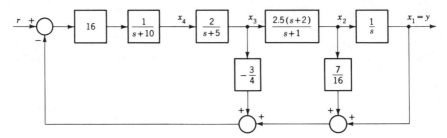

Fig. 9.4-5   Series compensation with $k_4 = 0$.

The system design as determined thus far is illustrated in Fig. 9.4-4. If the innermost loop is reduced, it is found that the equivalent series compensator is

$$G_c(s) = \frac{16}{s + 10} \tag{9.4-2}$$

Use of this equivalent series compensator removes the unwanted pole of $G(s)$ at the origin.   However, use of this series compensator, as indicated in Fig. 9.4-5, suffers from the objection that all the state variables are not fed back, and hence some stability and sensitivity benefits may be lost.   To demonstrate this point, let us investigate this mode of compensation a little further.

With $k_4 = 0$, and the series compensator of Eq. (9.4-2) in the system as in Fig. 9.4-5, $H_{eq}(s)$ becomes

$$H_{eq}(s) = \frac{0.138(s + 10)(s + 1.45)}{s + 2}$$

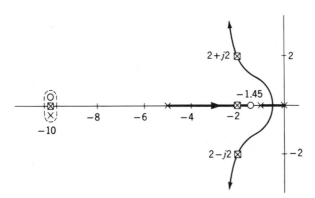

Fig. 9.4-6   Root locus for the system of Fig. 9.4-5.

and $G_c(s)G(s)$ is

$$G_c(s)G(s) = \frac{80(s+2)}{s(s+1)(s+5)(s+10)}$$

The root locus resulting for the open-loop transfer function $G_c(s)G(s)H_{eq}(s)$ is illustrated in Fig. 9.4-6. As before, the desired closed-loop poles are realized at $s = -2, -10$, and $-2 \pm j2$, but, as predicted, the asymptotes now go off at $\pm 90°$ rather than there being a single asymptote at $-180°$. The reason is that one zero of $H_{eq}(s)$ was lost by setting $k_4 = 0$.

Thus far we have tried two extreme values of possible added pole positions, 0 and -10. No doubt an intermediate value will produce the desired stability characteristics that we attribute to state-variable feedback. An interesting choice of an intermediate pole location is at $s = -2$. For the equivalent $G_c(s)$ still to be $16/(s+10)$, k_4 must be $\frac{1}{2}$, so that the resulting system is as in Fig. 9.4-7. With this value of k_4, $H_{eq}(s)$ becomes

$$H_{eq}(s) = \frac{8s^3 + 59s^2 + 166s + 160}{80(s+2)}$$

$$= \frac{(s+2.685)^2 + 1.68^2}{10}$$

Because of the choice of the added pole location to cancel the zero location in $G(s)$, $G(s)$ is

$$G(s) = \frac{80}{s(s+1)(s+5)}$$

and the root locus of the resulting system is identical to the root locus given previously in Fig. 9.3-3 except that a closed-loop pole exists at $s = -2$.

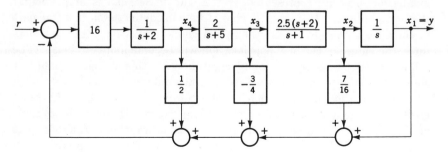

Fig. 9.4-7 Closed-loop system if compensator pole is at $s = -2$.

Thus with this choice of the compensation pole, the desired stability and sensitivity characteristics of state-variable feedback are realized. Furthermore, it is easily established that all the inner loops are also stable.

This example is important because it demonstrates that even in the case when cancellation compensation is used it is necessary to feed back the newly generated state variable. When the pole was added at $s = -2$, k_4 was not zero but one-half. Conventional methods of series compensation using lead, lag, or lead-lag networks often rely upon cancellation compensation. The state variables associated with these added networks are always available, but they are not fed back. This fact is pointed out as a further explanation of why conventional control methods never yield an optimum system.

On the basis of the examples of this section it is now possible to postulate a design procedure for those cases in which $y(s)/r(s)$ is to have no closed-loop zeros:

1. Choose the desired closed-loop transfer function $y(s)/r(s)$. A pole of $y(s)/r(s)$ must be located at each zero of $G(s)$.
2. Add a sufficient number of new poles to $G(s)$ to increase the order of the system such that it is compatible with the specified $y(s)/r(s)$.
3. Assume that all the state variables are available and represent the system by the usual state-variable-feedback configuration. Each of the new state variables is also fed back.
4. Find $y(s)/r(s)$ in terms of the feedback coefficients, making use of the $H_{eq}(s)$ reduction.
5. Equate the expressions for $y(s)/r(s)$ from steps 1 and 4 and solve for **k** and K by equating like powers of s.
6. If all the state variables are not available, use the known values of **k** and K to determine suitable series or minor-loop compensation.

Because of the arbitrary selection of the new pole positions, the evaluation procedure presented at the end of Sec. 9.3 is of particular importance here. In fact, this should be considered as an integral part of the design procedure. As the reader gains familiarity with the procedure, the choice of the new pole location will become more obvious. The following discussion presents one suggestion for this choice, although it should not be interpreted as a hard-and-fast rule.

The method involves placing the compensator poles at the same positions as some of the desired closed-loop poles. If this is done, zeros of $H_{eq}(s)$ are also at these same locations, so that branches of the root locus exist at each point. It is important to realize that if a pole of $G(s)$ and a zero of $H_{eq}(s)$ lie at the same point, this does not imply cancellation, since the zeros of $H_{eq}(s)$ do not appear as zeros of the closed-loop transfer function $y(s)/r(s)$. This procedure fixes m of the zeros of $H_{eq}(s)$ and therefore reduces the factoring problem involved in finding the zeros of $H_{eq}(s)$.

The example just worked can be used to illustrate this approach. A root-locus plot of $G(s)H_{eq}(s)$ for the modified simplest case contains no zeros of $G(s)$, as the zeros of $G(s)$ are also the poles of $H_{eq}(s)$, and these cancel. [It is the poles of $G(s)$ that are not canceled by the zeros of $H_{eq}(s)$.] Thus we may start a *tentative root-locus diagram* by marking on the s plane the open-loop poles of $G(s)$ and the desired closed-loop poles of $y(s)/r(s)$, as shown in Fig. 9.4-8a. In order to complete the root locus,

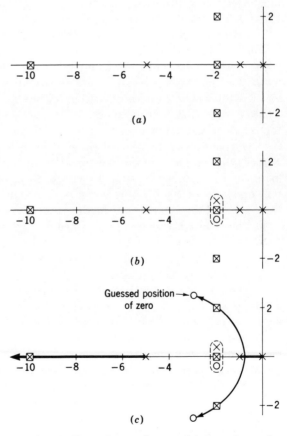

(a)

(b)

Guessed position → of zero

(c)

Fig. 9.4-8 Tentative root locus. (a) Open-loop poles of $G(s)$ and poles of $y(s)/r(s)$; (b) pole and zero added at $s = -2$; (c) final result.

the compensator pole must be selected, and the zeros of $H_{eq}(s)$ placed on the s plane.

The desired closed-loop response is given by Eq. (9.4-1) as

$$\frac{y(s)}{r(s)} = \frac{80(s+2)}{(s+2)(s+10)[(s+2)^2+2^2]}$$

Suppose we make use of the idea above and place the added pole at one of the desired closed-loop poles. Two choices are possible, either at $s = -2$ or at $s = -10$. Let us consider the choice of $s = -2$ first; then one of the three zeros of $H_{eq}(s)$ must also lie at $s = -2$, which ensures that the closed-loop pole is at this location, regardless of gain. Figure 9.4-8b illustrates the addition of this compensator pole and of the zero of $H_{eq}(s)$. These are not placed directly on the axis to avoid confusion.

Two more poles of $H_{eq}(s)$ must be located on the diagram before the root locus can be drawn. Of course, once $y(s)/r(s)$ has been chosen and the forward transfer function completely specified, it is possible to solve for $H_{eq}(s)$ and find its zeros. Here we are attempting to draw the root locus without knowing the locations of the remaining zeros of $H_{eq}(s)$. That is, we are attempting to determine whether our choice of compensator pole is a reasonable one.

Our tentative drawing of the root locus is indicated in Fig. 9.4-8c. Notice that the compensator pole and the zero of $H_{eq}(s)$ establish a closed-loop pole but that as far as the drawing of the root locus is concerned, this pole and zero pair contribute equal positive and negative angles. Thus their location does not affect the drawing of the root locus.

This is a tentative root locus, since the branches of the root locus that pass through the points $s = -2 \pm j2$ are a guess, and their termination points are unknown. However, it is known that the termination points are on the two remaining zeros of $H_{eq}(s)$.

There is no need to proceed any further, as we have accomplished what we set out to do. In order to force the branches of the root locus to pass through the desired closed-loop poles, the two remaining zeros of $H_{eq}(s)$ must lie somewhere to the left of $s = -2$. Of course, from our previous solution we know that the zeros of $H_{eq}(s)$ lie at $s = -2.685 \pm j1.68$ and that the final root locus is given in the previous section in Fig. 9.3-3.

One important point remains with respect to this example. The compensator pole was chosen at $s = -2$ because a closed-loop pole was desired there and not to cancel the zero in $G(s)$ that exists at $s = -2$. On the surface this looks like cancellation compensation, but in view of the feedback of k_4 around this compensator, it is clear that cancellation in the usual sense is not realized.

Let us consider the second possible choice of the compensator pole such that it would be located at another desired closed-loop pole location. This pole location is at $s = -10$. Again we follow the same procedure to investigate the suitability of this choice:

1. Indicate on the s plane the open-loop poles of $G(s)$ and the desired closed-loop poles of $y(s)/r(s)$.
2. Place the unknown compensator poles at desired closed-loop pole locations.
3. Draw the tentative root locus, based upon the assumption of positive gain.

This three-step procedure increases in complexity as we treat more general systems, but the idea of treating open- and closed-loop information on the same diagram remains unchanged. The positive-gain requirement is made in step 3 because of stability problems that result if negative gain is used.

It is tentatively decided to place the compensator pole at $s = -10$. The first step of the procedure to test whether this is a desirable compensator-pole position is identical to that indicated in Fig. 9.4-8a, since both $G(s)$ and the required $y(s)/r(s)$ are the same. Figure 9.4-9a illustrates step 2. Before the tentative root locus can be drawn, or rather as a part of drawing the tentative root locus, it is necessary to see how the remaining zeros of $H_{eq}(s)$ have to be placed on the root-locus diagram to ensure that the desired closed-loop response can be realized. Clearly a zero must be located between $s = -2$ and $s = -1$, so that the branch of the root locus starting at $s = -5$ will cross over the point $s = -2$. The tentative root locus is drawn in Fig. 9.4-9b; recall that there is still one more zero of $H_{eq}(s)$ to be located. The only possible place it can be located is to the left of $s = -10$. In actuality we know that it is located at infinity, since we considered this case in Figs. 9.4-5 and 9.4-6. It is coincidental for the compensator-pole location at $s = -10$ that k_4 turned out to be zero.

The only problem that remains is to decide which compensation scheme is the better, with the compensator pole at -2 or -10. The tentative root loci of Figs. 9.4-8c and 9.4-9b look approximately the same, with the important exception that the asymptotes in the latter figure are at $\pm 90°$. Because of this fact the system would have poor relative stability for changing gain, and we should choose the pole location at $s = -2$ as the more desirable one. It should be emphasized, however, that under the design conditions both systems are identical from an input-to-output point of view. Furthermore, a system designed with a Guillemin-Truxal

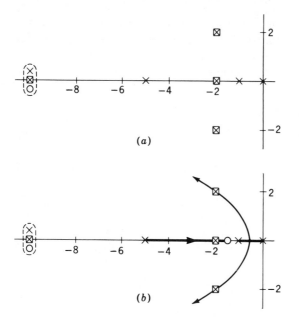

Fig. 9.4-9 (*a*) Compensation pole added at $s = -10$;
(*b*) tentative root locus.

equalizer would also behave in an identical fashion, assuming the design
conditions are the actual conditions that exist in the physical system.
Only if gains or pole locations are changed is the overall system performance
different.

Another method for choosing the location of the compensator pole
is based on system sensitivity (White, 1967). The sensitivity of a function $T(s,\lambda)$ with respect to a parameter λ is defined by Truxal (1955) as

$$S_\lambda^T(s) = \frac{d \ln T}{d \ln \lambda} = \frac{\lambda}{T} \frac{dT}{d\lambda} \tag{9.4-3}$$

In the application here, $T(s,\lambda)$ is the closed-loop transfer function
$y(s)/r(s)$, and λ is a system parameter, such as a gain, a feedback coefficient, or an open-loop pole position. Then $S_\lambda^{y/r}(s)$ is a measure of the
percentage change in $y(s)/r(s)$ for a percentage change in λ. The sensi-
tivity of the system performance is diminished if $|S_\lambda^{y/r}(j\omega)|$ is made to be
small.

In the problem discussed above, the values of the parameters δ and
k_4 are to be chosen. The selections are now made by considering $S_\delta^{y/r}(s)$

and $S_{k_4}^{y/r}(s)$. The closed-loop transfer function, written as a function of δ and k_4, is

$$
\begin{aligned}
&\frac{y(s)}{r(s)} \\
&= \frac{80(s + 2)}{s^4 + (6 + \delta + 16k_4)s^3 + [16 + 6(\delta + 16k_4)]s^2} \\
&\qquad\qquad\qquad\qquad\qquad + [126 + 5(\delta + 16k_4)]s + 160
\end{aligned}
$$

The sensitivity of $y(s)/r(s)$ with respect to δ is

$$
S_\delta^{y/r}(s) = \frac{\delta}{y/r}\frac{d(y/r)}{d\delta} = \frac{-\delta s(s + 1)(s + 5)}{\Delta_k(s)} \tag{9.4-4}
$$

where $\Delta_k(s)$ is the denominator of $y(s)/r(s)$. The sensitivity of $y(s)/r(s)$ with respect to k_4 is

$$
S_{k_4}^{y/r}(s) = \frac{k_4}{y/r}\frac{d(y/r)}{dk_4} = \frac{-16k_4s(s + 1)(s + 5)}{\Delta_k(s)} \tag{9.4-5}
$$

Recall that δ and k_4 are to be selected such that the equivalent $G_c(s)$ is $16/(s + 10)$. This requires that $\delta + 16k_4 = 10$. It may be noted that δ and k_4 appear in $\Delta_k(s)$ only as the quantity $\delta + 16k_4$. Thus, for allowable choices of δ and k_4, $\Delta_k(s)$ is not a function of δ and k_4. Therefore, it is seen from Eqs. (9.4-4) and (9.4-5) that $|S_\delta^{y/r}(j\omega)|$ and $|S_{k_4}^{y/r}(j\omega)|$ are proportional to $|\delta|$ and $|k_4|$ respectively. Usually it is desirable to decrease the sensitivity with respect to elements in the forward path and to accept higher sensitivities for the feedback coefficients, because the tolerances for the k_i's may be controlled. However, in this case the series compensator is also selected by the designer. A possible solution is to choose δ such that the sensitivities with respect to δ and k_4 are equal. From the sensitivity equations above, this requires $16k_4 = \delta$. This equation, along with the condition that $\delta + 16k_4 = 10$, yields

$$
\delta = 5 \qquad k_4 = \frac{5}{16}
$$

It should be noted that the sensitivity of $y(s)/r(s)$ with respect to the other parameters of the system does not depend on the values of δ and k_4 as long as these values satisfy $\delta + 16k_4 = 10$.

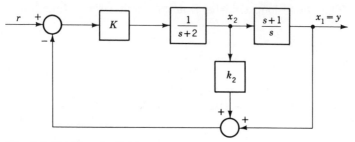

Fig. 9.4-10   Exercise 9.4-1.

By this method, the position of the compensating pole has been chosen by considering a quantitative measure of system sensitivity.

In all the above procedures we have made an arbitrary selection of the new pole locations and then solved for the associated feedback coefficients. An alternate procedure is to fix the feedback coefficients for the new state variables and solve for the associated pole locations.

In particular, it is convenient to set the new feedback coefficients to zero.   Once the pole locations are found, the transfer function of the series compensator may be realized by means of feedback in order to achieve the desired stability and sensitivity properties.   This procedure is discussed in detail in terms of the general case (Sec. 9.6).   Before considering the general case, however, we examine the problems associated with inaccessible state variables in terms of the simplest case.   This is done in the next section.

Exercises 9.4   *9.4-1.*   For the system shown in Fig. 9.4-10 find the values of K and k_2 such that the closed-loop transfer function of the system is

$$\frac{y(s)}{r(s)} = \frac{3}{s+3}$$

Plot a root locus of $G(s)H_{eq}(s)$.   Is the system stable for all gain?

answers:

$$K = 3 \qquad k_2 = -\tfrac{1}{3} \qquad \text{yes for } K > 0$$

9.4-2.   For the open-loop system shown in Fig. 9.4-11, find the values of the feedback coefficients and the gain K such that the closed-loop

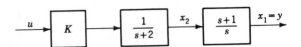

Fig. 9.4-11 Exercise 9.4-2.

transfer function is

$$\frac{y(s)}{r(s)} = \frac{2}{(s+1)^2 + 1^2}$$

Assume that the new pole is added at $s = -1$.

answer:

$K = 2$ $\mathbf{k} = \text{col } (1,0,0)$

9.4-3.   Find two other possible solutions for Exercise 9.4-2 by selecting two other locations for the added pole. Verify that stability properties of state-variable feedback are provided by these designs.

answer:

If the new pole location is at $s = -\delta$, then

$\mathbf{k} = \text{col } (1,0,(1 - \delta)/2)$ $K = 2$

9.4-4.   Show that if the system

$$\dot{\mathbf{x}} = \begin{bmatrix} -\alpha & \alpha \\ \alpha & -\alpha \end{bmatrix} \mathbf{x} + \begin{bmatrix} K \\ 0 \end{bmatrix} u$$

$$y = [1 \quad 1]\mathbf{x}$$

has a closed-loop transfer function

$$\frac{y(s)}{r(s)} = \frac{5}{s + 5}$$

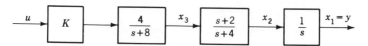

Fig. 9.4-12   Exercise 9.4-5.

then **k** = col (1,1) independent of α and $K = 5$.

9.4-5.   Find the appropriate series compensation, feedback coefficients, and gain such that the system shown in Fig. 9.4-12 has a closed-loop transfer function

$$\frac{y(s)}{r(s)} = \frac{450}{(s + 25)[(s + 3)^2 + 3^2]}$$

Plot the root locus of $G_c(s)G(s)H_{eq}(s)$.

answer:

If the added pole location is at δ,

$$\mathbf{k} = \text{col } (1, 0.133, -0.253, (21 - \delta)/112.5) \qquad K = 112.5$$

9.5   Inaccessible state variables

All the design sections of this book, with the exception of Sec. 7.6 on Kalman filters, have assumed that all the state variables are available for measurement and eventual use in the generation of the control $u(\mathbf{x})$. In this section we assume that the output variable is available but that one or more of the remaining state variables are inaccessible. The introductory remarks for Sec. 7.6 apply here as well. Briefly, it is often impossible, too expensive, or too difficult to measure all the state variables. The question, then, is what to do when this is the case.

This question was answered in Sec. 7.6, where the design criterion was an integral performance index. The approach there was quite elegant and required some knowledge of the noise components associated with the measurement of each of the state variables. Here the design criterion is the desired closed-loop transfer function. The approach in this section uses only conventional control theory and block-diagram manipulations. The results obtained here are somewhat obvious and not nearly so elegant as those reported in Sec. 7.6, although the results are not so complicated or difficult to implement. In many cases the approach presented here represents a reasonable compromise between the cost and complexity of a Kalman filter design and a practical approach to realize the benefits of state-variable feedback.

The method of dealing with inaccessible state variables discussed here applies in the general case of the next section, although our discussion centers about the situation treated in the two previous sections, namely, when $y(s)/r(s)$ has no zeros. We proceed here with this more restricted class of systems in order not to delay any longer this important practical problem. The reader will see that no difficulty is encountered in applying the same procedures to the general case. In addition, the restriction to the simplest case facilitates the initial discussion.

Two general methods are available to deal with the problem of inaccessible state variables. The first method utilizes minor-loop equalization, and the second uses series compensation. The simplest of these two methods is the use of minor-loop equalization. Instead of feeding back all the state variables through constant elements, minor-loop compensation makes use of dynamic elements in the feedback paths.

In the cases considered in Secs. 9.3 and 9.4 the design procedure centered about the knowledge of the final form of the control system, assuming that all the state variables are available. Here we continue to use the $H_{eq}(s)$ method to determine the k_i's and the state-variable feedback structure. Simple block-diagram manipulations are then used to indicate alternate means by which the desired closed-loop transfer function can be realized if some of the state variables are inaccessible.

The following example serves to illustrate the method in such a manner that the formal design procedure is almost self-explanatory. Assume that the given $G(s)$ is the same as has been used as the running example throughout this and the previous chapter; that is, $G(s)$ is

$$G(s) = \frac{10K}{s(s+1)(s+5)}$$

and the desired closed-loop response $y(s)/r(s)$ is, as before,

$$\frac{y(s)}{r(s)} = \frac{80}{s^3 + 14s^2 + 48s + 80}$$

The necessary values of K, k_2, and k_3 have been determined in Sec. 9.3

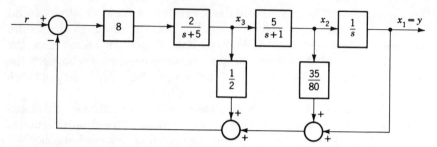

Fig. 9.5-1 Block diagram assuming all state variables are available.

to be

$$K = 8 \qquad k_2 = 0.437 = {}^{35}\!/_{80} \qquad k_3 = 0.5$$

A final block diagram is given in Fig. 9.5-1.

Assume now that x_2 is not available.   This is a reasonable assumption if one interprets the specific example in terms of the field-controlled dc motor because it has been assumed that x_2 was not directly available but had to be generated with a tachometer.   In terms of the hardware realization, the block diagram of Fig. 9.5-1 is actually that of Fig. 9.5-2. In terms of a block-diagram manipulation, the input to k_2 has been moved from the unavailable point x_2 through the integrator to x_1.   In general, as inputs to the various k_i's are moved to the right on the block diagram, powers of s begin to appear in the numerator of the equivalent feedback

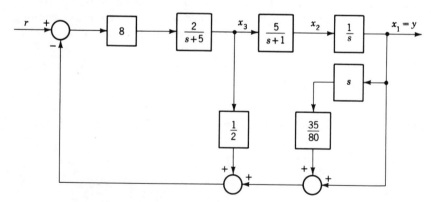

Fig. 9.5-2 Generation of x_2 by a tachometer.

elements. This is evident in this example and in our discussions of $H_{eq}(s)$. Clearly, an increasing response amplitude for ever-increasing frequency is not physically realizable. The use of a tachometer in this example is an exception. Although a tachometer gain eventually decreases if frequency is increased sufficiently, this is not evident in practice because of the motor's inability to respond at high frequencies.

In this example, the input to the k_2 block may also be moved from the point x_2 to x_3 by inserting an element $5/(s + 1)$ in series with k_2. This is indicated in Fig. 9.5-3a, and the resulting system is given in Fig. 9.5-3b. The final configuration of 9.5-3b is recognized as one form of a conventional minor-loop-equalization method. Such minor-loop equalization is a natural consequence of state-variable-feedback procedures when all the state variables are not available.

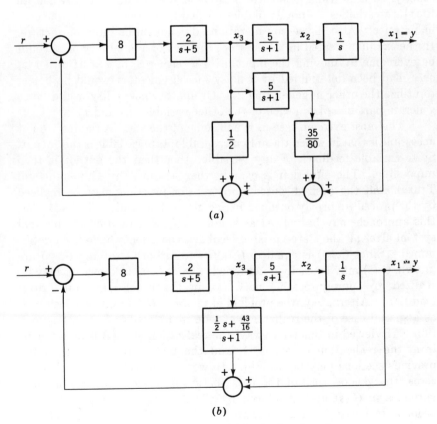

Fig. 9.5-3   (a) Generation of x_2 from x_3; (b) final minor-loop form.

On the basis of this simple example, the following design procedure is postulated:

1. Assume all state variables are available and use the $H_{eq}(s)$ method to determine the k_i's necessary to realize the desired response.
2. Use block-diagram-manipulation techniques to move inputs to the feedback constants from the inaccessible to accessible state variables.

The simplicity of this procedure is not proportional to its effectiveness. Since the block diagrams that result from step 2 yield the same $H_{eq}(s)$, all the stability benefits previously mentioned are still realized.

A note of caution is in order, however. In the above example a lack of knowledge of x_2 did not affect the design because we assume that the block $x_2(s)/x_3(s)$ is known exactly. Rarely is any time constant known exactly, so that while it is theoretically possible to do as well when all the state variables are not available as when they are, this is not the case in practice. Also, noise considerations did not enter into the picture. In the example treated in this section, the lack of availability of x_2 could be overcome by moving the input of k_2 to either x_1 or x_3. If either x_1 or x_3 had been determined by a noisy measurement, it would be better to utilize the other in generating x_2. Or another possibility would be to generate part of x_2 from each of the other variables, x_1 and x_3.

The most extreme case in which some of the state variables are not accessible is that in which the only measurable state variable is the output. State-variable feedback of any variable other than the output is then impossible. The situation is exactly that assumed by Guillemin and Truxal, and the desired closed-loop transfer function may be realized by the procedure briefly outlined in Sec. 9.2. The reader will recall that this approach may be viewed as simply a $G_{eq}(s)$ reduction of the final system after all the state-variable feedback coefficients have been determined. Since $G_{eq}(s)$ is equal to $G_c(s)G(s)$ and both $G(s)$ and $G_{eq}(s)$ are known, $G_c(s)$ may be easily determined. Once $G_c(s)$ is known, it may be realized by purely passive networks in the usual Guillemin-Truxal tradition. Alternately, the problem of realizing $G_c(s)$ may be considered as a special case of the realization of a desired closed-loop transfer function. If viewed in this latter way, the realization of $G_c(s)$ is no different from the realization of $y(s)/r(s)$, and the techniques outlined in the previous sections may be utilized. However, since $G_c(s)$ often contains zeros, the general case of the next section is needed. Since the state variables in $G_c(s)$ are introduced by the designer, there should be no problem in measuring these variables and using them to construct $u(\mathbf{x})$ partially.

In the example being considered (Fig. 9.5-1) let us assume that both x_2 and x_3 are unavailable. The first step in the block-diagram reduction to an equivalent $G_c(s)G(s)$ system has taken place in Fig. 9.5-3b. If the connection at x_3 is moved to the output of the amplifier, as in Fig. 9.5-4a, the final minor-loop realization has been determined. Of course, if this minor loop is combined with $K = 8$, the result is as shown in Fig. 9.5-4b, and this series equalizer is just the Guillemin-Truxal equalizer. The root locus for the Guillemin-Truxal system was given in Sec. 9.3 (Fig. 9.3-4). It is clear that this system is unstable for high K. The system of Fig. 9.5-4a is stable for all K. Of course, the Guillemin-Truxal system could be made stable for all K by realizing the amplifier gain with a high-gain amplifier with feedback of $\frac{1}{8}$ around it.

Before concluding this section, let us consider the case in which the plant to be controlled contains complex conjugate poles. This often happens when a hydraulic actuator is used as the power element. In such a case it is impossible to measure one of the states, the blocks no longer being separable, as was assumed thus far. It is then necessary to postulate an equivalent system, determine the k_i's, and then return to the physical case. The following example is typical of the required procedure.

The system to be controlled is given in Fig. 9.5-5a, and the ultimate

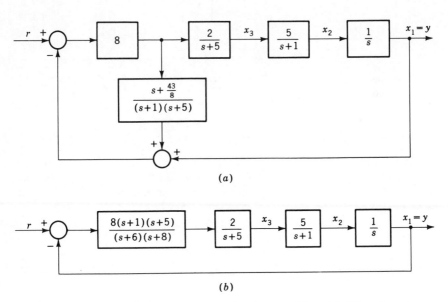

(a)

(b)

Fig. 9.5-4 Equalization with both x_2 and x_3 inaccessible. (a) Minor-loop form; (b) Guillemin-Truxal series form.

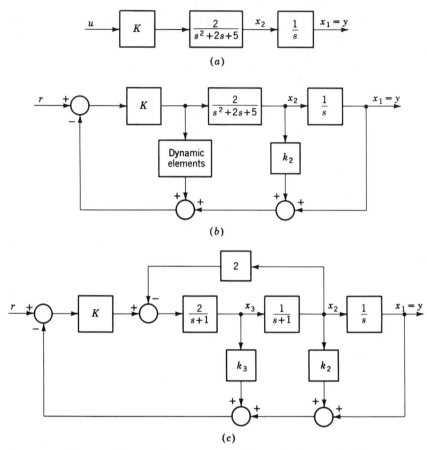

Fig. 9.5-5 System with complex conjugate poles.   (a) Plant; (b) ultimate state-variable-feedback configuration; (c) equivalent system: in the final design $K = 10$, $k_2 = \frac{7}{20}$, and $k_3 = \frac{1}{2}$.

state-variable-feedback configuration is given in Fig. 9.5-5b.   An equivalent system is shown in Fig. 9.5-5c.   The final design is independent of the equivalent representation of a complex conjugate block.   It is quite simple to find $H_{eq}(s)$ for the equivalent system as

$$H_{eq}(s) = k_3 s^2 + (k_2 + k_3)s + 1$$

Then if the desired closed-loop response is

$$\frac{y(s)}{r(s)} = \frac{20}{[(s+1)^2 + 1^2](s+10)} = \frac{20}{s^3 + 12s^2 + 22s + 20}$$

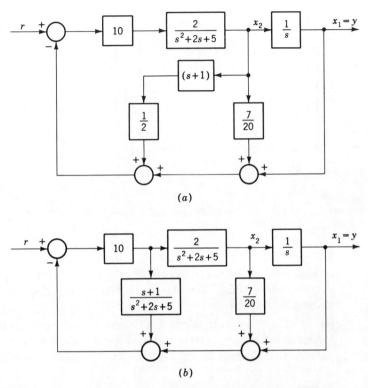

(a)

(b)

Fig. 9.5-6   Reduction of Fig. 9.5-5c to the form of Fig. 9.5-5b.   (a) First step in transformation; (b) final result.

the feedback coefficients of the equivalent system are determined by the procedure of the simplest case to be

$$k_2 = \tfrac{7}{20} \qquad k_3 = \tfrac{1}{2} \qquad K = 10$$

The final design for the equivalent system is shown in Fig. 9.5-5c. The easiest way of realizing the desired system configuration of Fig. 9.5-5b is indicated in a two-step fashion in Fig. 9.5-6a and b. Notice that the final design requires the realization of a transfer function with complex conjugate poles and one zero. Because this transfer function has a zero, it does not belong to the category of transfer functions that have been realized in either the simplest case or the modified simplest case. Hence we leave the discussion of the realization of this feedback network through state-variable feedback until later. The realization is similar to the

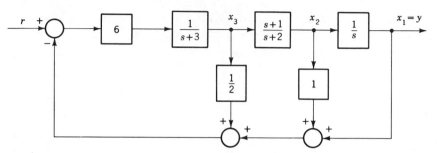

Fig. 9.5-7   Exercise 9.5-1.

means by which the complex conjugate poles in the plant were realized by feedback.

Exercises 9.5   *9.5-1*. Draw block diagrams for the system shown in Fig. 9.5-7 if (*a*) x_2 is inaccessible; (*b*) x_3 is inaccessible; (*c*) x_2 and x_3 are inaccessible. Use the minor-loop technique to generate inaccessible states.

9.5-2. Find the equivalent Guillemin-Truxal series compensator for Exercise 9.5-1c. Draw the root locus for the system and compare it with the root locus of $G(s)H_{eq}(s)$ for the system of Fig. 9.5-7.

answer:

$$G_c(s) = \frac{6.0(s + 2)(s + 3)}{(s + 1.43)(s + 12.56)}$$

9.5-3. Find the transfer function of the minor loop, $H_m(s)$, and the gain K such that the system shown in Fig. 9.5-8 has the closed-loop

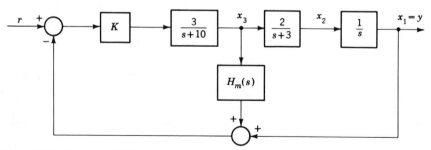

Fig. 9.5-8   Exercise 9.5-3.

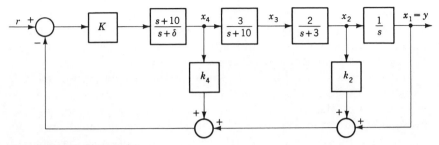

Fig. 9.5-9   Exercise 9.5-4.

transfer function

$$\frac{y(s)}{r(s)} = \frac{160}{[(s+2)^2 + 2^2](s+20)}$$

answer:

$$H_m(s) = \frac{11(s+5.27)}{80(s+3)} \qquad K = \frac{80}{3}$$

9.5-4.   Find the values of K, k_2, k_4, and δ for the system shown in Fig. 9.5-9 such that the closed-loop transfer function is

$$\frac{y(s)}{r(s)} = \frac{160}{[(s+2)^2 + 2^2](s+20)}$$

HINT: The answer of the previous problem may be useful. Note that this provides another method of generating inaccessible states.

answer:

One possible solution is $K = 80$, $\delta = 43$, and $k_4 = 0.025$. In all cases k_2 is $\frac{25}{160}$.

9.6   *H-equivalent method: the general case*

The preceding sections dealt with the application of the $H_{eq}(s)$ method to the simplest case, i.e., the case in which $y(s)/r(s)$ has no zeros. In this section we treat the general case in which $y(s)/r(s)$ is to have r zeros and n poles and the given $G(s)$ is inadequate to meet the requirements of the desired closed-loop transfer function. The most common case in which this situation arises is that in which zeros are required in the closed-loop transfer function. Usually $G(s)$ does not contain zeros, or if it does, they are not located in the desired places. In this situation series compensation must be added to realize the required zeros. This increases the order of the open-loop transfer function, and, as in Sec. 9.4, for each new state variable added two unknowns are also added, namely, the location of the compensator pole and the value of the feedback coefficient associated with the new state variable.

Before discussing the design procedure, it is well to indicate why one may desire zeros in the closed-loop response. The basic reason is to achieve control over the velocity-error coefficient K_v. If $y(s)/r(s)$ is written in time-constant form as

$$\frac{y(s)}{r(s)} = \frac{(s/z_1 + 1)(s/z_2' + 1) \, \cdots \, (s/z_r' + 1)}{(s/p_1' + 1)(s/p_2' + 1) \, \cdots \, (s/p_n' + 1)} \tag{9.6-1}$$

it is possible to show (Truxal, 1955) that

$$-\frac{1}{K_v} = \frac{1}{p_1'} + \frac{1}{p_2'} + \, \cdots \, + \frac{1}{p_n'} - \frac{1}{z_1'} - \frac{1}{z_2'} - \, \cdots \, - \frac{1}{z_r'} \tag{9.6-2}$$

Here the primes are used on the pole and zero locations to emphasize that these are the pole and zero locations of the *closed-loop* system and not of the open-loop $G(s)$.

In Eq. (9.6-2), $-1/K_v$ can be made zero to ensure zero position error for ramp inputs by setting

$$\frac{1}{p_1'} + \frac{1}{p_2'} + \, \cdots \, + \frac{1}{p_n'} = \frac{1}{z_1'} + \frac{1}{z_2'} + \, \cdots \, + \frac{1}{z_r'} \tag{9.6-3}$$

Thus there is an obvious advantage to including zeros in the closed-loop response. By satisfying Eq. (9.6-3) we can ensure an infinite velocity-error coefficient.

In the examples of this section we shall satisfy, or at least approximately satisfy, Eq. (9.6-3). Throughout the rest of this section it is assumed that $y(s)/r(s)$ is required to have r zeros and n poles. Actually, three separate situations may arise, depending upon m, the number of inherent zeros of $G(s)$, namely, m may equal r or it may be greater or less than r. Only the case when m is equal to r is discussed in detail here, since the variations in approach due to an inequality are only minor.

It is assumed that the inherent zeros of $G(s)$ are not located at the desired zero positions of $y(s)/r(s)$. Thus m zeros must be removed from the closed-loop transfer function and m new zeros added at the desired locations. This result can be accomplished by the addition of m series networks of the form

$$G_c(s) = \frac{s + \beta_i}{s + \delta_i} \qquad (9.6\text{-}4)$$

where the zeros are at the locations of the desired zeros of $y(s)/r(s)$. The addition of the mth-order series compensation increases the order of the open-loop system by m. The order of the closed-loop system is still effectively n, because m of the $n + m$ closed-loop poles that result are used to cancel the m unwanted zeros.

The series compensation of Eq. (9.6-4) may be realized in two possible ways, as shown in Fig. 9.6-1. While it is easy to demonstrate that the transfer function of each of the forms shown in Fig. 9.6-1 is equal to Eq. (9.6-4), this is where the similarity ends. In the standard form of Fig. 9.6-1a, for example, the output is labeled as x_{m+n}, while in the feedforward form the output is $x_{m+n} + u$ and the state x_{m+n} is an internal variable. In both cases it is assumed that the state indicated is a physical, measurable quantity.

In the standard-form realization, the differential equation for x_{m+n} is given by

$$\dot{x}_{m+n} = -\delta_m x_{m+n} + \dot{u} + \beta_m u$$

The appearance of $\dot{u}$ in this equation is a violation of the assumption that the system could be described by Eq. (**Ab**). This problem was mentioned briefly in Sec. 2.7 on physical variables. Here we investigate the consequences of this violation in more detail. Of primary interest is the fact that the zero at $s = -\beta_m$ does not appear as a pole in $H_{eq}(s)$.

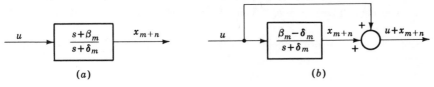

(a) (b)

Fig. 9.6-1 Two realizations of the series compensation of Eq. (9.6-4). (a) Standard form; (b) feedforward form.

If the feedforward form is used to realize the series compensation, then no violation of Eq. (**Ab**) occurs since $\dot{x}_{m+n}$ in this case is

$$\dot{x}_{m+n} = -\delta_m x_{m+n} + (\beta_m - \delta_m)u$$

and no $\dot{u}$ appears. Because Eq. (**Ab**) is not violated, no change occurs in the properties of $H_{eq}(s)$ discussed in Sec. 8.3. In particular $H_{eq}(s)$ continues to have a pole at every zero of $G_c(s)G(s)$.

The reader may wonder why we even bother to consider the standard realization since it violates Eq. (**Ab**) while the feedforward form does not. In the first place, it is hoped that the treatment of the standard form will enhance the reader's understanding of the possibilities of state-variable feedback. In addition, there are some physical systems, as discussed in Sec. 2.7, in which a violation of Eq. (**Ab**) occurs even before compensation is added. The treatment of such systems must be undertaken in the manner that the standard-form violation is treated here. For these reasons, we consider both of the possible forms for the series compensation in the following development.

Because the design philosophy to be used here is so similar to that of the previous sections, we may write it down immediately. The design procedure in the general case consists of the six following steps:

1. Choose the desired closed-loop transfer function $y(s)/r(s)$.
2. Add sufficient compensation of the form described by Eq. (9.6-4) to make the open-loop transfer function compatible with the desired $y(s)/r(s)$.
3. Assume that all the state variables are available and represent the system by the usual state-variable-feedback configuration. Each of the new state variables associated with the compensation networks is also fed back.
4. Find $y(s)/r(s)$ by making use of the $H_{eq}(s)$ reduction.
5. Equate the expressions for $y(s)/r(s)$ from steps 1 and 4 and solve for the unknown system parameters.
6. Use the known values of the system parameters to realize the final system configuration. If all the state variables are not available, the procedures of Sec. 9.5 must be used.

Steps 4 to 6 are not specified in detail because we wish to investigate several alternate procedures.

It has been noted previously that the introduction of compensation gives one new state variable and two unknowns: the value of the compensator pole and the value of the feedback coefficient associated with this new state variable. In Sec. 9.4 we chose the value of the compensator poles, either arbitrarily or from a tentative root-locus diagram, and then used these values to determine the values of **k** and K.

It was mentioned at the end of that section that another approach could have been taken. That is, we could have chosen the value of the feedback coefficients associated with the new state variables to be an arbitrary value, such as zero, and then solved for the compensator-pole positions. If we use this *series-compensation* approach in the general case, the $H_{eq}(s)$ reduction of step 4 involves only the feedback coefficients $k_1, k_2, \ldots, k_n$. On the other hand, the parameters mentioned in step 5 are these feedback coefficients, K and the m values of the *compensator-pole locations*. Step 6 would then imply the realization of the resulting series compensator by means of state-variable feedback.

This procedure is not advocated because the method does not make use of insight that can be gained from a consideration of a tentative root-locus diagram. However, it does give the correct answer in a straightforward way. A number of problems worked in this fashion will aid the reader in understanding the use of the tentative root locus.

This series-compensation design procedure is illustrated by the system shown in Fig. 9.6-2. Assume, as required by step 1, that the desired closed-loop response is given as

$$\frac{y(s)}{r(s)} = \frac{6(s+3)}{(s+3)^2+3^2} = \frac{6(s+3)}{s^2+6s+18}$$

Since there is a zero of $G(s)$ which we wish to cancel, we must actually realize

$$\frac{y(s)}{r(s)} = \frac{6(s+2)(s+3)}{(s+2)[(s+3)^2+3^2]} = \frac{6(s+2)(s+3)}{s^3+8s^2+30s+36} \qquad (9.6\text{-}5)$$

Here the open-loop gain has been selected to ensure a zero steady-state position error, and the new zero location has been chosen to satisfy Eq. (9.6-3). Thus the resulting system will have an infinite position-and-velocity-error coefficient.

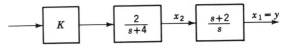

Fig. 9.6-2 Plant to be controlled such that
$$\frac{y(s)}{r(s)} = \frac{6(s+3)}{(s+3)^2+3^2}$$

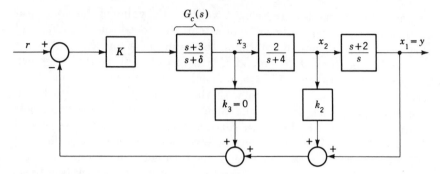

Fig. 9.6-3   Configuration for the series-compensation method.

The method by which this new $y(s)/r(s)$ is to be realized is indicated in Fig. 9.6-3, where the standard form is used for the series compensation. Since only one new zero is required in $y(s)/r(s)$, only one basic compensation element is added, and the zero of this unit is chosen to be the desired value of 3.   In Fig. 9.6-3, k_3 has been arbitrarily chosen to be zero, in line with the series-compensation design procedure that we are using.   It is not intended that k_3 be left at this zero value; this is just an intermediate step.   Thus the $H_{eq}(s)$ that is determined from the block diagram of Fig. 9.6-3 is only a tentative one, and this is indicated by the notation $H_{eq}^*(s)$.

From Fig. 9.6-3, $y(s)/r(s)$ may be written in terms of K, k_2, and δ as

$$\frac{y(s)}{r(s)} = 2K(s+2)(s+3)/\{s^3 + [\delta + 4 + 2K(k_2 + 1)]s^2$$

$$+ [4\delta + 4K + 6K(k_2 + 1)]s + 12K\} \quad (9.6\text{-}6)$$

If equal powers of s are equated in Eqs. (9.6-5) and (9.6-6), the following values result:

$$K = 3 \qquad k_2 = -\tfrac{4}{3} \qquad \delta = 6$$

In terms of these values $KG_c(s)$ and $H_{eq}^*(s)$ become

$$KG_c(s) = \frac{3(s+3)}{s+6}$$

and

$$H_{eq}^*(s) = \frac{-(s-6)}{3(s+2)}$$

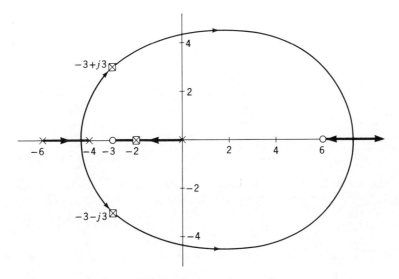

Fig. 9.6-4 Root-locus diagram for

$$G_c(s)G(s)H_{eq}^*(s) = \frac{-2K/3(s+3)(s-6)}{s(s+4)(s+6)}$$

The root locus for $G_c(s)G(s)H_{eq}^*(s)$ is shown in Fig. 9.6-4. Because of the negative sign in $H_{eq}^*(s)$, a $0°$ locus must be drawn. Observe that in this figure $H_{eq}^*(s)$ has a zero in the right half plane, and one asymptote go toward zeros at infinity. The realization of the compensation network by feedback as required by step 6 can be used to eliminate these difficulties.

The dashed portion of Fig. 9.6-5 indicates the portion of the system to be used to realize the series-compensation network $3(s+3)/(s+6)$. The equation that must be satisfied here is

$$\frac{K(s+3)/(1+Kk_3)}{s+(\delta_1+3Kk_3)/(1+Kk_3)} = \frac{3(s+3)}{s+6}$$

By equating the gains it is seen that

$$\frac{K}{1+Kk_3} = 3$$

or

$$K = \frac{3}{1-3k_3} \qquad\qquad (9.6\text{-}7)$$

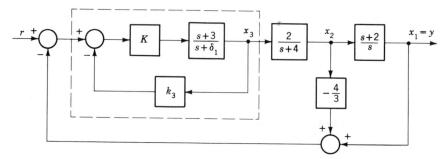

Fig. 9.6-5 Final system configuration; values for system parameters are $K = 12$, $\delta_1 = 15$, $k_3 = \frac{1}{4}$.

and by equating pole locations the equation that must be satisfied is

$$\frac{\delta_1 + 3Kk_3}{1 + Kk_3} = 6 \tag{9.6-8}$$

From Eq. (9.6-7) it is clear that for K to be positive, k_3 must be less than $\frac{1}{3}$. It is possible to place a lower bound on k_3 by requiring that the zeros of $H_{eq}(s)$ always lie in the left half plane so that stability for high gain is ensured. From Fig. 9.6-5, $H_{eq}(s)$ is

$$H_{eq}(s) = \frac{k_3 s^2 + (4k_3 - \frac{2}{3})s + 4}{2(s + 2)}$$

The use of Routh's criterion requires k_3 to be greater than $\frac{1}{6}$. Thus k_3 is bounded by

$$\frac{1}{6} < k_3 < \frac{1}{3}$$

if K is to be positive and the zeros of $H_{eq}(s)$ are to lie in the left-half s plane.

Let us assume that k_3 is the average of these two limits, so that $k_3 = \frac{1}{4}$. Then $H_{eq}(s)$ is

$$H_{eq}(s) = \frac{(s + \frac{2}{3})^2 + 3.96^2}{8(s + 2)}$$

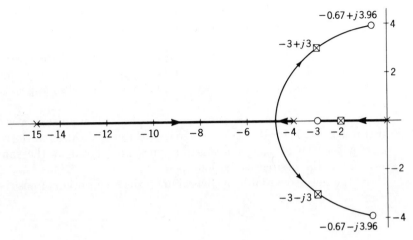

Fig. 9.6-6   Root locus of

$$G_c(s)G(s)H_{eq}(s) = \frac{3(s + 3)[(s + 0.67)^2 + 3.96^2]}{s(s + 4)(s + 15)}$$

and K and δ_1 are easily found to be

$$K = 12 \qquad \delta_1 = 15$$

Now the values of all unknown parameters in Fig. 9.6-5 are known, and $G_c(s)G(s)H_{eq}(s)$ is

$$G_c(s)G(s)H_{eq}(s) = \frac{3(s + 3)[(s + \frac{2}{3})^2 + 3.96^2]}{s(s + 4)(s + 15)}$$

The corresponding root locus is indicated in Fig. 9.6-6. The desired transfer function has been realized, with infinite position-and-velocity-error coefficients, and the resulting closed-loop system is stable for all gain.

Let us use an alternate approach to solve this same example. This time, rather than selecting k_3 to be zero and eventually realizing the resulting series compensator with state-variable feedback, let us select a value for δ by returning to the tentative root-locus construction procedure that was detailed in Sec. 9.4. There is one difference, however. Since the standard form was used for the series compensation, a zero appears in the left-hand block of the final system. Therefore $H_{eq}(s)$ does not cancel this zero, and it must appear on the s-plane plot of the poles and zeros of $G(s)H_{eq}(s)$. Let us repeat the procedure involved in drawing the tentative root-locus diagram:

1. Indicate on the s plane the open-loop poles of $G(s)$ and the desired closed-loop poles of $y(s)/r(s)$. If a zero appears in the left-hand block of the final compensated system, this zero must also appear on the s plane.
2. Place the unknown compensator poles on the s plane in such a way that it is possible for the root locus to pass through the desired closed-loop poles. Often the compensator poles are placed at the same location as the desired closed-loop poles.
3. Draw the tentative root locus, based upon the assumption of positive gain.

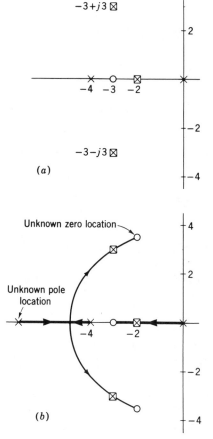

(a)

(b)

Fig. 9.6-7 Tentative root locus. (a) First step; (b) final result.

For the problem under discussion, step 1 is completed in Fig. 9.6-7a. In this case we are unable to place the compensator pole at the desired closed-loop pole location because then a pole would exist between $s = -3$ and $s = -4$, assuming positive gain. However, the pole may be placed anywhere to the left of $s = -3$, such that the resulting tentative root-locus diagram is as given in Fig. 9.6-7b. Thus the compensator being used here is a lead network. It is still not possible to state specifically what value should be assigned to δ. However, one might expect that if the pole is placed very near to $s = -3$, this would not be much of a lead circuit. A 5-to-1 lead circuit would place the pole location at $s = -15$, a value previously determined by choosing $k_3 = \frac{1}{4}$.

Let us assume that δ is chosen to be 15. The block diagram of the system of interest is shown in Fig. 9.6-8. For this system $H_{eq}(s)$ is given by

$$H_{eq}(s) = \frac{k_3 s^2 + (4k_3 + 2k_2 + 2)s + 4}{2(s + 2)} \qquad (9.6\text{-}9)$$

and $G_c(s)G(s)$ is

$$G_c(s)G(s) = \frac{2K(s + 2)(s + 3)}{s(s + 4)(s + 15)}$$

Note that as indicated previously $H_{eq}(s)$ does not have a pole at $s = -3$. The closed-loop transfer function of the system is therefore

$$\frac{y(s)}{r(s)} = \frac{2K(s + 2)(s + 3)/(1 + Kk_3)}{\begin{aligned}s^3 &+ s^2(19 + 7Kk_3 + 2Kk_2 + 2K)/(1 + Kk_3) \\ &+ [s(60 + 12Kk_3 + 6Kk_2 + 10K)]/(1 + Kk_3) \\ &+ 12K/(1 + Kk_3)\end{aligned}}$$
$$(9.6\text{-}10)$$

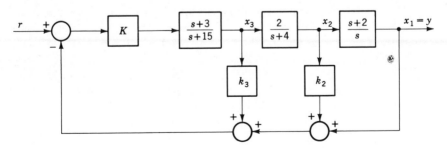

Fig. 9.6-8   Direct use of the $H_{eq}(s)$ method.

If equal powers of s are equated in Eqs. (9.6-5) and (9.6-10) the following three equations result:

$$\frac{19 + 7Kk_3 + 2Kk_2 + 2K}{1 + Kk_3} = 8$$

$$\frac{60 + 12Kk_3 + 6Kk_2 + 10K}{1 + Kk_3} = 30$$

$$\frac{12K}{1 + Kk_3} = 36$$

While these equations are nonlinear in K, k_2, and k_3, they may be easily changed into linear equations by crossmultiplying and treating K, Kk_2, and Kk_3 as variables. If this is done, one must solve the following three linear equations:

$$11 - (Kk_3) + 2(Kk_2) + 2K = 0$$
$$30 - 18(Kk_3) + 6(Kk_2) + 10K = 0$$
$$-36 - 36(Kk_3) + 12K = 0$$

These equations may be solved simultaneously to give $Kk_2 = -16$, $Kk_3 = 3$, and $K = 12$ or $k_2 = -\frac{4}{3}$, $k_3 = \frac{1}{4}$, and $K = 12$. The solution here is the same as previously determined using series-compensation approach. The final design is indicated in Fig. 9.6-5, and the root locus is once again given in Fig. 9.6-6.

Let us review the two design procedures that were used in connection with the example problem of Fig. 9.6-2. In the series-compensation approach k_3 was assumed to be zero, and the desired closed-loop transfer function was determined in terms of a series equalizer. This series equalizer was then realized by state-variable feedback for a particular value of k_3. The value of k_3 was chosen to ensure that the resulting K would be positive and that the zeros of $H_{eq}(s)$ would lie in the left half plane.

In the other method the pole location was chosen as a result of using the tentative-root-locus method. The constants k_2, k_3, and K were found by using the $H_{eq}(s)$ method. The resulting design was the same as above since δ was selected as 15.

Regardless of how the feedback elements are evaluated, notice that the resulting final design has the following desirable characteristics. Both feedback elements are near unity, so that large gains are not necessary in the feedback paths. The negative value of k_2 may be somewhat surprising. If the system of Fig. 9.6-5 is reduced to the $G_{eq}(s)$ form, it is noticed that none of the inner loops is unstable, even with this negative value of the feedback coefficient, which effectively produces positive feedback in that loop. Note, however, that the damping ratio of the system becomes quite small as the value of K increases.

As an alternate approach to the control of the plant shown in Fig. 9.6-2, let us use the feedforward compensation form of Fig. 9.6-1b rather than the standard form of Fig. 9.6-1a which has been used previously. The system configuration of interest is shown in Fig. 9.6-9a. The first

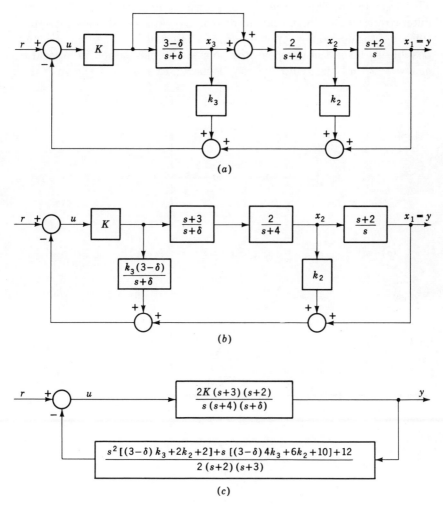

Fig. 9.6-9 Use of the feedforward form of series compensation. (*a*) System configuration; (*b*) first step in the $H_{eq}(s)$ reduction; (*c*) final $H_{eq}(s)$ representation.

step in forming the $H_{eq}(s)$ representation is to move the k_3 connection to the left and to combine the feedforward loop as shown in Fig. 9.6-9b. The completed $H_{eq}(s)$ representation is shown in Fig. 9.6-9c. Note that because the form of Eq. (**Ab**) is not violated by the feedforward compensator, $H_{eq}(s)$ now contains all of the zeros of $G_c(s)G(s)$. Because of this fact, one might expect that the final design will be somewhat different than before.

Once again we use the tentative-root-locus approach to choose δ. The first step of this procedure is shown in Fig. 9.6-10a. This figure differs from Fig. 9.6-7a in that the zero of $G_c(s)$ at $s = -3$ does not appear since it is canceled by a pole of $H_{eq}(s)$. Because of this fact it is now possible to place the compensator pole at the closed-loop pole location of $s = -2$ and the tentative root locus takes the form shown in Fig.

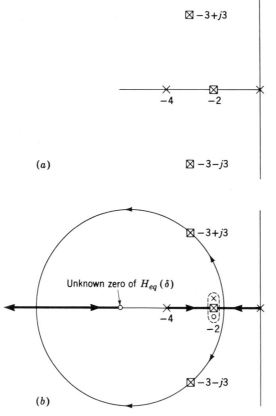

Fig. 9.6-10   Tentative root locus using feedforward
compensation.   (a) Basic pole-zero configuration; (b) final form.

9.6-10*b*. This design appears to be better than that shown in Fig. 9.6-6 for two reasons. First, the zero of $G(s)$ at $s = -2$ is canceled independent of the value of gain since a closed-loop pole always exists at $s = -2$. Second, the feedforward design has better stability characteristics than the standard-form design since, as the gain increases on the root locus of Fig. 9.6-10*b*, the damping ratio also increases rather than decreasing as in Fig. 9.6-6.

Let us assume that we decide to select δ as 2. The values for **k** and K may now be found by making use of the $H_{eq}(s)$ reduction to write $y(s)/r(s)$ as

$$\frac{y(s)}{r(s)} = \frac{2K(s+3)(s+2)}{s^3 + s^2(6 + Kk_3 + 2Kk_2 + 2K)} $$
$$+ s(8 + 4Kk_3 + 6Kk_2 + 10K) + 12K$$

$$(9.6\text{-}11)$$

Equating the coefficients of s in Eqs. (9.6-5) and (9.6-11), we find that $k_2 = -\tfrac{4}{3}$, $k_3 = \tfrac{4}{3}$, and $K = 3$. The exact root locus of $G_c(s)G(s)H_{eq}(s)$ is shown in Fig. 9.6-11, and we see that it is much as we had predicted from Fig. 9.6-10*b*.

Thus far the discussion of the general case has centered about one particular example, in which $m = r = 1$. All that was to be accomplished in this example was that the zero position was to be changed and the poles located as desired. If in this example m had been zero, a similar procedure would have been required. In order to add a zero in the closed loop, a basic series-compensation unit consisting of a pole and a zero would have had to be added in front of the fixed plant. Since there would be no existing zero in the closed loop to cancel, the resulting closed-loop transfer function would have been of order $n + 1$. This fact would be realized early in the study of the problem, and any difficulty that this might introduce could be overcome by specifying a $y(s)/r(s)$ of order $n + 1$ or by placing the additional pole far enough to the left in the s plane so that the additional pole would not affect the desired nth-order response.

Similarly, if m is greater than r, poles of the closed-loop plant can be placed under the unwanted zeros, with a resulting closed-loop transfer function of order $n - (m - r)$. If nth-order response is desired, $m - r$ poles can be added in front of the existing plant and necessary compensation. Regardless of the relative size of m and r, the design procedures are very much the same, and we shall not dwell further on this topic. The problems at the end of this section consider some of the various relations that may exist between m and r. In the case when $m > r$,

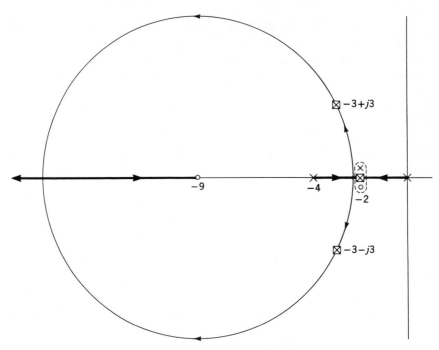

Fig. 9.6-11   Final root locus of $G_c(s)G(s)H_{eq}(s)$ for the system of Fig. 9.6-9.

the input compensation block can always be selected as just a pole and the equations are of the form (**Ab**) for either of the forms shown in Fig. 9.6-1.

In a sense it is ironic that zeros in $G(s)$ cause additional complexity in system design.   Zeros in $G(s)$ have always been thought of as a desirable stabilizing feature.   From the point of view of state-variable feedback the zeros give no advantage unless they are located in a place that is desired in the closed-loop transfer function.

In this section we have discussed several alternate procedures for determining the feedback coefficients in the general case where $y(s)/r(s)$ may have arbitrarily located zeros.   While these procedures are a powerful and almost universally applicable tool for the design of closed-loop systems, there are some special cases in which exceptional closed-loop behavior can be achieved.   These situations are discussed in the next section.

Exercises 9.6   *9.6-1.*   For the system shown in Fig. 9.6-12 find the values of the feedback coefficients and the gain such that the

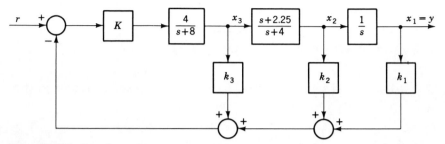

Fig. 9.6-12   Exercise 9.6-1.

closed-loop transfer function is

$$\frac{y(s)}{r(s)} = \frac{4K(s + 2.25)}{[(s + 3)^2 + 3^2](s + 9)}$$

Plot the root locus for $G(s)H_{eq}(s)$. What is the minimum value that the damping ratio will have as the gain is varied from zero to infinity?

answer:

$\mathbf{k} = $ col $(1, 0.349, -0.308)$ $K = 18$

Minimum damping ratio is $\sim$0.7.

9.6-2. Find the feedback coefficients, the gain, and the series equalizer such that the closed-loop transfer function of the system shown in Fig. 9.6-13 is

$$\frac{y(s)}{r(s)} = \frac{6(s + 3)}{(s + 3)^2 + 3^2}$$

Work this exercise by both the series-compensation and the direct $H_{eq}(s)$ method using the standard-form compensation. Plot the root loci of $G_c(s)G(s)H_{eq}(s)$ for the resulting systems.

answer:

If the series equalizer is $(s + 3)/(s + 10)$,

$\mathbf{k} = $ col $(1, -\frac{4}{3}, \frac{4}{21})$ $K = 7$

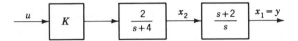

Fig. 9.6-13   Exercise 9.6-2.

9.6-3.   Find the values of **k**, K, and the series compensation in the feedforward form for the system

$$\dot{x} = \begin{bmatrix} 0 & 1 \\ 0 & -2 \end{bmatrix} x + \begin{bmatrix} 0 \\ 4K \end{bmatrix} u \qquad y = x_1$$

such that the closed-loop transfer function is

$$\frac{y(s)}{r(s)} = \frac{80(s + 1)}{[(s + 2)^2 + 2^2](s + 10)}$$

Plot the root locus of the final design.

answer:

If the pole of the compensation is at $s = -10$,

k = col (1.0,0.7,0.3) $K = 20$

9.7   Special procedures

This section considers two procedures for selecting the zeros of $H_{eq}(s)$ as an integral part of the design method. Both methods tend to make the resulting closed-loop system insensitive to variations in the gain K.

The first method makes use of the fact that for high gain the branches of the root locus terminate on the zeros of $H_{eq}(s)$. If state-variable feedback is used, $H_{eq}(s)$ always has $n - 1$ zeros, and on the s plane the asymptote associated with the root locus of $G(s)H_{eq}(s)$ is at $-180°$. Therefore at high gain one of the closed-loop poles goes toward minus infinity while the other closed-loop poles approach the zeros of $H_{eq}(s)$. This suggests designing systems to approximate a desired $y(s)/r(s)$ by placing the $n - 1$ zeros of $H_{eq}(s)$ at $n - 1$ of the desired closed-loop-pole locations and letting the system run at high gain. Such a procedure would not normally be possible for unity-ratio-feedback systems because of stability problems. With the $n - 1$ zeros available in $H_{eq}(s)$, stability is not a problem, as long as the system is modeled adequately and all the significant state variables are fed back.

In order to illustrate this method, consider once again the system of Fig. 9.3-1, where it is assumed $y(s)/r(s)$ is given by

$$\frac{y(s)}{r(s)} = \frac{80}{[(s+2)^2 + 2^2](s+10)} = \frac{80}{(s^2 + 4s + 8)(s+10)}$$

Here $H_{eq}(s)$ has two zeros, which we assume are located at the desired closed-loop conjugate-pole locations so that

$$H_{eq}(s) = \frac{s^2 + 4s + 8}{8}$$

On the other hand, $H_{eq}(s)$ may be determined in terms of the feedback coefficients as

$$H_{eq}(s) = \frac{s^2 + s(k_3 + 5k_2)/k_3 + 5/k_3}{5/k_3}$$

If these two forms for $H_{eq}(s)$ are equated, we find that

$$k_2 = \tfrac{3}{8} \quad \text{and} \quad k_3 = \tfrac{5}{8}$$

For these values, $G(s)H_{eq}(s)$ becomes

$$G(s)H_{eq}(s) = \frac{1.25K(s^2 + 4s + 8)}{s(s+1)(s+5)} \tag{9.7-1}$$

The root locus corresponding to this $G(s)H_{eq}(s)$ in indicated in Fig. 9.7-1. Gain values are marked along the root locus to indicate the degree of approximation for the various values of gain. It is seen that for $K > 25$, the complex conjugate poles are approximated quite closely.

This approach has the advantage of being very simple. Furthermore, the zeros of $H_{eq}(s)$ are sure to lie in the left half plane, assuming the desired closed-loop system is stable. Also, the designer can work directly from the root-locus diagram, and although this method is only approximate, the approximation made to the desired closed-loop poles is often as good as the knowledge of the open-loop-pole positions. There is no use in establishing closed-loop-pole positions exactly if this positioning is based upon imperfectly known open-loop-pole and zero positions.

The second special situation to be considered in this section involves those cases in which the input amplifier gain is subject to variation. This

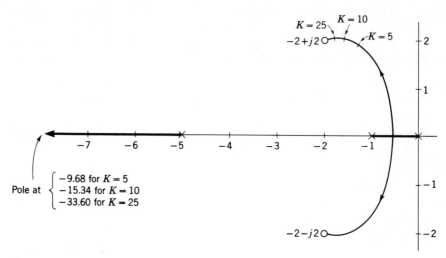

Fig. 9.7-1   Root locus for

$$G(s)H_{eq}(s) = \frac{10K(s^2 + 4s + 4)}{8s(s + 1)(s + 5)}$$

is effectively the situation in star-tracking systems.   Bright stars give
large error signals for small tracking error, while dim stars give only a
small error signal for the same tracking error.

The idea suggested here is to position all the open-loop poles, except
the integration, at the desired closed-loop poles (Herring, 1967).   This
may be done with series compensation, feedback, or a combination of both.
Then the zeros of $H_{eq}(s)$ are forced to lie at the same place, thereby fixing
these pole locations.   The following example illustrates the approach.

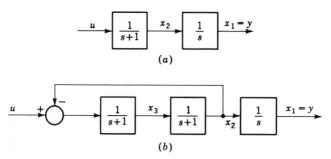

Fig. 9.7-2   Gain-insensitive design.   (*a*) Plant to be controlled;
(*b*) modification so that open-loop poles are at $s =$
$-1 \pm j1$.

Assume that the system to be controlled is given in Fig. 9.7-2a and that the desired closed-loop response is

$$\frac{y(s)}{r(s)} = \frac{2}{(s+1)^2 + 1^2} = \frac{2}{s^2 + 2s + 2}$$

Two open-loop poles of $G(s)$ are forced to lie at the desired closed-loop poles by the addition of a series compensator and feedback, as indicated in Fig. 9.7-2b. Here a series compensator had to be added so that the pole at $s = 0$ was not disturbed, since zero steady-state position error is desired.

Now consider the system of Fig. 9.7-2b as the open-loop system to be controlled, with the transfer function

$$G(s) = \frac{1}{s[(s+1)^2 + 1^2]}$$

The state variables are now fed back in the usual way, as shown by the system of Fig. 9.7-3. For this system

$$H_{eq}(s) = k_3 s(s+1) + k_2 s + 1 = \frac{s^2 + s(k_2 + k_3)/k_3 + 1/k_3}{1/k_3}$$

The numerator of $H_{eq}(s)$ is forced to equal $s^2 + 2s + 2$, so that the zeros of $H_{eq}(s)$ are at the desired closed-loop pole locations. Thus $k_2 = \frac{1}{2}$ and $k_3 = \frac{1}{2}$. The open-loop transfer function is therefore

$$G(s)H_{eq}(s) = \frac{K(s^2 + 2s + 2)}{2s(s^2 + 2s + 2)}$$

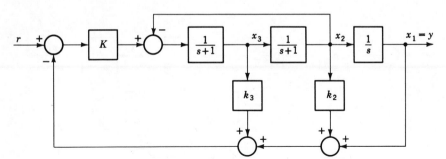

Fig. 9.7-3 Final form of the closed-loop system; final system parameters are $k_2 = \frac{1}{2}$, $k_3 = \frac{1}{2}$.

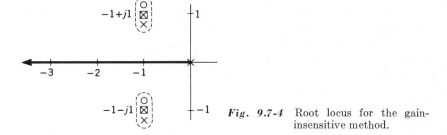

Fig. 9.7-4 Root locus for the gain-insensitive method.

As before, the poles of $G(s)$ and the zeros of $H_{eq}(s)$ do not cancel but establish a branch of the root locus at a point. The root locus corresponding to this $G(s)H_{eq}(s)$ is indicated in Fig. 9.7-4.

Note that the desired closed-loop response has been realized only approximately, since an extra pole exists on the negative real axis. But as gain is increased, this pole moves to the left and its residue decreases rapidly. Therefore, for any gain past, say, 10, the contribution of this pole to the total response is negligible, and the closed-loop system performs as though its poles were at $s = -1 \pm j1$ *regardless of gain.*

In this section we have considered two procedures which allow one to position the poles of $y(s)/r(s)$ approximately. These techniques are very easy to use and provide amazing results. In both cases the resulting closed-loop system is relatively gain-insensitive. In the high-gain approach the closed-loop poles move only a small amount once some minimum gain level is achieved. In the other approach complete gain insensitivity is achieved, except for one real pole, which moves toward infinity. Hence these methods are very effective in systems where gain levels may vary appreciably.

Exercises 9.7   *9.7-1.* Use the high-gain approach on the system shown in Fig. 9.7-5 to achieve approximately a closed-loop transfer

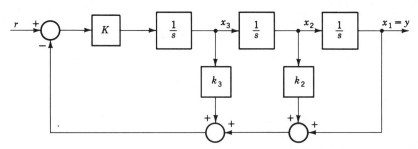

Fig. 9.7-5 Exercise 9.7-1.

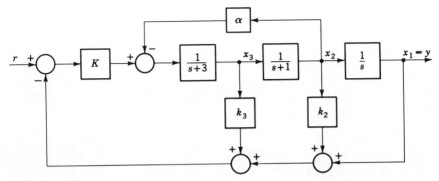

Fig. 9.7-6 Exercise 9.7-2.

function of

$$\frac{y(s)}{r(s)} = \frac{8}{(s+2)^2 + 2^2}$$

Plot the root locus of $G(s)H_{eq}(s)$ and determine the value of K necessary to place the real pole exactly at $s = -10$.

answer:

$\mathbf{k} = \text{col } (1,0.5,0.125)$ $K = 125$

9.7-2. For the system shown in Fig. 9.7-6 find the values of α, k_2, k_3 to make the system have a closed-loop response of approximately

$$\frac{y(s)}{r(s)} = \frac{8}{(s+2)^2 + 2^2}$$

independent of the gain K. What must be the minimum value of K such that the real pole is to the left of $s = -10$?

answer:

$\alpha = 5.0$ $\mathbf{k} = \text{col } (1,0.375,0.125)$ $K > 80$

9.7-3. For the system

$$\dot{\mathbf{x}} = \begin{bmatrix} -\alpha & \alpha \\ \alpha & -\alpha \end{bmatrix} \mathbf{x} + \begin{bmatrix} K \\ 0 \end{bmatrix} u$$

$$y = x_1 + x_2$$

find the feedback coefficients using the high-gain approach such that the closed-loop transfer function is approximately

$$\frac{y(s)}{r(s)} = \frac{2.5(s + 2\alpha)}{s + 5\alpha}$$

Plot the root locus for the system and determine the gain such that one closed-loop pole is at $s = -5\alpha - \delta$.

answer:

$$\mathbf{k} = \text{col}\ (0.4, 1.6) \qquad K = \frac{2.5(5\alpha + \delta)(3\alpha + \delta)}{\delta}$$

9.8   Summary and conclusion

This chapter has dealt with the design of linear single input–single output control systems through the use of state-variable feedback. The design techniques discussed relied completely upon the Laplace transform methods in the frequency domain. These methods differ considerably from those in Chap. 7, although the problems being treated are the same. The relationship between the performance index and the choice of the desired $y(s)/r(s)$ was established through the use of Kalman's equation. When $y(s)/r(s)$ is chosen so that $|1 + G(s)H_{eq}(s)| \geq 1$, the two approaches are equivalent. This inequality may be violated, however, and the methods of design based on the choice of $y(s)/r(s)$ are still applicable even though no quadratic performance index exists.

The major portion of this chapter has been directed toward relating the vast existing knowledge of frequency-domain methods concerning control-system synthesis to the state-variable-feedback problem. This chapter could have been based on matrix methods rather than block-diagram manipulations. Since $G(s)$ is

$$G(s) = \mathbf{c}^T \mathbf{\Phi}(s) \mathbf{b}$$

and $G(s)H_{eq}(s)$ is

$$G(s)H_{eq}(s) = \mathbf{k}^T \mathbf{\Phi}(s) \mathbf{b}$$

then $y(s)/r(s)$ may be written as

$$\frac{y(s)}{r(s)} = \frac{G(s)}{1 + G(s)H_{eq}(s)} = \frac{\mathbf{c}^T \mathbf{\Phi}(s) \mathbf{b}}{1 + \mathbf{k}^T \mathbf{\Phi}(s) \mathbf{b}}$$

This matrix expression could then be equated to the desired $y(s)/r(s)$ and the values of $\mathbf{k}$ and K determined. This approach was not used because it is difficult to envision developing insight with matrix equations to the same degree that is gained through the use of the root locus, for example. However, in actually determining the feedback coefficients and gain in higher-order systems, the matrix formulation may be easily programmed on a digital computer (Melsa, 1967) and solutions may then be obtained without difficulty.

However, one should not forget that the frequency-domain methods are considerably more restricted in their scope than those approaches usually classified as modern control theory. Unless the system is linear, the control interval infinite, and the performance index quadratic, the frequency-domain methods are not equivalent and may not even be applicable. For example, Laplace transform methods are of little assistance in the solution of minimum-time or minimum-fuel types of problem.

Although this book has concentrated on the analysis and design of linear systems, attempts have been made throughout to indicate how the methods may be applied to the broader class of nonlinear and time-varying systems. It is hoped that the reader has been inspired to seek out further information on these more difficult problems in the many advanced texts available.

The only way in which this book can logically end is with the words "feed back *all* the state variables."

9.9 Problems

9.9-1. Find the feedback coefficients for the system shown in Fig. 9.9-1 such that the closed-loop transfer function is

$$\frac{y(s)}{r(s)} = \frac{20}{[(s+1)^2 + 1](s+10)}$$

(*a*) by the $H_{eq}(s)$ method of this chapter and (*b*) by finding the associated performance index and using the methods of Chap. 8.

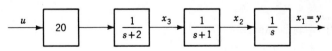

Fig. 9.9-1   Prob. 9.9-1.

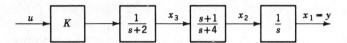

Fig. 9.9-2   Prob. 9.9-5.

9.9-2.   Find the feedback coefficients and series compensation for the system of Prob. 9.9-1 such that the closed-loop transfer function is

$$\frac{y(s)}{r(s)} = \frac{20(s+1)}{[(s+1)^2+1](s+2)(s+5)}$$

Ensure that the closed-loop system is stable for all gain.   Find the performance index for this augmented system.

9.9-3.   Find the feedback coefficients for the system

$$\dot{\mathbf{x}} = \begin{bmatrix} 0 & 1 & 0 \\ 0 & 0 & 1 \\ 0 & -5 & -4 \end{bmatrix} \mathbf{x} + \begin{bmatrix} 0 \\ 0 \\ K \end{bmatrix} u$$

$$y = x_1$$

by using the high-gain method of Sec. 9.7 such that the closed-loop transfer is approximately

$$\frac{y(s)}{r(s)} = \frac{8}{(s+2)^2+2^2}$$

How large must the gain be so that the real pole is left of $s = -10$?

9.9-4.   Repeat Prob. 9.9-3 using the gain-insensitive approach of Sec. 9.7.

9.9-5.   Find the feedback coefficients and series compensation for the system shown in Fig. 9.9-2 such that the closed-loop transfer function is

$$\frac{y(s)}{r(s)} = \frac{5(s+2)}{[(s+1)^2+1](s+5)}$$

Do the problem by each of the three methods of Sec. 9.6.

9.9-6.   Find minor-loop configurations for the closed-loop system of Prob. 9.9-5 if

(a) x_2 is inaccessible
(b) x_3 is inaccessible
(c) x_2 and x_3 are inaccessible

9.9-7. Find the feedback coefficients for the unstable open-loop system

$$\dot{\mathbf{x}} = \begin{bmatrix} 0 & 1 & 0 \\ 0 & 2 & 1 \\ 0 & 0 & -1 \end{bmatrix} \mathbf{x} + \begin{bmatrix} 0 \\ 0 \\ K \end{bmatrix} u$$

$$y = x_1$$

such that the closed-loop transfer function is

$$\frac{y(s)}{r(s)} = \frac{80}{[(s + 2)^2 + 2^2](s + 10)}$$

References

Herring, J. E.: "Design of Linear and Nonlinear Control Systems via State Variable Feedback," doctoral dissertation, University of Arizona, Tucson, Ariz., 1967.

Melsa, J. L.: A Digital Computer Program for the Analysis and Design of State Variable Feedback Systems, University of Arizona, Engineering Experiment Station Report, March, 1967.

Schultz, D. G.: A New Method of the Design of Linear Systems, NASA Contractor Report, CR-77901, August, 1966.

Truxal, J. G.: "Automatic Feedback Control System Synthesis," McGraw-Hill Book Company, New York, 1955.

White, R. C.: "Sensitivity and State Variable Feedback," M.S. thesis, University of Arizona, Tucson, Ariz., 1967.

index